The Human Body in Health and Disease

The Human Body in Health and Disease

RUTH LUNDEEN MEMMLER, M.D.

Professor Emeritus, Life Sciences; Formerly Coordinator, Health, Life Sciences and Nursing, East Los Angeles College, Los Angeles

and

RUTH BYERS RADA, M.A.

Professor of Life Sciences and Assistant Dean of Instruction, East Los Angeles College, Los Angeles

3rd EDITION

J. B. LIPPINCOTT COMPANY
PHILADELPHIA • TORONTO

THIRD EDITION

Distributed in Great Britain by
Blackwell Scientific Publications, Oxford, London, and Edinburgh

Paperbound: ISBN-0-397-54105-8
Clothbound: ISBN-0-397-54106-6

Library of Congress Catalog Card Number 78-124392
Printed in the United States of America

9 8 7

PREFACE

The primary aim of the authors is to introduce the student to principles of the biological and physical sciences that contribute to his understanding of human body processes in normal and in certain abnormal conditions. In addition to the sciences of body structure (anatomy), dynamics and function (physiology), disease (pathology), and considerations of microbiology, there is a new chapter on the basic concepts of chemistry as they relate to the life processes, as well as some elementary principles of physics. This additional content serves to make this edition a more completely integrated science text. As in previous editions, by comparing the normal with the abnormal at every opportunity, the student is gradually oriented to the clinical setting with a scientific foundation that facilitates an understanding of the rationale underlying care and cure processes.

This new edition is distinguished by emphasis on cellular metabolism, which should heighten the student's understanding of homeostasis and disease entities and permit a more complete explanation of physiologic and pathologic processes throughout.

The order of the chapters has been changed, following the suggestions of some of the instructors who used the second edition. The chapter covering the nervous system is presented earlier in the sequence than previously, hoping that it will foster a more meaningful understanding of important body processes, such as the control of circulation and respiration which are discussed later in the text. However, any order of presentation which best adapts itself to the overall curriculum of the school may well be followed.

Every effort has been made to revise the content according to recent research findings and new methods of treatment. Among the latter are therapeutic measures, such as heart and kidney transplants (with a discussion of the rejection syndrome) and the use of dialysis machines. To further clarify the relationships of various body structures, an 8-page color insert of anatomic plates has been included. The addition of 14 new illustrations, many of which serve to illustrate the dynamics of physiology, with a revision of the original 61 drawings, also strengthens the usefulness of the book.

The pronunciation key which has proved helpful and time-saving to the beginning student with no background in using medical terminology has been retained. An indication of the correct pronunciation is given in parentheses following the introduction of many of the scientific words. To further assist the student in pronouncing and understanding the meaning of words, a list of commonly used roots, combining forms, prefixes, and suffixes, and an extensive glossary have been added to the book.

The authors realize the limitations of such a short book on such a complex subject and it is hoped that the student will be referred to more detailed texts for additional study. It is also hoped that the flexibility of the book will serve as a basic guide to the instructor who may wish to introduce additional conditions of illness as normal and abnormal body structure and function are compared.

The authors are deeply indebted to the many people whose encouragement and suggestions have helped in the revision of this book. Eugene Memmler and Carol M. Woike are responsible for the new artwork, as well as the relabeling and revision of the original illustrations. The authors are also grateful to the staff of the publishers, particularly to Miss Anna May Jones, Associate Editor, Nursing Education, for her guidance and help.

CONTENTS

CHAPTER 1

THE GENERAL PLAN
OF THE HUMAN BODY

Living matter and cells ▪ Organs and organ-systems ▪ Directions
and locations in the body ▪ Dorsal and ventral body cavities.

WHAT ARE LIVING THINGS MADE OF?

According to a nursery rhyme children are made of sugar and spice, or perhaps of
puppy dogs' tails, depending on which sex we are discussing. More accurately, the
"stuff" of which all living things are made is called **protoplasm** (pro'to-plazm). This
word is made up of 2 Greek words: *proto*, meaning "original," and *plasm*, meaning
"substance." Chemically, protoplasm is composed of quite ordinary elements, such
as carbon, oxygen, hydrogen, sulfur, nitrogen and phosphorus. There is nothing
extraordinary, either, in the appearance of protoplasm; it looks very much like the
white of an egg. Yet, nobody has been able to explain why protoplasm has that
characteristic which we call life. We will learn more about this intricate substance
in Chapter 3.

If the building material of all living things, both plants and animals, is protoplasm,
the building blocks made of this are called **cells** (see Fig. 1). Cells vary a great deal
in size. Something as small as a worm may be composed of millions of cells, yet we
all are familiar with at least one of the larger kinds of cell, of which an egg is a
perfectly good example. In fact, if we keep the egg in mind, the construction of the
cell will be quite easy to visualize. Let us work our way from the outside to
the center.

First comes the outer covering, called the **cell membrane.** Next is the main
substance of the cell, the **cytoplasm** (si'to-plazm), which might be likened to the
white of the egg. The cytoplasm contains water, food particles, pigment and other
specialized materials. In the center of the cell, comparable with the egg yolk, is a
globule called the **nucleus** (nu'kle-us), containing the chromatin network. The
nucleus controls some of the activities of the cell, including its reproduction. Within
the nucleus is still another tiny globule of matter called the **nucleolus** (nu-kle'o-lus),

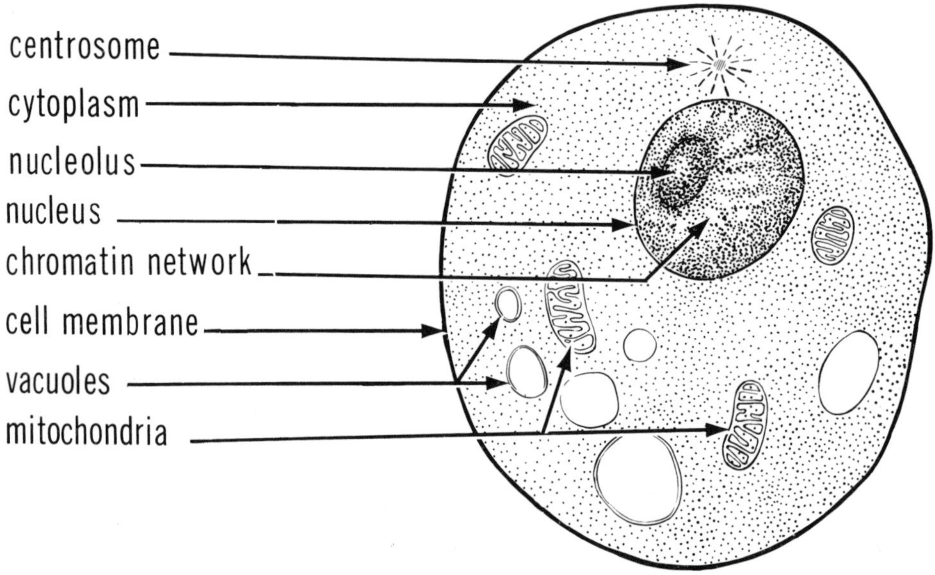

centrosome
cytoplasm
nucleolus
nucleus
chromatin network
cell membrane
vacuoles
mitochondria

FIG. 1. A typical cell. The entire structure is made of protoplasm.

the function of which is related to reproduction. The unique ability of a cell to reproduce itself will be discussed in Chapter 4.

The cell, then, is the basic unit of all life. When you study the causes of disease, you will encounter a number of primitive living things which are composed of but one cell. However, for the moment we shall confine our discussion to the human body, which is made up of many millions of cells. The body is composed of specialized groups of cells, the first of which are called **tissues.** Various tissues combine to form **organs,** and several organs and parts grouped together for certain functions form **systems.**

BODY SYSTEMS

The body systems have been variously stated to be 9, 10, or 11 in number, depending on how much detail one wishes to include.
Here is one list of systems:

1. The **skeletal system.** The basic framework of the body is a system of over 200 bones with their joints, collectively known as the skeleton.

2. The **muscular system.** Body movements are due to the action of the muscles which are attached to the bones. Other types of muscles are present in the walls of such organs as the intestine and the heart.

3. The **circulatory system.** The heart, blood vessels, lymph vessels and lymph nodes all make up the system whereby blood is pumped to all the body tissues,

bringing with it food, oxygen and other substances, and carrying away waste materials.

4. The **digestive system.** This system comprises all organs which have to do with taking in food and converting the useful parts of it into substances that the body cells can use. Examples of these organs are the mouth, the teeth, and the alimentary tract (esophagus, stomach, intestine and accessory organs such as the liver and the pancreas).

5. The **respiratory system.** This includes the lungs and the passages leading to and from them. The purpose of this system is to take in air, and from it extract oxygen which is then dissolved into the blood and conveyed to all the tissues. A waste product of the cells, carbon dioxide, is taken by the blood to the lungs, whence it is expelled to the outside air.

6. The **integumentary system.** The word "integument" (in-teg'u-ment) means "skin." The skin is considered by some authorities to be a separate body system. It includes the hair, nails, sweat and oil glands, and other related structures.

7. The **urinary system.** This is also called the excretory system. Its main components are the kidneys, the ureters, the bladder and the urethra. Its purpose is to filter out and rid the body of certain waste products taken by the blood from the cells. (Note that other waste products are removed via the digestive and the respiratory systems.)

8. The **nervous system.** The brain, the spinal cord and the nerves all make up this very complex system by which all parts of the body are controlled and coordinated. The organs of special sense (eyes, ears, taste buds, organs of smell, etc.), sometimes classed as a separate **sensory system,** together with the sense of touch, receive stimuli from the outside world, which are then converted into impulses that are transmitted to the brain. The brain determines to a great extent the body's responses to messages from without and within, and in it occur such higher functions as memory and reasoning.

9. The **endocrine system.** A few scattered organs known as endocrine glands produce special substances called hormones, which regulate such body functions as growth, food utilization within the cells, and reproduction. Examples of endocrine glands are the thyroid and the pituitary.

10. The **reproductive system.** This system includes the external sex organs and all related inner structures which are concerned with the production of new individuals.

DIRECTIONS IN THE BODY

Because it would be awkward and incorrect to speak of bandaging the "southwest part" of the chest, a number of terms have been devised to designate specific regions and directions in the body. Some of the more important of these are listed as follows (note that they refer to the body in the "anatomic position"—upright with palms facing forward):

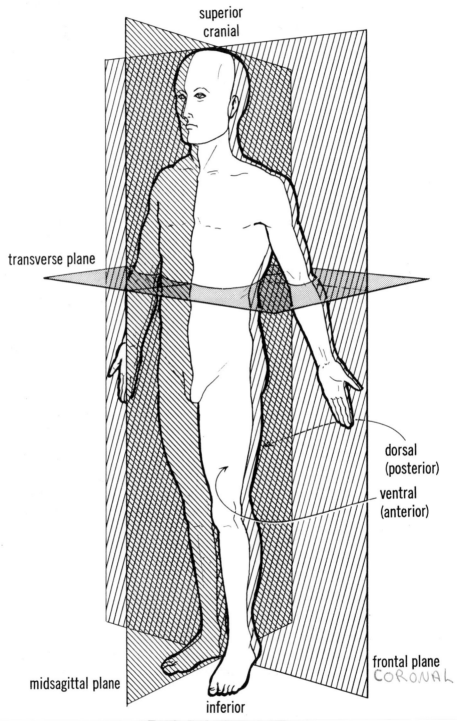

FIG. 2. Body planes and directions.

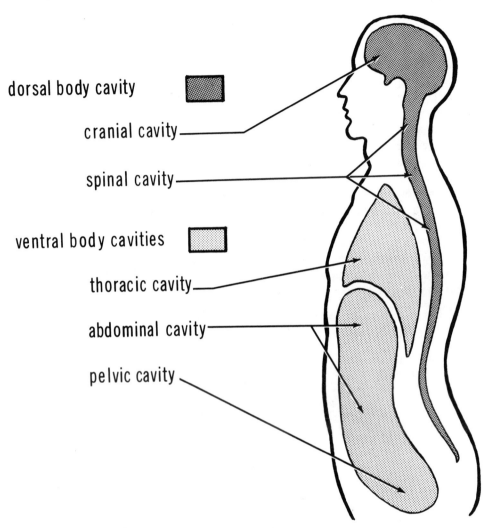

dorsal body cavity

cranial cavity——

spinal cavity——

ventral body cavities

thoracic cavity——

abdominal cavity——

pelvic cavity

Fig. 3. Side view of body cavities.

1. **Superior** is a relative term meaning "above" or "in a higher position." Its opposite, **inferior,** means "below" or "lower." The heart, for example, is superior to the intestine.

2. **Ventral** and **anterior** mean the same thing in humans: "located near the belly surface or front of the body." Their corresponding opposites, **dorsal** and **posterior,** refer to locations nearer the back.

3. **Cranial** means "near the head"; **caudal,** "near the sacral region of the spinal column" (i.e., where the tail is located in lower animals).

4. **Medial** means "near an imaginary plane that passes through the midline of

the body, dividing it into left and right portions." **Lateral,** its opposite, means "farther away from the midline," toward the side.

5. **Proximal** means "nearest the origin of a structure"; **distal,** "farthest from that point." For example, the part of your thumb where it joins your hand is its proximal region. The tip of the thumb is its distal region.

For convenience in visualizing the spacial relationships of various body structures to each other, anatomists have divided the body by means of 3 imaginary planes. Think of a body plane as a huge cleaver (see Fig. 2).

1. The **midsagittal** (mid-saj′i-tal) **plane.** If the cleaver were to cut the body in two down the middle in a fore-and-aft direction, separating it into right and left portions, the sections you would see would be midsagittal.

2. The **frontal plane.** If, instead of the above operation, the cleaver were held in line with the ears and then were brought down the middle of the body, creating a front and a rear portion, you would see a front (anterior or ventral) section and a rear (posterior or dorsal) section.

3. The **transverse plane.** If the cleaver blade were swung horizontally, it would divide the body into an upper (superior) part and a lower (inferior) portion. There could be many such cross sections, each of which is on a transverse plane.

BODY CAVITIES

The body contains a few large internal spaces or **cavities** within which various organs are located. There are 2 groups of cavities: **dorsal** and **ventral** (see Fig. 3).

DORSAL CAVITIES

There are 2 dorsal cavities: (1) the **cranial cavity,** containing the brain; and (2) the **spinal canal,** enclosing the spinal cord Both of these cavities join, hence they are a continuous space.

VENTRAL CAVITIES

The ventral cavities are much larger than the dorsal ones. There are 2 ventral cavities: (1) the **thoracic cavity,** containing mainly the heart, the lungs and the large blood vessels, and (2) the **abdominal cavity.** This latter space is subdivided into 2 portions, one containing the stomach, most of the intestine, the kidneys, the liver, the gallbladder, the pancreas and the spleen; and a lower one called the **pelvis,** or pelvic cavity, in which are located the urinary bladder, the rectum and the internal parts of the reproductive system.

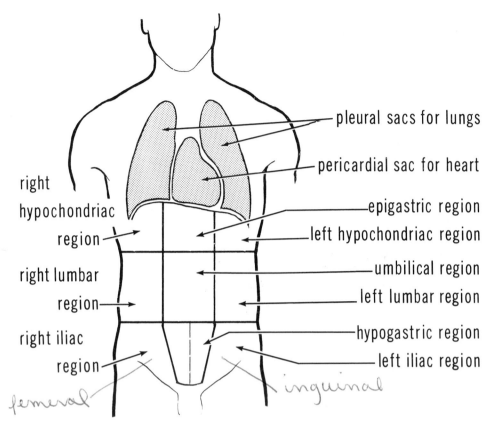

FIG. 4. Front view of body cavities and the regions of the abdomen.

Unlike the dorsal cavities, the ventral cavities are not continuous. They are separated by a muscular partition, the **diaphragm** (di'ah-fram), the function of which is discussed in Chapter 16.

Regions in the Abdominal Cavity. Because the abdominal cavity is so large, it has been found helpful to divide it into 9 regions. These are shown in Figure 4. The 3 central regions are the **epigastrium** (ep-i-gas'tre-um), located just below the breastbone; the **umbilical** (um-bil'i-kal) **region** about the umbilicus (um-bil-i'kus), commonly called the navel; and the **hypogastric** (hi-po-gas'trick) **region,** the lowest of all of the midline regions. At each side are the right and left **hypochondriac** (hi-po-kon'dre-ak) regions, just below the ribs; then the right and left **lumbar** regions; and finally, the right and left **iliac,** or **inguinal** (in'gwi-nal), regions. A much simpler division into 4 quadrants (right upper, left upper, right lower, left lower) is now less frequently used.

SUMMARY

1. **Living matter.**
   A. Basic substance: protoplasm.
   B. Structural unit: cell.
   C. Principal parts of cell: cell membrane, cytoplasm, nucleus, nucleolus.
   D. Organization of body cells: tissues, organs, systems.
2. **Body systems:** skeletal, muscular, circulatory, digestive, respiratory, integumentary, urinary, nervous (and sensory), endocrine, reproductive.
3. **Body directions.**
   A. Superior, near head; inferior, away from head.
   B. Ventral (anterior) near belly; dorsal (posterior) near back.
   C. Cranial, near head; caudal, near end of spinal column.
   D. Medial, near midsagittal plane; lateral, toward side.
   E. Proximal, near origin; distal, distant from origin.
   F. Body division by planes.
      (1) Midsagittal: left and right portions.
      (2) Frontal: front and rear portions.
      (3) Transverse: top and bottom portions.
4. **Body cavities.**
   A. Dorsal.
      (1) Cranial.
      (2) Spinal.
   B. Ventral.
      (1) Thoracic.
      (2) Abdominal.
         (a) 9 regions include epigastric, umbilical, hypogastric, right and left hypochondriac, right and left lumbar, and right and left iliac, or inguinal.
         (b) 4 quadrants (no longer extensively used).
   C. Dorsal cavities continuous, abdominal cavities separated by diaphragm.

QUESTIONS AND PROBLEMS
1. Of what substance is living matter composed?
2. Define a cell. Name 4 main components of a typical cell.
3. Define: tissue, organ, body system.
4. List the body systems, including a brief description of each with respect to its function.
5. List the opposite term for each of the following body directions: superior, ventral, anterior, cranial, medial, proximal. Define each item in the complete list.
6. What are the 3 main body planes? Explain the division of each.
7. Make a rough sketch of the 2 principal groups of body cavities, indicating the 9 divisions of the largest cavity.

CHAPTER 2

DISEASE AND DISEASE-PRODUCING ORGANISMS

The nature of disease ▪ The study of disease ▪ Disease terminology ▪ Diagnosis, treatment and prevention ▪ Infection ▪ The microorganisms ▪ Bacteria ▪ Fungi ▪ Rickettsiae ▪ Viruses ▪ Protozoa ▪ Parasitic worms ▪ Microbial control ▪ Aseptic methods ▪ Chemotherapy ▪ Laboratory identification of pathogens.

WHAT IS DISEASE?

Disease may be defined as the abnormal state in which part or all of the body is not properly adjusted or is not capable of carrying on all the required functions. There are marked variations in the extent of the disease and in its effect on the person. Disease can have a number of direct causes such as the following:

1. **Disease-producing Organisms.** Certain of these will be discussed in this chapter. These are believed to play a part in at least one half of the human illnesses in the world.

2. **Malnutrition.** This means a lack of essential vitamins, minerals, proteins, or other substances required for normal life processes to take place.

3. **Physical Agents.** These include excessive heat or cold, or injuries that cause cuts, fractures, or crushing damage to tissues.

4. **Chemicals.** Certain ones may be poisonous or otherwise injurious if present in excess, such as lead compounds (in paints), carbolic acid (in certain antiseptic solutions), certain laundry aids, etc.

5. **Birth Defects.** Those abnormalities of structure and function which are present at birth are termed either **inherited** or **congenital** (kon-jen′i-tal). An inherited abnormality (such as the blood disease hemophilia) is one which has been passed on by the parents through their reproductive cells. A congenital abnormality (such as a harelip) is one which has been acquired during the process of development within the mother's womb (uterus), but which probably has nothing to do with inheritance.

9

6. **Degenerative Process. Degeneration** (de-jen-er-a'shun) means breaking down. With aging, there is deterioration of tissue so that it becomes less active and less capable of performing its normal functions. Such degenerative processes may be caused by continuous infection, by repeated minor injuries to tissues by poisonous substances, or by the normal "wear and tear" of life. Thus degeneration is an anticipated result of aging.

7. **Neoplasms.** This word (ne'o-plazm) means "new growth" and refers to cancer and other types of tumors. Neoplasms are discussed in greater detail in Chapter 4.

Other factors entering into the production of a disease are known as **predisposing causes.** While a predisposing cause may not in itself give rise to a disease, it increases the probability of a person's becoming ill. Examples of predisposing causes include:

Age. As we saw, the degenerative processes of aging can be a direct cause of disease. But a person's age also can be a predisposing factor. For instance, measles is more common in children than in adults.

Sex. Certain diseases are more characteristic of one sex than the other. Men are more susceptible to heart disease, while women are more prone to develop diabetes.

Heredity. Some individuals inherit a "tendency" to acquire certain diseases—particularly diabetes and many allergies.

Living Conditions and Habits. A person who habitually drives himself to exhaustion, does not have enough sleep, or pays little attention to his diet is highly vulnerable to the onslaught of disease. Overcrowding invites epidemics, and lack of sunshine can cause rickets in children. The use of narcotics and the abuse of alcohol and tobacco also can lower vitality and predispose to disease.

Occupation. A number of conditions are classified as "occupational diseases." For instance, miners are susceptible to lung damage caused by the constant inhalation of stonedust.

Physical Exposure. Undue chilling of all or part of the body, or prolonged exposure to heat, can lower the body's resistance to disease.

Preexisting Illness. Any preexisting illness, even as mild a one as the common cold, increases the chances of contracting another disease.

Psychogenic Influences. "Psycho" refers to the mind, "genic" to origin. Some physical disturbances are due either directly or indirectly to emotional upsets caused by conditions of stress and anxiety in daily living. Peptic ulcers and so-called nervous indigestion are examples.

THE STUDY OF DISEASE

Our brief survey of the human body should give us a glimpse into 3 different studies which are considered the fundamentals of medical science. These are:

1. **Anatomy** (ah-nat'o-me)—the science of the structure of the body and the relationship of its parts to each other.

2. **Physiology** (fiz-e-ol′o-je)—the science which deals with the activities or dynamics (functions) of the body and its parts.

3. **Pathology** (pah-thol′o-je)—the science which treats of the essential nature of disease, including the structural and functional changes produced by the disorders.

The modern approach to the study of disease emphasizes the close relationship of the pathological and physiological aspects and the need to understand the fundamentals of each in treating any body disorder. The term used for this combined study in medical science is **pathophysiology.**

Underlying the basic medical sciences are the yet more fundamental subjects of physics and chemistry. A knowledge of both of these is essential to any real understanding of the life processes.

It is interesting to note that many other sciences have grown up about the study of disease and that each has become a specialty in itself. Some examples of these more specialized sciences include:

1. **Bacteriology** (bac-te-re-ol′o-je), which includes a study of the many beneficial as well as disease-producing plantlike organisms called bacteria.

2. **Microbiology** (mi-kro-bi-ol′o-je), which is the science of microscopic plants and animals, usually emphasizing the bacteria. This term sometimes is synonymous with bacteriology.

3. **Protozoology** (pro-to-zo-ol′o-je), a study of one-celled animals.

4. **Parasitology** (par-ah-si-tol′o-je), the general study of parasites, a **parasite** being any organism which lives on or within another (called the **host**) at the host's expense.

5. **Helminthology** (hel-min-thol′o-je), the study of worms, particularly parasitic ones.

DISEASE TERMINOLOGY

The study of the cause of any disease, or the theory of its origin, is **etiology** (e-te-ol′o-je). Any study of a disease usually includes some indication of its **incidence,** which means its range of occurrence and its tendency to affect certain groups of individuals more than others. Information concerning its geographic distribution and its tendency to appear in one sex, age group, or race more or less frequently than another is usually included in a presentation on disease incidence.

Diseases are often classified on the basis of severity and duration as:

1. **Acute:** Those that are relatively severe but usually last a short time.

2. **Chronic:** Those that are often less severe but likely to be continuous or recurring for long periods of time.

3. **Subacute:** Those that are intermediate and fall between acute and chronic, not being quite so severe as acute infections nor as long-lasting as chronic disorders.

Still another term used in describing certain diseases is **idiopathic** (id-e-o-path′ik), which means "self-originating" or "without a known cause."

A **communicable** disease is one which can be transmitted from one person to another. If many people in a given region acquire a certain disease at the same time, that disease is said to be **epidemic.** If a given disease is found to a lesser extent but continuously in a particular region, the disease is **endemic** to that area.

DIAGNOSIS, TREATMENT AND PREVENTION

In order to treat a patient, the doctor obviously must first determine the nature of the illness—that is, make a **diagnosis.** A diagnosis is the conclusion drawn from a number of facts put together. The doctor must know the **symptoms,** which are the changes in body function felt by the patient; and the **signs** (also called **objective symptoms)** which the doctor himself can observe. Sometimes a characteristic group of signs (or symptoms) accompanies a given disease. Such a group is called a **syndrome** (sin'drome). Frequently certain laboratory tests are performed and the results evaluated by the physician in making his diagnosis.

Although nurses do not diagnose, they play an extremely valuable role in this process by observing closely for signs, encouraging the patient to talk about himself and his symptoms, and then reporting this information to the doctor. Once the patient's disorder is known, the doctor prescribes a course of treatment, also referred to as **therapy.** Many measures in this course of treatment are carried out by the nurse under the physician's orders.

In recent years physicians, nurses and other health workers have taken on increasing responsibilities in **prevention.** Throughout most of medical history, the physician's aim has been to cure a patient of an existing disease. However, the modern concept of prevention seeks to stop disease before it actually happens—to keep people well through the promotion of health. A vast number of organizations exist for this purpose, ranging from the World Health Organization (WHO) on an international level down to local private and community health programs. A rapidly growing responsibility of the nursing profession is educating individual patients toward the maintenance of total health—physical and mental.

INFECTION

The predominant cause of disease in humans is the invasion of the body by disease-producing **microorganisms** (mi-kro-or'gan-izms). The word "organism" means "anything having life;" "micro" means "small." Hence, a microorganism is a tiny living thing, too small to be seen by the naked eye. Another term for microorganism is **microbe** or, more popularly, "germ."

Although the great majority of microorganisms are beneficial to man, or at least are harmless, a certain few types cause illness; that is, they are **pathogenic** (path-o-jen'ic). Any disease-causing organism is a **pathogen.** If the body is invaded by pathogens with adverse effect, the condition is called an **infection.** If the infection is restricted to a relatively small area of the body, it is **local.** A generalized or

systemic (sis-tem'ik) infection is one in which the whole body is affected. Generalized infections usually are spread by the blood stream.

THE MICROORGANISMS

ANIMAL, VEGETABLE OR WHAT?

Microorganisms are living things of a very primitive order. Higher forms of life, with which we all are familiar, are composed of vast numbers of cells engaged to a greater or lesser degree in specialized tasks. Most microorganisms, however, are composed of but one cell in which are carried on all the processes of life—nutrition, growth, reproduction and so forth. Some microbes are classed as plants and others as animals. At this level the difference is based on the type of food compounds that they can use. While plants can manufacture food from simple substances in the soil, water and air in which they live, no animal can do this. Animals obtain food from other living things. Still other types of microorganisms cannot be assigned with certainty to either the plant or the animal kingdom. The following is a simplified grouping of the microorganisms:

Plants

Algae (no pathogenic forms)
Bacteria
Fungi

Animals

Protozoa

Unclassified

Viruses
Rickettsiae

BACTERIA

The bacteria are one-celled plants. Although they comprise the largest group of pathogens, most bacteria are not only harmless to man but are absolutely essential to the continuation of all life on earth. It is through the action of bacteria that dead animals and plants are decomposed and transformed into substances which enrich the soil. Sewage is rendered harmless by bacteria. One type of bacteria transforms the nitrogen of the air into a form usable by plants, a process called **nitrogen fixation.** Farmers take advantage of this by allowing a field to lie fallow (untilled) so that the nitrogen of its soil can be replenished. There are so many different types

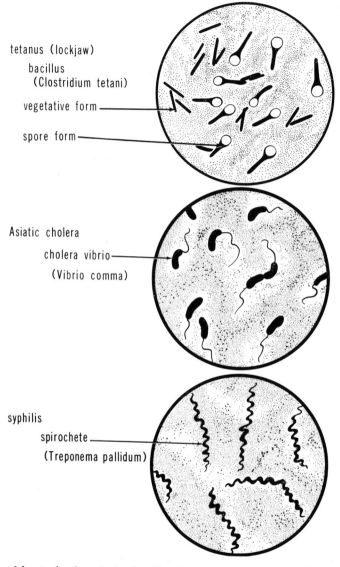

FIG. 5. Bacteria of the elongated type.

tetanus (lockjaw)
  bacillus
    (Clostridium tetani)
  vegetative form ———
  spore form ———

Asiatic cholera
  cholera vibrio ———
    (Vibrio comma)

syphilis
  spirochete ———
    (Treponema pallidum)

of bacteria that their classification is very complicated. For our purposes, a convenient and simple grouping is based on the shape and arrangement of their cells as seen with a microscope.

1. Rod-shaped cells: **bacilli** (bah-sil′i). Cells are straight and slender, like matchsticks. Some are cigar-shaped with tapering ends. Typical bacillary diseases include tetanus, diphtheria, tuberculosis and typhoid fever.

2. Spherical cells: **cocci** (kok′si). Cells resemble dots. Cocci are seen in character-

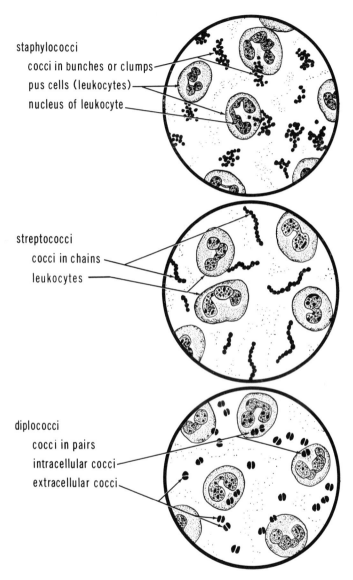

FIG. 6. Bacteria of the spherical type.

staphylococci
    cocci in bunches or clumps
    pus cells (leukocytes)
    nucleus of leukocyte

streptococci
    cocci in chains
    leukocytes

diplococci
    cocci in pairs
    intracellular cocci
    extracellular cocci

istic arrangements Some are in pairs and are called **diplococci** (*diplo*-double). Another type is arranged in chains, like a string of beads. These are the **streptococci** (*strepto*-chain). A third group is seen in large clusters and is known as **staphylococci** (staf-i-lo-kok′si) (*staphylo*-bunch of grapes). Diplococci cause gonorrhea and meningitis among others; streptococci and staphylococci are responsible for a wide variety of infections.

    3. Curved rods. One type has only a slight curvature, like a comma, and is

called **vibrio** (vib're-o). Another form resembles a corkscrew and is known as **spirillum** (spi-ril'um) (plural **spirilla).** Bacteria very similar to the spirilla, but capable of waving and twisting motions, are called **spirochetes** (spi'ro-ketes). Cholera is caused by a vibrio. The most serious and widespread spirochetal infection is syphilis.

Bacteria can be seen only under a microscope. As a rough indication of their size, from 10 to 1000 bacteria (depending upon the species) could, if lined up, span a pinhead. Bacteria live in an environment of moisture and food materials. Some types are capable of swimming rapidly about by themselves by means of threadlike appendages called **flagella** (flah-jel'ah). Their requirements as to water, food, oxygen, temperature and other factors vary according to the species. Not surprisingly, the pathogenic bacteria are most at home within the "climate" of the human body. When living conditions are ideal, the organisms reproduce (by splitting in two) with unbelievable rapidity. If they succeed in overcoming the body's natural defenses, they can cause damage in two ways: by producing poisons, or **toxins,** and by entering the body tissues and growing within them. In Table 1 of the Appendix are listed some typical pathogenic bacteria and the diseases which they cause.

FUNGI

The **fungi** (fun'ji) are another large group of simple plants. Only a very few types are pathogenic. Although the fungi are much larger and more complicated than the bacteria, they are still a low order of plant life, lacking the green pigment chlorophyll which enables higher plants to utilize the energy of sunlight in carrying out their life processes. Like bacteria, the fungi prefer dark and damp places in which to grow.

Familiar examples of fungi are mushrooms, puffballs, bread molds and yeasts (commercial yeast cakes used in baking and brewing). Of the fungi only **yeasts** and **molds** include pathogenic types. Diseases caused by fungi are called **mycotic** infections (*myco*-fungus). Examples of these are athlete's foot and ringworm. Although few diseases are caused by fungi, some are very dangerous and all are difficult to cure.

Table 2 of the Appendix is a list of typical fungous diseases.

RICKETTSIAE

Early in this century Dr. Howard T. Ricketts discovered this hitherto unknown type of organism. The **rickettsiae** (rik-et'se-e) probably belong to the plant kingdom and are similar in appearance to bacteria, though so much smaller as to be barely visible in the ordinary light microscope. A great difference between the rickettsiae and bacteria, however, is that the rickettsiae cannot exist outside living tissue. This

Fig. 7. Protozoa

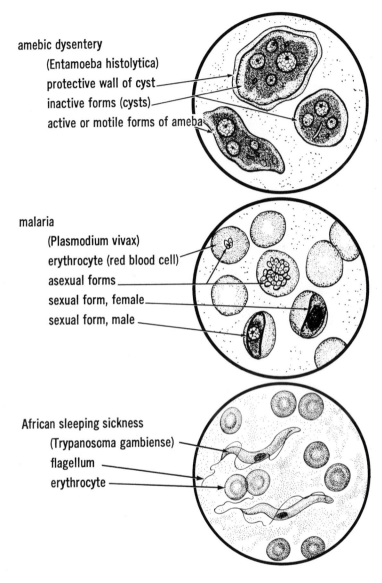

amebic dysentery
    (Entamoeba histolytica)
    protective wall of cyst
    inactive forms (cysts)
    active or motile forms of ameba

malaria
    (Plasmodium vivax)
    erythrocyte (red blood cell)
    asexual forms
    sexual form, female
    sexual form, male

African sleeping sickness
    (Trypanosoma gambiense)
    flagellum
    erythrocyte

is a true **parasitic** (par-ah-sit′ik) relationship, and because the rickettsiae must remain within living cells, they are **obligate** parasites.

The rickettsiae are the cause of a number of serious diseases in man such as typhus and Rocky Mountain spotted fever. In almost every instance, these organisms are transmitted through the bites of such creatures as lice, ticks and fleas. In Table 3 are listed a few common rickettsial diseases.

VIRUSES

If the bacteria and the rickettsiae seem small, they are enormous in comparison to the **viruses.** These latter are so tiny as to be invisible in the ordinary light microscope and can be seen only in an electron microscope. Viruses are the smallest known living things. Much current research is concentrated on viruses. Like the rickettsiae, they can grow only within living tissues.

At present there is no universally accepted classification of viruses. For our purpose, we can think of them in relation to the diseases which they cause. There is a considerable number of them—measles, polio, hepatitis, smallpox and the common cold, to name a few. In Table 4 are listed representative viral diseases.

PROTOZOA

With the **protozoa** (pro-to-zo'ah) we come to the one and only group of microbes which can be definitely classed as animals because of their mode of nutrition. Although the protozoa are one-celled, like the bacteria, they are much larger. Protozoa are found in almost any body of water from moist grass to mud puddles to the sea.

There are 4 main divisions of the protozoa:

1. **Amebae** (ah-me'bae). An ameba is an irregular blob of protoplasm which propels itself by extending a branch of itself (a "false foot") and then flowing over it. Amebic dysentery is caused by a pathogen of this group.

2. **Ciliates** (sil'e-ates). These organisms are covered with tiny hairs called cilia which produce a wave motion to propel the creature.

3. **Flagellates** (flaj'e-lates). These organisms are propelled by the long whiplike filaments called flagella.

4. **Sporozoa** (spo-ro-zo'ah). Unlike other protozoa, the sporozoa cannot propel themselves. They are parasites, unable to grow outside the host. A member of this group causes malaria.

Table 5 is a list of typical pathogenic protozoa with the diseases for which they are responsible.

PARASITIC WORMS

Many species of worms (also referred to as **helminths**) are parasitic by nature and select the human organism as their host. Whereas invasion by any form of organism is usually called an infection, the presence of parasitic worms in the body also can be termed an **infestation.**

COMMON ROUNDWORM

The most common of the intestinal worms is the large rounded **ascaris** (as'kah-ris), which is very prevalent in China but is believed to infest more than one third of the

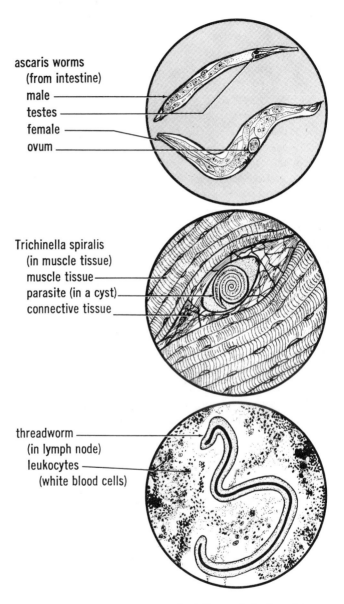

Fig. 8. Common parasitic worms.

ascaris worms
(from intestine)
male
testes
female
ovum

Trichinella spiralis
(in muscle tissue)
muscle tissue
parasite (in a cyst)
connective tissue

threadworm
(in lymph node)
leukocytes
(white blood cells)

rural population of the United States as well. In the United States it is found especially frequently in the children of the rural South. This worm resembles the earthworm (fishworm) in appearance and may be present in such large numbers that intestinal obstruction ensues. The eggs produced by the adult worms are very resistant so that they can live in soil during either freezing or hot, dry weather and cannot be destroyed even by strong antiseptics. The embryo worms develop within the eggs deposited with excreta in the soil, and later reach the digestive system of a victim by means of contaminated food. Discovery of this condition may be made by a routine stool examination.

PINWORMS

Another fairly common infestation, particularly in children, is the seat or **pinworm** (*Enterobius vermicularis*), which is also very hard to control and eliminate. The worms average somewhat less than one half inch in length and live in the lower part of the alimentary tract. The adult female moves outside to the vicinity of the anus to lay its thousands of eggs. These eggs are often transferred by the child's fingers from the itching anal area to the mouth. In the digestive system of the victim the eggs develop to form new adult worms, and thus a new infestation is begun. The child also may infect others by this means. Patience and every precaution, with careful attention to the doctor's instructions, are necessary if the patient is to be rid of the worms. Washing the hands, keeping fingernails clean, and avoiding finger sucking are all essential.

HOOKWORMS

Hookworms are parasites that live in the small intestine. They are dangerous because they suck blood from the host and also do great physical damage to the tissues, causing such a severe anemia (blood deficiency) that the victim becomes sluggish, both physically and mentally. Most victims become susceptible to various chronic infections because of greatly reduced resistance following such a great and continuous blood loss. Hookworms lay thousands of eggs, which are distributed in the soil by contaminated excreta. The eggs develop into small larvae which are able to penetrate the intact skin of bare feet. They enter the blood, and by way of the circulating fluids, the lungs and the upper respiratory tract finally reach the digestive system. Prevention of this infestation is accomplished best by the proper disposal of excreta, attention to sanitation, and the wearing of shoes in areas where the soil is contaminated.

OTHER ROUNDWORMS

While most roundworms are transmitted via excreta, the small **Trichinella** (trik-i-nel'ah) found in pork and other muscle foods is an exception. These tiny round worms become enclosed in a cyst, that is, a sac, inside the muscles of the rat, the pig and man. If the pork is not well cooked, these sacs or cysts are dissolved by the host's digestive juices, and the tiny worms mature and travel to the muscles

Fig. 9. Tapeworm. The many segments (proglottids) may be lost without injuring the parasite as long as the head is attached to the host's intestine.

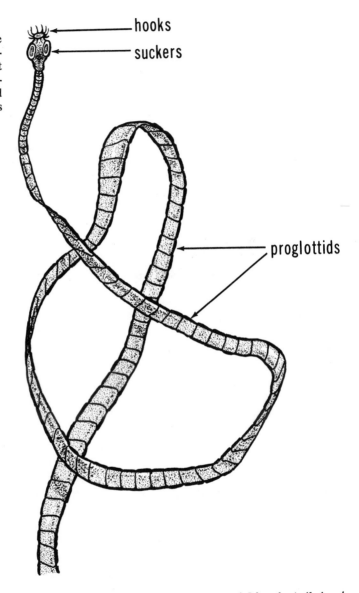

hooks

suckers

proglottids

where they again become encased. This disease is known as **trichinosis** (trik-i-no′ sis). Another threadlike worm causes **filariasis** (fil-ah-ri′ah-sis). This tiny worm is transmitted by such biting insects as flies and mosquitoes. The worms grow in large numbers, causing various body disturbances. If the lymph vessels become clogged by them, there results a condition called **elephantiasis** (el-e-fan-ti′ah-sis) in which the lower extremities and the scrotum may become tremendously enlarged. Filariasis is most common in tropical and subtropical lands, such as southern Asia and many of the South Pacific islands.

FLATWORMS

Some flatworms resemble long ribbons, while others are shaped like a leaf. Tapeworms may grow in the intestinal tract to a length of from 5 to 50 feet (see Fig. 9). They are spread by infected improperly cooked meats, including beef, pork and fish. As is the case with most intestinal and worm parasites, the reproductive systems are very highly developed, so that each worm produces an almost unbelievable number of eggs which then may contaminate food, water and soil. The leaf-shaped flatworms are known as flukes; they may invade various parts of the body including the blood, the lungs, the liver and the intestine.

MICROBIAL CONTROL

THE SPREAD OF MICROORGANISMS

There is scarcely a place on earth which is naturally free of microorganisms. One exception is the interior of normal body tissue. But on external body surfaces, on lining membranes and inside of tubes and organs that are connected with the outside—such as the mouth, throat, nasal cavities, and large intestine—both harmless and pathogenic microbes live in abundance. As will be explained in Chapter 20, the body has natural defenses against these organisms. If these natural defenses are sound, a person may harbor many microbes without ill effect. However, if his resistance becomes lowered, an infection can result.

Microbes are spread about through an almost infinite variety of means. The simplest way is by person-to-person contact. The more crowded the conditions, the greater the chances of epidemics breaking out. The atmosphere is a carrier of microorganisms. Although microbes cannot fly, the dust of the air is alive with them. In close quarters the atmosphere is further contaminated by bacteria-laden droplets discharged by sneezing, coughing, and even normal conversation. Pathogens also are spread by such pests as rats, mice, fleas, lice, flies and mosquitoes. Microbial growth is further abetted by the prevalence of dirt and the lack of sunlight. In slum areas there is often a combination of crowded conditions and poor sanitation. In addition, many of the inhabitants have lowered resistance because of poor nutrition and other undesirable health practices. As a result, epidemics are apt to begin in these districts.

MICROBES AND PUBLIC HEALTH

An institution of all civilized societies is the establishment and legal enforcement of measures designed to protect the health of their members. Most of these practices are concerned with preventing the spread of infectious organisms. A few examples of fundamental public health considerations are listed:

Sewage and Garbage Disposal. In times past, when people disposed of the household "slops" by the simple expedient of throwing them out the window, great epidemics were inevitable. Modern practice is to divert sewage into a processing plant in which harmless bacteria are put to work in destroying the pathogens. The resulting noninfectious "sludge" makes excellent fertilizer.

Purification of the Water Supply. Drinking water which has become polluted with untreated sewage may be contaminated with such dangerous pathogens as typhoid bacilli, the viruses of polio and hepatitis, and dysentery amebae. The municipal water supply usually is purified by a filtering process, and a close and constant watch is kept on its microbial population.

Prevention of Food Contamination. Various national, state and local laws all seek to prevent outbreaks of disease through contaminated food. Not only can certain animal diseases (tuberculosis, tularemia) be passed on, but food is a natural breeding place for many dangerous pathogens. Two organisms which cause food poisoning are the rod-shaped botulism bacillus (*Clostridium botulinum*) and the grapelike "staph" (*Staphylococcus aureus*). For further information see Table 1 of the Appendix.

Most cities have sanitary regulations requiring, among other things, compulsory periodic inspection of food-handling establishments and medical examination of personnel.

Milk Pasteurization. Milk is rendered free of pathogens by pasteurization, a process in which it is heated to 145° F. for 30 minutes and then is allowed to cool rapidly before being bottled. Pasteurized milk still contains microbes, but no harmful ones.

ASEPTIC METHODS

In the practice of medicine, surgery, nursing and other health fields, specialized procedures are performed for the purpose of reducing to a minimum the influence of pathogenic organisms. The word "sepsis" means "poisoning due to pathogens"; **asepsis** (ah-sep'sis) is its opposite: a condition in which no pathogens are present. Those procedures which are designed to kill, remove, or prevent the growth of microbes are called aseptic methods.

There are a number of terms designating aseptic practices, many of which are often confused with one another. Some of the more commonly used terms and their definitions are as follows:

Sterilization. To sterilize an object means to kill *every* living microorganism on it. In operating rooms and delivery rooms especially, as much of the environment is kept sterile as is practicable—for instance, the gowns worn by operating room personnel and the instruments used. The usual sterilization agent is live steam under pressure, or else dry heat. Most pathogens can be killed by exposure to boiling

water for 4 minutes. However,—and this is a vitally important fact to remember—
a very few types of pathogenic bacteria are capable of developing a highly resistant
armorlike coat. The resulting stage is called a **spore.** Spores are very difficult to kill
To insure destruction of all spore-forming organisms, the time and temperature for
sterilization are much greater than are required to kill most pathogens.

Disinfection. Disinfection refers to any measure which kills all pathogens (except
spores), but not necessarily all harmless microbes as well. Most disinfecting agents
(disinfectants) are chemical. Examples are iodine and phenol (carbolic acid). Two
other terms for bacteria-killing agents, synonymous with disinfectant, are **bactericide**
and **germicide.**

Antisepsis. This term refers to any process in which pathogens are not necessarily
killed, but are prevented from multiplying, a state called **bacteriostasis** (bak-te-re-
os'tah-sis). **Antiseptics** are less powerful than disinfectants.

CHEMOTHERAPY

Chemotherapy (ke-mo-ther'ah-pe) is the treatment of disease by the administration
of chemical substances which kill or prevent the growth of pathogenic organisms
within the body. Unlike disinfectants, which cannot be taken into the body without
damage to its tissues, chemotherapeutic agents exert what is called a selective
action; that is, they act against the parasites without harm to the host. For instance,
quinine (made from the bark of a tree) kills the malaria parasite but does not
injure the body tissues. A large group of chemotherapeutic agents are the sulfon-
amide ("sulfa") compounds, used against a number of disease organisms. Because
these drugs can be toxic to the body in some cases, they have been largely
superseded by the antibiotics.

Antibiotics. An antibiotic is a chemical substance, produced by *living* cells. It
has the power to kill or arrest the growth of pathogenic microorganisms by upsetting
vital chemical processes within them. Most antibiotics are derived from molds and
soil bacteria. Penicillin, the most widely used antibiotic, is made from a common
blue mold, *Penicillium.* Another large group of antibiotics is produced by *Strepto-
myces,* a type of soil bacteria; a well-known example of this group is streptomycin.

Although the development of antibiotics has been of incalculable benefit to
mankind, it has also given rise to serious complications. One danger is that of
secondary infection. For example, an antibiotic may be given to combat the bacteria
causing a specific disease. Now, it may well be that coexisting in the body with
these pathogens is a second type of disease organism—say a fungus. Up to the time
of the administration of the drug the fungus had been no danger to the body because its growth had been suppressed by the bacteria. If the fungus's natural enemy
now is eliminated, and the fungus happens to be unaffected by the antibiotic, there
is nothing to prevent it from growing unrestrainedly and setting up a new infection
which is very difficult to cure.

Another danger in the use of antibiotics is the development of allergy (an abnormal reaction) to these substances within certain individuals. This complication can have very dangerous consequences.

Finally, the widespread use of antibiotics has resulted in the natural evolution of strains of pathogens which are resistant to such medications. One of the greatest problems in hospitals today is the prevalence of antibiotic-resistant ("drug-fast") staphylococci, which cause serious infections that may be unresponsive to chemotherapy.

LABORATORY IDENTIFICATION OF PATHOGENS

The nurse, physician or laboratory worker may obtain specimens from the patient in order to identify bacteria and other organisms. Specimens most frequently studied include blood, spinal fluid, feces, urine and sputum, as well as swabbings from other areas. Swabs are used to collect specimens from the nose, throat, eyes, and cervix, and from ulcers or other infected areas.

There are so many different kinds of bacteria requiring indentification that the laboratory must use a number of procedures for determining which organism is present in the material obtained from the patient. One of the most frequently used methods for beginning the process of identification involves the application of colored dyes, known as stains, to a thin smear of the specimen on a glass slide. After being stained with a reddish dye (carbolfuchsin), the smear may be treated with acid. Most bacteria quickly lose their stain upon application of the acid, but the organisms that cause tuberculosis and leprosy remain colored. Such organisms are said to be **acid-fast.**

Another commonly used procedure is known as the **Gram stain.** A bluish dye (such as methyl violet or gentian violet) is applied and then a weak solution of iodine is added. This causes a color-fast combination within certain organisms so that the use of alcohol or other solvents does not remove the dye. These bacteria are said to be **Gram-positive.** Examples are the pathogenic staphylococci and streptococci, the cocci that cause certain types of pneumonia, and the bacilli that produce diphtheria, tetanus, and anthrax. Other organisms are said to be **Gram-negative** because the coloring can be removed from them by the use of a solvent, such as acetone or alcohol. Examples of Gram-negative organisms are those diplococci that cause gonorrhea and epidemic meningitis, and the bacilli that produce typhoid fever, influenza, and 1 type of dysentery. The colon bacillus, normally found in the bowel, is also Gram-negative, as is the cholera vibrio. A few organisms do not stain with any of the commonly used dyes, such as the spirochete of syphilis and the rickettsiae. Special staining techniques must be used to identify those organisms.

In addition to the various staining procedures, other laboratory techniques include; (1) growing bacteria for study by culture, a process using substances called media (such as nutrient broth or agar) that bacteria can use as food; (2) studying the ability of bacteria to act on (ferment) various carbohydrates (sugars); (3) counting bacteria in a given specimen by specialized processes; (4) inoculating animals and analyzing their reactions to the injections; and (5) studying bacteria by serologic (blood) tests, mostly based on the antigen-antibody reaction (see Chap. 20). These are but a few of the many laboratory procedures that play a vital part in the process of diagnosing disease.

SUMMARY

1. **Disease:** abnormal state of part or all of the body.
2. **Direct causes of disease:** pathogenic organisms, malnutrition, physical and chemical agents, congenital and inherited abnormalities, degeneration, neoplasms.
3. **Predisposing factors:** age, sex, heredity, living conditions and habits, occupation, physical exposure, preexisting illness, psychogenic influences.
4. **Fundamental medical sciences:** anatomy, physiology, pathology.
5. **Terminology.**
    A. Etiology: study of causation.
    B. Incidence: range of occurrence.
    C. Disease description.
        (1) Acute: severe, short duration.
        (2) Chronic: less severe, long duration.
        (3) Subacute: intermediate between above in severity and duration.
        (4) Idiopathic: unknown cause.
        (5) Communicable: transmissible.
        (6) Epidemic: widespread in a given region.
        (7) Endemic: characteristic of a given region.
    D. Diagnosis: determination of the nature of an illness.
    E. Symptom: change in body function felt by patient.
    F. Sign: change in body function observable by others.
    G. Syndrome: characteristic group of signs and symptoms.
    H. Therapy: course of treatment.
    I. Prevention: removing potential causes of disease.
6. **Infection:** invasion of the body by microorganisms.
7. **Microorganisms** (also called microbes or germs).
    A. Microscopic living things.
    B. Disease-causing microorganisms are called pathogens.
8. **Bacteria.**
    A. One-celled plants.
    B. Classified according to shape.
        (1) Bacilli (straight rods).
        (2) Cocci (dot-shaped).
            (a) Diplococci: pairs.
            (b) Streptococci: chains.
            (c) Staphylococci: bunches.

(3) Curved rods.
    (a) Vibrios: comma shaped.
    (b) Spirilla: corkscrew or wavy shaped.
    (c) Spirochetes: like spirilla but flexible body.
  C. Pathogenic species produce toxins or growth within body cells.

9. **Fungi.**
  A. Simple plants, larger than bacteria.
  B. Yeasts and molds include pathogenic species.

10. **Rickettsiae:** smaller than bacteria, obligate parasites.

11. **Viruses:** smallest microorganisms, obligate parasites.

12. **Protozoa.**
  A. Only microbes in animal kingdom.
  B. Divisions: amebae, ciliates, flagellates, sporozoa.

13. **Parasitic worms** (helminths).
  A. Roundworms: ascaris, pinworms (both intestinal parasites); Trichinella (encysted in muscle tissue); threadworms (clog lymph vessels).
  B. Hookworms: intestinal parasites, cause anemia.
  C. Flatworms: tapeworms (intestinal parasites); flukes (invade intestine, lungs, liver, etc.).

14. **Microbial controls.**
  A. Spread of microorganisms.
    (1) Body normally harbors parasites.
    (2) Microbes spread by direct contact, dust, droplets, vermin.
  B. Public health measures: sewage disposal, water purification, food inspection, milk pasteurization.
  C. Aseptic methods: sterilization (total removal of organisms); disinfection (destruction of pathogens except spores); antisepsis (bacteriostasis).
  D. Chemotherapy.
    (1) Purpose: to kill or inhibit microbes in body without tissue damage.
    (2) Principal agents: antibiotics.
    (3) Disadvantages of antibiotics: allergy, secondary infection, drug-fast strains.

15. **Laboratory identification of pathogens.**
  A. Examples of acid-fast organisms: those causing tuberculosis and leprosy.
  B. Examples of Gram-positive organisms: those causing diphtheria, tetanus, anthrax, and certain types of pneumonia.
  C. Examples of Gram-negative organisms: those causing gonorrhea, epidemic meningitis, typhoid fever, influenza, and 1 type of dysentery.

QUESTIONS AND PROBLEMS

1. What is disease: List 5 direct and 5 indirect causes.
2. Define: etiology, incidence, acute, chronic, idiopathic, epidemic, endemic, diagnosis, symptom, sign, syndrome, therapy, infection, pathogen.

3. What are the 3 characteristic shapes of bacterial cells? Name a typical disease caused by each group.
4. In what ways are bacteria beneficial to man?
5. How do bacteria differ from rickettsiae and viruses from the point of view of size and living habits?
6. What is the typical mode of transmission of rickettsial infections?
7. What microbial group is classed as animals? Name 2 diseases caused by these.
8. Name 2 types of pathogenic fungi, and 1 common fungous infection.
9. List 4 viral diseases and 2 rickettsial diseases.
10. Name 3 shapes of parasitic worms.
11. What are the most common ways by which disease organisms are spread? What measures do communities take to prevent outbreaks of disease?
12. Define: asepsis, sterilization, disinfection, antisepsis.
13. What are some disadvantages in the use of antibiotics?
14. What are laboratory stains and why are they used? What are examples of acid-fast, Gram-negative, and Gram-positive organisms?

CHAPTER 3

CHEMISTRY, MATTER AND LIFE

Definition of chemistry ▪ Atoms and elements ▪ Molecules, compounds and mixtures ▪ Ions and electrolytes ▪ The chemistry of living matter ▪ DNA.

WHAT IS CHEMISTRY?

Recently the greatest strides toward understanding living organisms, including the human being, have come to us through **chemistry,** the science that deals with the composition of matter. It is through knowledge of chemistry that we are able to understand the normal and the abnormal functions of the body and its parts. The digestion of food in the intestinal tract, the production of urine by the kidneys, the regularity of breathing, all body processes are based on chemical principles. Chemistry also forms the foundation of microbiology and pharmacology (the study of drugs). Antiseptics, such as hexachlorophene used to cleanse the skin before a surgical operation, are chemicals, as are aspirin, penicillin and all other drugs used in treating disease. In order to have some understanding of the importance of chemistry in the health field, this chapter will briefly describe the **atoms, elements, molecules, compounds,** and **mixtures** which are the fundamental units of matter.

A LOOK AT ATOMS AND ELEMENTS

Atoms are inconceivably small particles that form the building blocks of matter, the smallest complete units of which all matter is made. To visualize the size of an atom, one can think of placing millions of them on the sharpened end of a pencil and still having room for more. Everything about us, everything we can see or touch, is made of atoms—the food we eat, the atmosphere, the water in the oceans, the smoke coming out of the chimney.

Despite the fact that the atom is such a tiny particle, it has been carefully studied and has been found to have a definite structure. An atom is made up of a **nucleus**

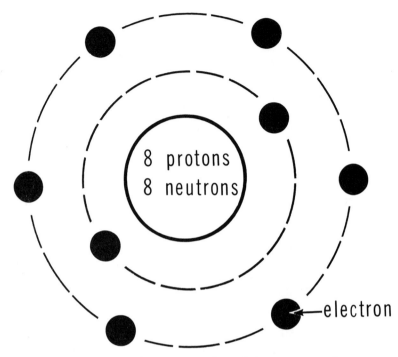

FIG. 10. Diagrammatic representation of the structure of an oxygen atom with 8 protons and 8 neutrons in the central nucleus, around which the electrons revolve.

(not to be confused with the cell nucleus) which contains positively charged electric particles called **protons** and noncharged particles called **neutrons.** The protons and the neutrons determine the weight of an atom and also whether it is radioactive (to be discussed later). Surrounding the nucleus in rapidly revolving orbits or rings are negatively charged electric particles called **electrons,** equal in number to the protons in the nucleus (see Fig. 10). An atom of one substance differs from the atom of another in the arrangement of these "subatomic" particles. For example, an atom of hydrogen has 1 electron whirling around 1 proton in the nucleus, while an atom of oxygen has 8 electrons whirling around 8 protons in the nucleus. The atom has been likened to the solar system in that the electrons orbit the nucleus as the planets orbit the sun.

Any substance that is composed of atoms of just 1 type is called an **element.** An element cannot be decomposed—that is, changed into something else—by physical means (e.g., by the use of heat, pressure, electricity), nor can it be broken up by chemical methods. Examples of elements include various gases, such as hydrogen, oxygen and nitrogen; liquids, such as the mercury used in thermometers and blood pressure instruments; and many solids, such as iron, aluminum, gold, silver and carbon. Graphite (the so-called lead in a pencil), coal, charcoal, and the diamond are examples of the element carbon. The entire universe is made up of about 100 elements. However, most are combined with others to form the compounds we will discuss in the next section.

No discussion of elements and the atoms they are made of is complete without reference to the part some play in the diagnosis and treatment of disease. Atoms of an element may exist in several forms called **isotopes.** These forms are alike in their chemical reactions but differ in weight. For example heavy oxygen is much like regular oxygen except for its weight. This greater weight is due to the presence of a larger number of neutrons in the nucleus of the heavier isotope. Isotopes may be stable and maintain a contant character; others fall apart (disintegrate) as they give off small particles called rays, and these are said to be **radioactive.** Radioactive ·elements may occur naturally as is the case with such very heavy isotopes as radium and uranium. Others may be produced artificially from non-radioactive elements such as iodine and gold by bombarding (smashing) the atoms in special machines.

The rays given off by radioactive elements have the ability to penetrate and destroy tissues and so are used in the treatment of cancer and other illnesses. Radioactive materials may be placed in a special apparatus called a bomb, as with radioactive cobalt in the **cobalt bomb** used in the treatment of deep-seated cancer.

In addition to its therapeutic values, radiation is extensively used in diagnosis. X-rays penetrate the tissues and produce an impression of their interior on a photographic plate. Radioactive iodine and other "tracers" show the workings of many body organs. Rigid precautions must be followed by hospital personnel to protect themselves and the patient when using radiation in diagnosis or therapy because the rays can destroy healthy as well as diseased tissues.

In addition to its value in medicine, radioactivity plays an important part in industry. Certain synthetic plastic material, such as the polyethylene ware used in hospitals, retains its shape and usefulness at considerably higher temperatures after having been exposed to radioactivity. An example is the tubing used in some laboratories. There is also extensive research being carried on involving the "irradiation" of various types of foods to retain their quality longer. It may be that in the near future we will be able to buy ten pounds of potatoes instead of five without having to worry about their sprouting before being used.

MOLECULES, COMPOUNDS AND MIXTURES

When 2 or more atoms unite, a **molecule** is formed. It can be made of *like* atoms, as in the case of the oxygen molecule which is made of 2 identical atoms. More often, however, we think of molecules as including 2 or more different atoms. For example, a molecule of sodium chloride, which is common table salt, includes one atom of sodium and one of chlorine. Those substances that contain molecules formed by the union of 2 or more different atoms are called **compounds.** Compounds may be made of a few elements in a simple combination or they may be very complex. The simplest compound would be one whose molecule contains one atom of each of the 2 elements which unite to form the compound. An example of such a compound is the gas carbon monoxide, which contains 1 atom of carbon and 1 atom of oxygen. Most of the compounds that are classified as organic (because they were first found only in living organisms) are very complex. The starch found in potatoes, the fatty layer of tissue under the skin and the majority of drugs are organic compounds.

It is interesting to observe how different a compound is from any of its constituents. For example, 2 atoms of hydrogen, which we know as a gas, unite with 1 atom of oxygen, also a gas, to form a molecule of a liquid, water. Water is remarkably different in its appearance and its properties from its component gases. Another example is a form of sugar, glucose, a thick syrupy liquid. Its constituents include 12 atoms of the gas hydrogen; 6 atoms of the gas oxygen; and 6 atoms of the solid element carbon. In this case, the component gases and the solid carbon do not in any way resemble the glucose.

It is fortunate that not all elements or compounds combine chemically when brought together. If such were the case, we would be unable to keep intact the hundred or so different compounds in blood plasma while it is dried or frozen. Dried (powdered) plasma may be sent long distances easily and inexpensively. It may then be reconstituted by adding sterile water as it is needed in a war zone or at the scene of a major disaster. The many valuable compounds in the plasma remain separate entities with their own properties. Such combinations are called **mixtures.** Salt water is a mixture, both the salt and the water remaining separate compounds. The substances in a mixture can be present in any proportion, while in a compound the elements combine in definite proportions. You can stir any amount of salt into a given amount of water and still have a mixture. However, if one more atom of oxygen were added to a water molecule, you would have an entirely new compound called hydrogen peroxide, not water. Air is a mixture of gases, and any room with people in it will contain less oxygen than an empty room. Seawater is a mixture of water and dissolved solids; the amount of each will vary in different places, the water being less salty near the mouths of rivers. The compounds in a mixture can usually be separated by mechanical means, such as dissolving or boiling. If salt water is boiled, the compound water will eventually escape as steam or vapor, which, if collected in a bottle and cooled, regains its water state. The compound salt will remain in the pan appearing as the original white granules.

To better understand the relationship of mixtures, compounds, elements, molecules and atoms, we can follow the changes that occur in the transfer of a mixture to the individual atom. As was previously mentioned, salt and water in a salt water mixture regain their original properties by simple boiling. If we were able to take one grain of salt and cut it into halves, cut one section in half again, and continue doing so, we would still have the same properties as salt. The smallest particle obtainable that would still have the properties of salt is the salt molecule, which is made up of 1 atom of the element sodium, and 1 atom of the element chlorine. Thus we have regressed from the mixture to the atom. To summarize, we can say that salt water, a mixture, is made up of 2 compounds, salt and water. The components of salt are atoms of the element sodium, and atoms of the element chlorine. The water, of course, can be broken down in like manner to its atoms of hydrogen and oxygen.

IONS AND ELECTROLYTES

When discussing the structure of the atom, we mentioned the positively charged protons that are located in the nucleus, with the corresponding number of negatively charged electrons orbiting in the surrounding space and neutralizing the protons. If we can imagine removing a single electron from the sodium atom, it would leave 1 proton not neutralized, and the atom would have a positive charge. This can actually happen—the freely whirling electron can leap out of its orbit. Likewise atoms can gain electrons so that there are more electrons than protons. Such an atom is negatively charged. An atom with a positive or negative charge is called an **ion.** An ion that is positively charged is a **cation,** while a negatively charged ion is an **anion.**

When an atom loses an electron, it searches for another electron and will attach itself to an anion that has an extra one. The anion, in turn, is eager to give up its extra one to the cation. Let us imagine a positively charged sodium ion coming in contact with a negatively charged chlorine atom. The chlorine atom readily gives up its extra electron to the needy sodium ion and the 2 particles, because of their opposite charges which attract each other, will cling together and produce the compound sodium chloride. As was previously mentioned, this is ordinary table salt. A vast number of chemical compounds are made by this method of *electron transfer*.

In the tissue fluids and in the cells of the body, ions make it possible for materials to be altered, broken down, and recombined to form new substances. Calcium ions are necessary for the clotting of blood, the normal relaxation of muscle, and the health of bone tissue. Carbonate ions are required for the regulation of acidity and alkalinity of the tissues. The stable condition of the normal organism, called **homeostasis** (ho-me-o-sta′sis), is influenced by ions (see Chap. 7).

Compounds that form ions whenever they are in solution are called **electrolytes** (e-lek′tro-lites). Electrolytes are responsible for the acidity and the alkalinity of solutions. They include a variety of mineral salts, such as sodium and potassium chloride. Electrolytes must be present in exactly the right quantities in the fluid within the cell (intracellular) and outside the cell (extracellular) or there will be very damaging effects on the cells in the body, preventing them from functioning properly.

Since ions are charged particles, electrolytes can conduct an electric current. Records of electric currents in tissues are valuable indications of the functioning or malfunctioning of tissues and organs. The **electrocardiogram** (e-lek-tro-kar′de-o-gram) and the **electroencephalogram** (e-lek-tro-en-sef′ah-lo-gram) are graphic tracings (recorded by special instruments) of the electric currents generated by the heart muscle and the brain respectively (see Chaps 10 and 12).

THE CHEMISTRY OF LIVING MATTER

Perhaps the most interesting and baffling of all substances is **protoplasm,** the component of all living cells and tissues that was mentioned briefly in Chapter 1. Living matter is made up of atoms and molecules that are readily identifiable. Nevertheless, scientists have tried in vain over the years to produce protoplasm in the laboratory. Of the 100 or so elements that have been found in nature, only a relatively few, and those the lighter ones, are important components of protoplasm. Hydrogen, oxygen, carbon, and nitrogen are the elements that make up about 99 per cent of protoplasm. Calcium, sodium, potassium, phosphorus, sulfur, chlorine, and magnesium are the 7 elements that make up most of the remaining 1 per cent of the tissue elements. There are a number of others that are present in trace amounts, such as iron, copper, iodine, and fluorine.

From these elements the compounds that are formed and are most important in the human organism include the proteins, carbohydrates, and lipids (fatlike substances). The carbohydrates and lipids contain carbon, hydrogen, and oxygen as their chief and usually only elements. Proteins contain nitrogen as an important addition to the carbon, hydrogen, and oxygen.

As was previously mentioned, in appearance, protoplasm resembles the white of an egg.

Protoplasm is not of a uniform composition but includes a variety of substances, intricately organized. Dissolved in the water of protoplasm are mineral (inorganic) salts, simple sugars, and other substances. In addition to this complex solution, there is a variety of protein and fat molecules which seem to change from a fluid or *sol* state to a semisolid condition, known as the *gel* state. If we think of Jello or gelatin, we may remember that changes in temperature can cause it to become liquid with warmer conditions or solid with colder states. Such factors as the concentration of salts, pressure, agitation (shaking), as well as temperature variations cause changes back and forth between the sol state and the gel state within the protoplasm.

One of the general characteristics of protoplasm is its ability to grow and reproduce. If protoplasm could not reproduce, a man might eventually be without the outer layer of his skin, the cells of which continuously have to be replaced as a result of constant shedding. Other characteristics include the ability to move and to respond to a change in the environment. When you use the muscles in your finger to bend it, the cells in the muscle tissue becomes shorter and thicker to bring about the movement of the bones to which they are attached. When a stimulus is applied to a nerve cell, thus changing its environment, an electric impulse travels along its fibers. There are very few of us who have not experienced the sensation of pain when the dentist strikes a nerve-ending with his drill. Finally, protoplasm carries on the amazing complex process of metabolism which enables it to build protein and produce energy. Each body cell is constantly receiving food and oxygen and passing out waste products through its wall (see Chap. 4). This enables it to carry on its many busy chemical activities.

DNA

Among the most interesting of the complex compounds that are found in the protoplasm is one called **DNA** or **deoxyribonucleic** (de-ok-se-ri-bo-nu-kle'ik) **acid.** It is found in the cell nucleus and is believed to be the chief (or possibly only) component of the genes, the hereditary factors in each cell. The nucleus is the control center of the cell and DNA is a sort of master blueprint. Scientists think this and a few other complex and very large molecules found in the cell may very well contain the clue to the mystery of life.

SUMMARY

1. **Chemistry.**
    A. Deals with composition of matter.
    B. Includes study of atoms, elements, molecules, compounds, and mixtures.
2. **A look at atoms and elements.**
    A. Atoms are the smallest building blocks of all matter.
    B. Atomic nucleus consists of protons and neutrons.
    C. Electrons orbit around nucleus.
    D. Elements made of 1 type of atom.
    E. Elements cannot be subdivided chemically.
    F. Radioactivity important in medicine and industry.
3. **Molecules, compounds and mixtures.**
    A. Molecules contain 2 or more atoms, mostly of different kinds.
    B. Molecules may be simple and contain only 2 atoms.
    C. Molecules in human tissues may be very complex.
    D. Compounds contain 2 or more elements.
    E. Complex molecular structure in many organic compounds.
    F. Substances in a mixture are not combined chemically.
    G. Mixtures are made of substances in any proportions.
4. **Ions and electrolytes.**
    A. Atoms with electronic charges are ions.
    B. Many chemical compounds are made by electron transfer.
    C. Homeostasis is influenced by ions.
    D. Electrolytes are compounds that ionize when in solution.

5. **The chemistry of living matter.**
   A. Hydrogen, oxygen, carbon, and nitrogen are elements in largest quantity in protoplasm.
   B. Proteins, carbohydrates and lipids are compounds in protoplasm.
   C. Protoplasm can change back and forth from the fluid (sol) to the semisolid (gel) state.
6. **DNA.** The chief (and possibly only) component of genes, the hereditary factors in the cell nucleus.

QUESTIONS AND PROBLEMS
   1. Define chemistry and tell something about what is included in this study.
   2. What are atoms and what is known of their structure?
   3. What is an element and what are some examples of elements?
   4. What is meant by radioactivity and what are some of its practical uses?
   5. Define molecule, compound and mixture.
   6. What are organic compounds and what element is found in all of them?
   7. How does a mixture differ from a compound?
   8. What are ions and how are they related to electrolytes? What are some examples of ions and of what importance are they in the body?
   9. What elements are found in the largest amounts in protoplasm?
  10. What are some of the important groups of chemicals found in protoplasm?
  11. What is meant by the sol state and the gel state of protoplasm?
  12. Describe some of the general characteristics of protoplasm and give examples of how they enable the body to function.
  13. What is the importance of DNA?

CHAPTER 4

CELLS, TISSUES AND TUMORS

What happens in cells ▪ Tissues and tissue fluid ▪ Four kinds of tissue ▪ The supporting fabric of the body ▪ Gray and white matter ▪ Kinds of muscle tissue ▪ Benign and malignant tumors.

MORE ABOUT CELLS

In Chapter 1 we learned that the cell is the fundamental building block of all life, no matter whether the living thing, plant or animal, is made of but one cell or many millions of them. The cell may live alone, or may be only one unit of a complex structure; but whatever its state, cell changes, including energy production and cell division (reproduction) go on constantly.

Careful microscopic studies of the cell protoplasm have revealed the presence of tiny structures called **organelles** (or-gah-nels') that are concerned with a variety of functions within the cell. Among these organelles are rod-shaped bodies called **mitochondria** (mit-o-kon'dre-ah). The mitochondria are responsible for the chemical combinations that result in the release of energy. This chemical activity involves the use of oxygen and nutrient materials and is accomplished by means of enzymes within the mitochondria. *the power house of the cell*

Enzymes are complex proteins which act as catalytic agents, that is, they increase the speed of chemical reactions without being changed themselves. The vast majority of chemical reactions that go on in living things are catalyzed by enzymes. In addition to performing many functions within the cell itself, some enzymes are active outside of the cell in secretions as, for example, in the digestive juices. Enzymes act in a very specific manner, as if they are too choosey to have anything to do with any substances except the particular ones to which they are attracted.

A cell reproduces by dividing in two. Exactly why it does is a tantalizing mystery; but the process of cell division is easy to visualize. First there is a division of the **centrosome** (sen'tro-som), a specialized structure just outside the nucleus of the cell containing two bodies called **centrioles** (sen'tri-ols). The divided centrioles then

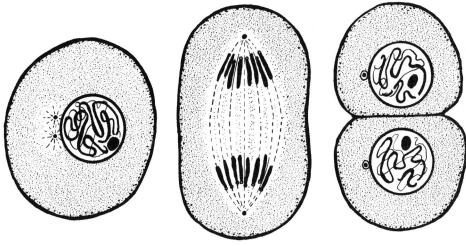

FIG. 11. Cell undergoing mitosis (simplified sequence). Note the divided centrosome, the change of the chromatin material of the nucleus into rod-shaped chromosomes, and the new cell membrane with the formation of 2 daughter cells.

move to opposite sides of the cell, trailing threadlike substances which form a structure resembling a spindle stretched across the cell.

During every cell division the most spectacular changes take place in the nucleus. The chromatin material found in the usual resting cell changes to become rod-shaped bodies called **chromosomes** (kro'mo-soms). These contain the **genes** (jenes) which are responsible for the inherited traits of each cell and eventually, those of the entire organism. The chromosomes split and separate, and half are drawn to each end of the cell, following the threadlike substances of the spindle that was formed by the centrioles.

Then the nucleus begins to elongate, becoming pinched in the middle until it begins to resemble a dumbbell. The cell wall takes on the same shape. The midsection between the 2 halves of the dumbbell becomes smaller and smaller until finally the cell splits in two. We now have 2 cells where there was but one. Each of these 2 **daughter** cells (the original is called, logically enough, the **parent** cell) usually receives exactly half the cell wall, half the cytoplasm, half the nucleus and other material of its parent. The name for this cell division is **mitosis** (mi-to'sis) (see Fig. 11). During the later phases of mitosis new pairs of centrioles are formed in preparation for the next cell division.

So far, so good; we have 2 new cells, but since each cell has only half the material that its parent contained, it is small and must grow before it is able to function or to reproduce itself in turn. Cells are alive, and all living things need food to grow and to produce energy; therefore the cell must receive nourishment somehow. This would seem to be a problem, since we learned that most cells are

FIG. 12. Diagram to show the diffusion of gaseous molecules throughout a given space. The bottle could contain a chlorine bleach, perfume, or a spray of some kind. In any case, there is a tendency for the molecules to spread throughout the area.

surrounded by a protective wall. However, if the cell is bathed in a liquid containing dissolved food materials, an interesting thing happens: the liquid with the dissolved food particles passes through the cell membrane. Not only do the nutrient molecules pass in, but waste products pass out of the cell in the opposite direction. The membrane also keeps valuable protein and other substances from leaving the cell and prevents the admission of undesirable substances. For this reason, the cell wall is classified as a **semipermeable** (sem-e-per′me-ah-ble) membrane, being very selective in what it allows to enter and to leave the cell. It is permeable or passable to some molecules but is impassable to others.

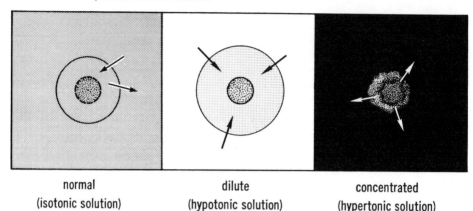

| normal | dilute | concentrated |
| (isotonic solution) | (hypotonic solution) | (hypertonic solution) |

FIG. 13. Diagram to illustrate osmosis. Water molecules moving through a cell membrane into a solution of salts in high concentration. The normal saline solution has a concentration nearly the same as that inside the cell; the dilute solution causes the cell to swell and eventually rupture because of so many water molecules moving into the cell; the concentrated solution causes the water molecules to move out of the cell, leaving it shrunken.

A combination of various physical processes is responsible for the phenomenon of exchanges through the cell wall or through the tissue membranes that are made up of a combination of many cells. Some of these are:

1. **Diffusion,** the movement of molecules from a region of relatively high concentration to one of lower concentration. Molecules, especially those in solution, tend to spread throughout an area, as do gases, seemingly in an effort to become evenly distributed (see Fig. 12).

2. **Osmosis,** the passage of a solvent, usually water, through a semipermeable membrane, with the molecules going from the less concentrated solution to the one that is more concentrated (the reverse of what happens in diffusion). The effect, however, still is a tendency to equalize the concentrations of the various substances in a given area (see Fig. 13).

3. **Filtration,** the passage of water containing dissolved materials through a membrane as a result of a greater mechanical force on one side (see Fig. 14). An example of filtration in the human body is the formation of urine in the microscopic functional units of the kidney as described in Chapter 17.

The liquid that surrounds the cells of the body has dissolved in it not only food materials but oxygen as well, both of which have been transported to the cells by means of the blood and other fluids. After the food and oxygen pass into the cell, a sequence of chemical reactions occurs. This whole process is given the broad, general name of **metabolism** (me-tab'o-lizm). Here is what actually goes on in metabolism. When the food enters the cell, the oxygen that accompanies it "touches off" a chemical reaction that is aided by the enzymes in the mitochondria. Some of

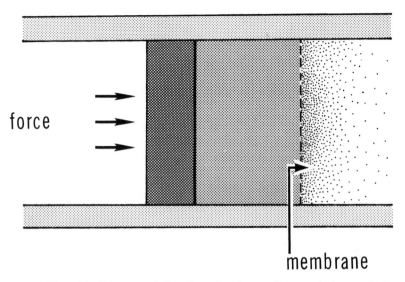

force

membrane

FIG. 14. Diagram of filtration, showing a substance being pushed through a membrane by a mechanical force.

the food is used by the cell to produce heat and energy and some to build up new protoplasm. As happens after any fire, waste products are left over. These are removed from the cell, to be carried away by the blood and other fluids. We see now that a cell is very much like a tiny factory, complete with its own power plant.

Thus the cell consumes food, builds itself up, generates heat and energy, and discharges waste materials. We already have investigated its reproductive process. Two other general traits of cells remain. The first of these is the ability to adapt itself to changing outside conditions. The second is the ability to discharge fluids through the cell wall. This latter trait was, of course, partially covered in the discussion of waste disposal. However, some specialized cells discharge other fluids as well, which are called **secretions.** These are substances that are produced in the cell by chemical modification of materials taken into the cell. Often these secretions serve a useful purpose elsewhere in the body.

The foregoing section should be concluded with a few qualifications. Some kinds of cells reproduce more readily than others; certain types, if they die, are not replaced at all. On the other hand, many thousands of new cells are formed daily in the skin and other tissues to replace those destroyed by injury, disease, or certain natural processes. As a person ages, characteristic changes in the overall activity of his body cells take place. One example of these is the slowing down of repair processes. The fracture of a bone, for example, takes considerably longer to heal in an aged person than in a young one.

At this point we are ready to proceed from the individual cell to the specialized groups of cells of which our bodies are made. Such groups are known as **tissues.**

ON TISSUES IN GENERAL

Although the basic structure of cells, as well as certain behavior patterns, remains constant regardless of the type of cell under discussion, cells themselves vary enormously with respect to shape, size, color and specialty. Many cells, for example, are transparent; some of these form the "window" of the eye. Other cells may have extensions in the form of thin fibers over a yard long, as in the case of some nerve cells. Some produce secretions; others transmit electrical impulses.

Tissues are groups of cells of the same type which have been brought together for a common purpose. In some ways the tissues in our bodies might be compared with the different materials which we use to clothe ourselves. Think for a moment of the great variety of materials employed in covering the body according to the degree of protection needed, the time of year, and so forth—wool, cotton, silk, rayon, leather, and even straw. All of these have different properties, as do tissues.

Before we begin a more detailed discussion of tissues, it might be interesting to note the surprising fact that we are virtually living in water. The tissues are full of it. The cells of which tissues are made contain from 60 per cent to 99 per cent water. Gases, liquids and solids dissolve in this water. Chemical reactions that are necessary for proper body function are carried on much more readily in a watery solution. Substances which do not go into solution may be suspended in the various liquids of the body, many of which circulate; and thus they may be moved from place to place. Water is indispensable for cell life, and lack of water causes death more rapidly than the lack of any other dietary constituent.

The solution of water and other materials in which the tissues are bathed is slightly salty, an interesting reminder of the first living cells which were created in the sea ages ago. This substance is called **tissue fluid.** Later, when we study the functions of the blood, we shall find out how food and oxygen manage to reach the cells of the tissues by way of the blood and the tissue fluid.

In connection with tissue fluid, it might be appropriate here to mention that an insufficiency of tissue fluid is called **dehydration,** and an abnormal accumulation of this fluid causes a condition called **edema** (e-de′mah), which shows up as a puffiness of the affected tissue.

TISSUE CLASSIFICATION

The 4 main groups of tissue are:
1. **Epithelium**—forms glands, covers surfaces and lines cavities.
2. **Connective tissue**—holds all parts of the body in place.
3. **Nerve tissue**—conducts nerve impulses.
4. **Muscle tissue**—designed for power-producing contractions.

Blood sometimes is considered a sort of tissue, since it contains cells and performs many of the functions of tissues. However, the blood has so many other unique characteristics and purposes that it will be taken up in a chapter of its own.

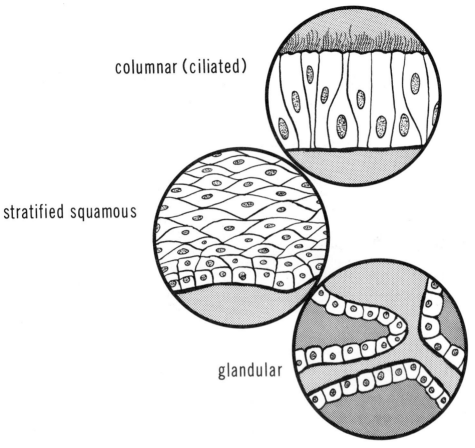

columnar (ciliated)

stratified squamous

glandular

FIG. 15. Three types of epithelium.

EPITHELIUM

Epithelium (ep-e-the'le-um) forms a protective covering for the body and all its organs; in fact, it is the main tissue of the outer layer of the skin. It forms the lining of the intestinal tract, the respiratory and urinary passages, the blood vessels, the uterus and other body cavities.

Epithelium has many forms and many purposes, and the cells of which it is composed vary accordingly. For instance, the cells of some kinds of epithelium produce secretions, such as **mucus** (mu'kus) (a clear, sticky fluid), digestive juices, perspiration, and other substances. The digestive tract is lined with a special kind of epithelium whose cells not only produce secretions but also are designed to absorb digested foods. The air that we breathe passes over yet another form of

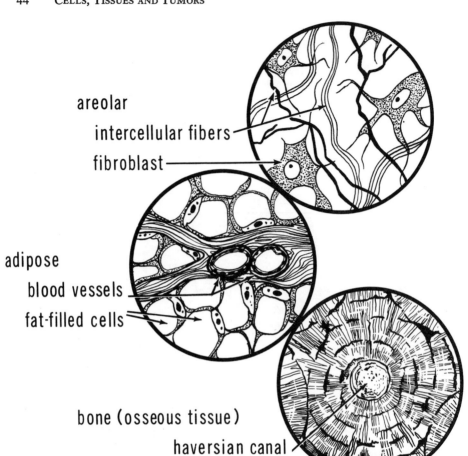

areolar

intercellular fibers

fibroblast

adipose

blood vessels

fat-filled cells

bone (osseous tissue)

haversian canal

(for nerves and blood vessels)

FIG. 16. Forms of connective tissue.

epithelium that lines the respiratory tract. This lining secretes mucus and also is provided with tiny hairlike projections called **cilia** (sil'e-ah) (see Fig. 15). Together, the mucus and the cilia help to trap bits of dust and other foreign particles which could otherwise reach the lungs and damage them. Some organs, such as the urinary bladder, must vary a great deal in size during the course of their work; and for this purpose there is a special wrinkled, crepelike type of epithelium which is capable of great expansion, yet will return to its original form once the tension is removed —as when, in this case, the bladder is emptied. Certain areas of the epithelium that forms the outer layer of the skin are capable of modifying themselves for greater strength whenever they are subjected to unusual wear and tear; the growth of calluses is a good example of this.

Epithelium will repair itself very quickly if it is injured. If, for example, there is a cut, the cells near and around the wound immediately form daughter cells which grow until the cut is closed. Sometimes, however, particularly after repeated injury, abnormal growths will occur; and these are given the general name of **tumors.** Some tumors remain localized. Others spread; and these are called **cancers.** Various kinds of abnormal growths will be discussed later on in this chapter.

CONNECTIVE TISSUE

The supporting fabric of the organs and the other parts of the body is connective tissue. If we were able to dissolve all the tissues except connective tissue, we would still be able to recognize the contour of the parts and the organs of the entire body. There are 2 distinct kinds of connective tissue, which are classified quite simply:

1. **Soft** connective tissues.
2. **Hard** connective tissues.

SOFT CONNECTIVE TISSUES

This group of connective tissues serves a number of different purposes. One group, called **adipose** (ad′e-pose) tissue, stores up fat for use by the body as a reserve food, a heat insulator, and as padding for various structures (see Fig. 16). Another kind of soft connective tissue serves as a binding between organs, as well as a framework for some organs which are otherwise made of epithelium. There is yet another form of this tissue which is particularly strong, being built up of fibers much like the strands of a cable. And, like a cable, this form of tissue serves to support certain organs which are subjected to powerful strains. A good example of this kind of tissue is a tendon.

There is another interesting function of soft connective tissue, and this is its use by nature to repair muscle and nerve tissue as well as to repair connective tissue itself. A large gaping wound will require a correspondingly large growth of this new connective tissue, as will an infected wound, and this new growth is called scar tissue. The process of repair includes stages in which new blood vessels are formed in the wound, followed by the growth of the scar tissue. An excessive development of the blood vessels in the early stages of repair may lead to the formation of so-called proud flesh. Normally, however, the blood vessels are gradually replaced by white fibrous connective tissue which forms the scar. Suturing (sewing) the edges of a clean wound together, as is done in the case of operative wounds, decreases the amount of scar tissue needed and hence reduces

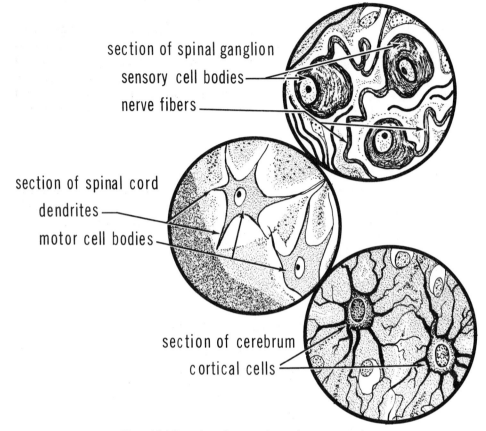

FIG. 17. Samples of nerve tissue (gray matter).

the size of the resulting scar. Such scar tissue may be stronger than the original tissue.

HARD CONNECTIVE TISSUES

The hard connective tissues, which, as the name suggests, are more solid than the other group, include cartilage and bones. Cartilage, popularly called gristle, is a tough, elastic and translucent material which is found in such places as between the segments of the spine and at the ends of the long bones. In these positions cartilage acts as a shock absorber as well as a bearing surface which reduces the friction between moving parts. Cartilage is found in other structures also, such as the nose, the ear, the epiglottis (the leaf-shaped structure below the throat) and other parts of the larynx, or "voice box."

The tissue of which the bones are made, called **osseous** (os'e-us) tissue (see Fig. 16), is very much like cartilage in its cellular structure. In fact, the bones of the unborn baby, in the early stages of development, are (except for some of the skull bones) nothing but cartilage. However, gradually this tissue becomes impregnated with calcium salts; and since calcium is another word for lime, we see that a mineral deposit is going on which finally leaves the bones in their characteristically hard and stony state. Within the bones are nerves, blood vessels, bone-forming cells, and a special form of tissue in which certain ingredients of the blood are manufactured.

A final comment on connective tissue in general is that, like epithelium, it repairs itself easily. In connective tissue, too, there may be abnormal growths of cells which form tumors.

NERVE TISSUE

The human body is made up of countless structures both great and small, each of which (with a few notable exceptions) contributes something to the action of the whole. This aggregation of structures might be considered as an army, all of whose members must work together. In order that they may, there must be a central coordinating and order-giving agency somewhere; otherwise chaos would ensue. In the body this central agency is the brain. Each structure of the body is in direct communication with the brain by means of its own set of telephone wires, called nerves. The nerves from even the most remote parts of the body all come together and form a great trunk cable called the spinal cord, which in turn leads directly into the central switchboard of the brain. Here, messages come in and orders go out 24 hours a day. This entire communication system, brain and all, is made of nerve tissue.

The basic structural unit of nerve tissue is called a **neuron** (nu'ron) (see Figs. 17, 37 and 38). A neuron consists of a nerve cell body plus small branches like those of a tree. These are called **fibers.** One group of these fibers carries nerve impulses (i.e., messages) to the nerve cell body. Another group of fibers carries impulses away from the nerve cell body. Neurons can be tremendously long; for example, the one that reaches from the big toe to the brain spans many feet—and this involves but one cell.

Nerve tissue (i.e., clusters of neurons) is supported by ordinary connective tissue everywhere except in the brain. Here, the supporting tissue is of a special kind, and it is suspected of having a unique purpose of its own. So far, however, nobody knows exactly what this special purpose is.

All the nerves outside the brain and the spinal cord, called the **peripheral** (peh-rif'er-al) nerves, have a thin coating known as **neurilemma** (nu-ri-lem'mah). Neurilemma is a part of the mechanism by which the peripheral nerves repair themselves when damaged. The brain and the spinal cord, on the other hand, have no neurilemma; so that if they are injured, the injury is permanent. However, even in the peripheral nerves, repair is a slow and uncertain process.

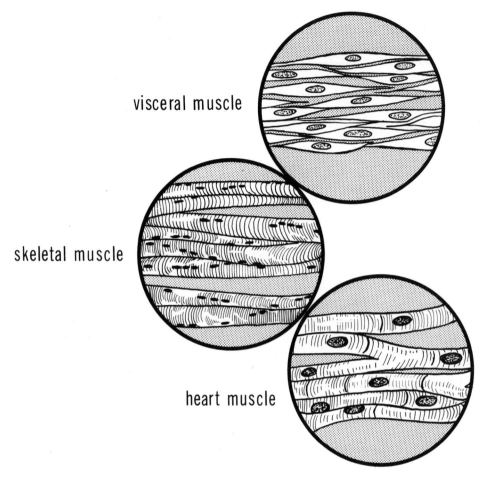

visceral muscle

skeletal muscle

heart muscle

FIG. 18. The 3 kinds of muscle tissue.

Telephone wires are insulated to keep them from short-circuiting, and so are nerve fibers, which actually do transmit something very much like an electric current. The insulating material of nerve fibers is called **myelin** (mi'el-in), and groups of these fibers form "white matter," so-called because of the color of the covering; it looks and is very much like fat. Not all nerves have myelin, however; some of the nerves of the system which controls the action of the glands, the smooth muscles (to be discussed shortly) and the heart do not have myelin. The cell bodies of all nerve cells also are uncovered (i.e., without myelin). Since all nerve cells are gray to begin with, and large collections of cell bodies are found in the brain, the great mass of brain tissue is popularly termed "gray matter."

MUSCLE TISSUE

Muscle tissue, whatever its kind, is designed to produce power by a forcible contraction. The cells of muscle tissue are long and threadlike, and so are called muscle fibers. If a piece of well-cooked meat is pulled apart, small groups of these muscle fibers can be observed. Muscle tissue usually is classified as follows:

1. **Skeletal muscle,** which combines with connective tissue to form the body muscles proper (to be studied later along with the skeleton). These provide for the movement of the body. This type of tissue also is known as **voluntary** muscle, since it can be made to contract by those nerve impulses from the brain which originate from an act of will. In other words, in theory at least, any of your skeletal muscles can be made to contract as you want them to.

The next 2 groups of muscle tissue are known as **involuntary** muscle, since they typically contract independently of the will. In fact, most of the time we do not think of their actions at all. These are:

2. **Cardiac muscle,** which forms the bulk of the heart wall and is known also as **myocardium** (mi-o-kar'de-um). This is the muscle which produces the regular contractions known as heart beats.

3. **Visceral muscle,** known also as **smooth** muscle, which forms the walls of the **viscera** (vis'er-ah), meaning the organs of the ventral body cavities (with the exception of the heart). Some examples of visceral muscles are those which move the food and waste materials along the digestive tract. Visceral muscles are found in other kinds of structures as well. Many tubular structures contain them, such as the blood vessels and the tubes which carry urine from the kidneys. Even certain structures at the bases of the body hairs have this type of muscle. When they contract, there results the skin condition that we call gooseflesh. Other types of visceral muscles will be taken up when we study the body systems (see Fig. 18).

There is a general disorder of muscles which might well be mentioned here. It is called **spasm** and is a sudden, violent and involuntary contraction of a muscle. A spasm is always painful. A spasm of the visceral muscles is called **colic,** and a good example of colic is the spasm of the intestinal muscles often referred to as bellyache. Spasms may occur also in the skeletal muscles; and if the spasms happen in a series, the condition may be called a **convulsion.** Specific diseases of which these abnormal muscle contractions are symptomatic will be taken up later.

Muscle tissue, like nerve tissue, repairs itself only with difficulty or not at all, once an injury has been sustained. These tissues when injured become replaced frequently with scar (connective) tissue.

TUMORS, BENIGN AND MALIGNANT

In the study of cells and tissues we gain some insight into the laws of growth. For reasons that still remain obscure, cells develop various forms, and those which are of the same kind congregate to form one of the basic tissues. These tissues become, in turn, the specialized organs. In the early stage of the body's development the cells multiply rapidly, and hence the body with all its structures grows in size until a point of maximum growth has been reached. From here on, cell division is not so rapid; it continues, however, at a rate sufficient to replace cells which for one reason or other have become used up and discarded. This complete picture of growth is neat and logical: the tissues are maintained, and every cell and formation of cells has its purpose.

It may happen, however, that the normal pattern of growth is broken by an upstart formation of cells having no purpose whatever in the body. As we have already noted, any abnormal growth of cells is called a tumor. If the tumor is confined to a local area and does not spread, it is called a **benign** (be-nine'), or **innocent,** tumor (these terms are used interchangeably). If the tumor spreads to neighboring tissues or to distant parts of the body, it is called a **malignant** (mah-lig'nant) tumor. The general term for any type of malignant tumor is **cancer.**

The ultimate reason for the formation of abnormal growths is still unknown but is the subject of intensive research at the present time. It is known that certain factors are conducive to tumor growth. One of these probably is an inherited tendency to develop such growths. Another factor is the presence of constant irritation. For example, skin cancer may begin in tissue that has been subjected to continued exposure to sunlight, x-rays, chemicals and such. If the tissue has been damaged previously, it is even more susceptible to the formation of cancer cells. Old scars, for example, are likely sites of cancerous formation. If cancer begins its development in some organ within the body, it is possible that it was encouraged by an abnormal stimulation of the organ by some secretion. The possibility of bacteria as a cause of cancer has been fairly well discounted, but some types of virus are under suspicion. It is quite certain, however, that there is no one cause of tumor formation.

Tumors are found in all kinds of tissue, but they occur most frequently in those tissues which repair themselves most quickly: namely epithelium and connective tissue, in that order.

BENIGN TUMORS capsule

Benign tumors, theoretically at least, are not dangerous in themselves; that is, they do not spread. Benign tumors grow as a single mass within a tissue, lending themselves neatly to complete surgical removal. Of course, some innocent tumors can be anything but innocent in their effect; they may grow within an organ, increase in size, and cause considerable mechanical damage. A benign tumor of the brain, for example, can kill a person just as can a malignant one. Ordinarily, however, benign tumors are not dangerous. Here are some examples of them (note that most of the names end in "oma," which means "tumor"):

handwritten notes:
Prefix Lipid - fat
suffix oma - tumor

1. **Papilloma** (pap-i-lo'mah). These grow in epithelium as projecting masses. Example: warts.

2. **Adenoma** (ad-e-no'mah). These are epithelial, growing in and about the glands ("aden" means "gland").

3. **Lipoma** (lip-o'mah). These are connective tissue tumors, originating in fatty (adipose) tissue.

4. **Osteoma** (os-te-o'mah). These also are connective tissue tumors, but originate in the bones.

5. **Myoma** (mi-o'mah). These are tumors of muscle tissue. Rare in voluntary muscle, they are common in some types of involuntary muscle, particularly the uterus (womb). When found in this organ, however, they ordinarily are called **fibroids.**

6. **Angioma** (an-je-o'mah). This tumor usually is one composed of small blood or lymph vessels, and includes the type of discoloration known as the port-wine stain or birthmark.

7. **Nevus** (ne'vus). These are small skin tumors of various tissues. Some are better known as moles. Some are angiomas. Ordinarily they are harmless but can become malignant through constant irritation.

MALIGNANT TUMORS *crab*

Malignant tumors, unlike benign tumors, can cause death no matter where they occur. The word "cancer" means "crab," and this is descriptive: a cancer sends out clawlike extensions into neighboring tissue. Not only does this happen, but also a cancer literally spreads its own seeds which plant themselves in other parts of the body. These "seeds" are, of course, cancer cells; and they are transported everywhere by either the blood or the lymph (a fluid related to the blood). When the cancer cells reach their destination, they immediately form new (secondary) growths. Malignant tumors, moreover, grow much more rapidly than benign ones.

Malignant tumors generally are classified in 2 categories according to the type of tissue in which they originate:

1. **Carcinoma** (kar-si-no'mah). These are cancers originating in epithelium and are by far the most common type of cancer. The usual sites of carcinoma are the skin, the mouth, the lung, the breast, the stomach and the uterus. These are usually spread by the lymphatic system (see Chap. 14).

2. **Sarcoma** (sar-ko'mah). These are cancers of connective tissue of all kinds and hence may be found anywhere in the body. Their cells are usually spread by the blood stream, and they often form secondary growths in the lungs.

There are other types of malignant tumors: for example, those which originate in a nevus, called **melanosarcomas** (mel-ah-no-sar-ko'mahs), and those which arise in the connective tissue that separates the nerve cells of the brain.

THE TREATMENT OF TUMORS

Benign tumors, as has been mentioned, can be removed completely by surgery. Malignant tumors cannot be handled so easily, for a number of reasons. If cancerous tissue is removed surgically, there is always the probability of a few hidden cells being left behind, to grow anew. If the cells have spread to distant parts of the body, there is little that anyone can do. On the other hand, cancer is curable if discovered early enough, before it has begun to spread. Not only surgery is employed, but also radiation, either by x-rays or radium, which has the effect of destroying rapidly growing cells. When used properly, therefore, radiation will kill cancer cells but will spare the more slowly growing cells of normal tissue.

Other methods for treating cancer include the use of a number of drugs that act selectively on tumor cells, and the **laser** (la'zer), a device that produces a very highly concentrated and intense beam of light. The laser can be used to destroy the tumor, or it can be employed as a cutting device for removing the growth. One important advantage of the laser is its ability to coagulate blood so that bleeding is largely prevented. It should be mentioned at this point that there are all sorts of quack cancer remedies on the market. All are useless, and some may even encourage the growth of cancer cells.

THE SYMPTOMS OF CANCER

Everyone should be familiar with certain signs which may be indicative of early cancer, so that they can be reported immediately before the condition can spread. It is unfortunate that early cancer is painless; otherwise, cancer would not be the problem that it is. Early symptoms may include unaccountable loss of weight, any unusual bleeding or discharge, persistent indigestion, chronic hoarseness or cough, changes in color or size of moles, any kind of sore that does not heal in a reasonable time, the presence of any unusual lump, and the presence of white patches inside the mouth or white spots on the tongue.

SUMMARY

1. **Characteristics of cells.**
    A. The building block of living things.
    B. Organelles are responsible for various functions within the cell.
    C. Enzymes are catalytic agents.
    D. The cell reproduces by mitosis.
    E. Physical and biological processes bring materials through the semipermeable cell wall.
    F. Chemical action within the cell is called metabolism.
2. **Characteristics of tissues.**
    A. Made of specialized cells.
    B. Tissue compares with cloth; properties vary with function.

C. Contain tissue fluid, which is mostly water.

D. Insufficiency of fluid: dehydration. Too much: edema.

3. **Tissue classification.**

A. Epithelium.

B. Connective tissue.

C. Nerve tissue.

D. Muscle tissue.

4. **Epithelium.**

A. Forms protective covering of the body and its organs.

B. Forms lining of the intestinal tract, respiratory and urinary passages, blood vessels, uterus and other body cavities.

C. May produce secretions.

D. May have cilia or other special characteristics.

E. Some types are wrinkled.

F. Repairs itself quickly and easily.

G. Most susceptible to tumor formation.

5. **Connective tissue.**

A. Supports organs and other body structures.

B. Divided into types:

(1) Soft. Stores fat, binds organs, forms organ framework, supports organs with heavy strains, forms scar tissue.

(2) Hard. Bones and cartilage.

C. Repairs itself easily and can grow tumors.

6. **Nerve tissue.**

A. Basic structure is neuron.

B. Composes coordinating and communication system of the body.

C. Neurons vary greatly in length.

D. Neurilemma helps nerves to repair themselves. Peripheral nerves have neurilemma, brain and spinal cord do not, so are incapable of repair.

E. Myelin insulates some nerves.

F. Repair of nerves even with neurilemma is slow and uncertain.

7. **Muscle tissue.**

A. Primary purpose to provide forcible contractions.

B. Fiberlike cells.

C. Three kinds.

(1) Skeletal. Forms the body muscles proper, also called voluntary muscle.

(2) Cardiac. Contracts regularly to produce heart beat. An involuntary muscle.

(3) Visceral. Known also as smooth muscle. Forms the walls of internal organs (heart excepted) including tubular structures.

D. Muscle disorders: spasm, colic, convulsion.

E. Repairs itself with difficulty or not at all. Injured tissue may be replaced with scar tissue.

8. **Tumors.**
    A. Characteristics.
        (1) Abnormal cell growths.
        (2) Causes (probable): heredity, irritation, possibly virus.
        (3) Found mainly in epithelium and connective tissue.
    B. Kinds of tumors.
        (1) Benign.
        (2) Malignant.
    C. Benign tumors.
        (1) Do not spread.
        (2) Completely removable by surgery.
        (3) Examples: papilloma, adenoma, lipoma, osteoma, myoma, angioma, nevus.
    D. Malignant tumors.
        (1) Send out appendages into neighboring tissue.
        (2) Cells spread to other parts of the body and cause secondary growths.
        (3) Cells grow more rapidly than those of benign tumors.
        (4) Can kill victim no matter where they grow.
        (5) Categories of malignant tumors (cancer):
            (a) Carcinoma. Epithelial, usually spread by lymphatic system. Most common.
            (b) Sarcoma. Connective tissue cancer. Usually spread by blood steam.
    E. Treatment of tumors: surgery, radiation, drugs, laser.
    F. Cancer symptoms: unaccountable weight loss, cough, persistent indigestion; unusual lumps, bleeding, discharge; nonhealing sores; change in color or size of moles, white patches inside the mouth or on the tongue.

QUESTIONS AND PROBLEMS
1. Define each of the following: organelle, mitochondria, enzyme, semipermeable membrane.
2. Outline the various stages of cell division. What is the name of this process?
3. What are some examples of processes that are responsible for the exchange of materials through membranes?
4. What goes on inside the cell once it receives these materials? Give the name for this process.
5. Define a tissue. Give a few general characteristics of tissues.
6. Define epithelium and give 2 examples. How easily does it repair itself?
7. Define connective tissue. Name the main kinds of connective tissue and give an example of each. How easily does it repair itself?
8. What is the main purpose of nerve tissue? What is its basic structural unit called?
9. Define neurilemma. Where is it present or absent?

10. Define myelin. Where is it found?
11. How easily does nervous tissue repair itself?
12. Name the 3 kinds of muscle tissue and give an example of each.
13. What is the difference between voluntary and involuntary muscle?
14. Name a general disorder of muscle tissue. Name 2 different variations of this and define them.
15. How easily does muscle tissue repair itself?
16. What is a tumor? In what kinds of tissue are they most commonly found?
17. Name the 2 general categories of tumors.
18. Name 3 factors which influence tumor growth.
19. Name 4 examples of benign tumors and tell where each is found.
20. What is the difference between a benign and a malignant tumor?
21. Name the 2 categories of malignant tumors. In what kind of tissue are they found? Which is the most common?
22. In what ways is cancer treated?
23. Name some early symptoms of cancer.

CHAPTER 5

MEMBRANES

Characteristics of membranes ▪ Kinds of membranes ▪ Epithelial membranes ▪ Connective tissue membranes ▪ Membranes and disease.

Now that we have studied the fundamental cell groupings—the tissues—we are ready to proceed to the next step and see in what ways the tissues are combined to form the actual body structures. The simplest of these tissue combinations are called **membranes.**

The word "membrane" means "any thin sheet of material which may separate 2 groups of substances." In our study of cells we encountered the word "membrane" for the first time, and saw that a membrane composed the wall of a cell through which various materials in solution (oxygen, food materials) could enter, and other substances (waste materials, secretions) could pass out. The cell wall is called the **cell membrane.**

In this chapter, however, we shall study only those membranes which are made up of a multitude of cells—that is, of tissues. These are known as **tissue membranes;** but, for the sake of convenience, they shall henceforth be referred to simply as membranes.

Membranes are thin, skinlike layers of tissue. Their properties vary; some are fragile, and others are tough. Some are transparent while others are opaque, which is just the opposite. Membranes may serve as dividing partitions, or may line hollow organs and body cavities. They may contain secreting cells that produce lubricants which make for ease of movement on the part of such organs as the heart and the joints. Other membranes serve to anchor various organs.

KINDS OF MEMBRANES

There are 2 broad categories of membranes. The first of these are the **epithelial membranes,** so-called because their outer surfaces are faced with epithelium. Their deep surfaces, however, have a layer of connective tissue, which strengthens the membrane. Epithelial membranes are in turn divided into 2 subgroups:

1. **Mucous** (mu'kus) **membranes,** which line tubes and other spaces that open to the outside of the body.

2. **Serous** (se'rus) **membranes,** which line closed cavities within the body.

The second category of membranes are known as fibrous (fi'brus) **connective tissue membranes.** Unlike epithelial membranes, those of this group are composed entirely of connective tissue. This category of membranes also can be divided into 2 subgroups:

    1. **Fascial** (fash'e-al) **membranes,** which serve to anchor and support the organs.

    2. **Skeletal membranes,** which cover bone and cartilage.

EPITHELIAL MEMBRANES

Epithelial membranes are made of closely crowded active cells, which manufacture lubricants and protect the deeper tissues from invasion by microorganisms. Mucous membranes produce a rather thick and sticky substance called mucus, while serous membranes secrete a much thinner lubricant. (Note that the adjective in each case contains an "o," while the nouns naming the secretion do not.)

In referring to the mucous membrane of a particular organ the noun **mucosa** (mu-ko'sah) may be used, while the special serous membrane covering an organ is called the **serosa** (se-ro'sah).

Mucous Membranes

Mucous membranes form extensive continuous linings in the digestive, the respiratory, the urinary, and the reproductive systems, all of which are connected with the outside. They vary somewhat both in structure and function. The cells that line the nasal cavities and most parts of the respiratory tract are supplied with tiny hairlike extensions of the protoplasm, called cilia, which have been mentioned previously. These microscopic cilia move in a wavelike manner that forces the secretions outward away from the deeper parts of the lungs. In this way millions of pathogens, trapped in the sticky mucus, are prevented from causing harm. Ciliated (sil-i-a'ted) epithelium is found also in certain tubes of both the male and the female reproductive systems.

The mucous membranes which line the digestive tract have their own special functions. For example, the mucous membrane of the stomach serves to protect the deeper tissues from the action of certain powerful digestive juices. If for some reason a portion of this membrane were injured, these juices would begin to digest a part of the stomach itself—which, incidentally, is exactly what happens in the case of peptic ulcers. Mucous membranes located farther along in this system are designed to absorb food materials which then are transported to all the cells of the

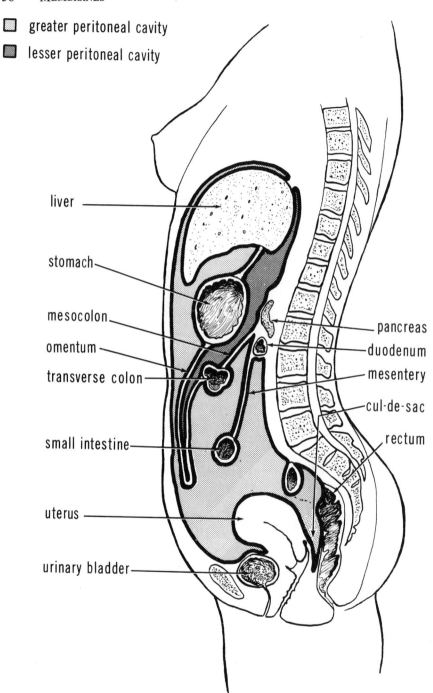

greater peritoneal cavity

lesser peritoneal cavity

liver

stomach

mesocolon

omentum

transverse colon

small intestine

uterus

urinary bladder

pancreas

duodenum

mesentery

cul-de-sac

rectum

FIG. 19. Abdominal cavity showing peritoneum.

body. But we are getting too far ahead in our story; other mucous membranes will be discussed when we encounter them later.

SEROUS MEMBRANES

Serous membranes, unlike mucous membranes, do not usually communicate with the outside of the body. This group lines the closed spaces known as body cavities. There are 3 main body cavities, and hence 3 serous membranes, which are:

1. The 2 **pleurae** (ploor′e) or pleuras (ploor′ahs), which form 2 separate sacs, one for each lung.

2. The **pericardium** (per-e-kar′de-um), which is a sac that covers the heart. It fits into a space in the chest between the 2 lungs.

3. The **peritoneum** (per-i-to-ne′um), which is much the largest, and which lines the abdominal cavity (see Fig. 19).

The epithelium which covers serous membranes is of a special kind called **mesothelium** (mes-o-the′le-um), which is smooth and glistening, and lubricated so that movements of the organs can take place with a minimum of friction.

Serous membranes are so arranged that one layer forms the lining of the closed sac, while the other layer of the membrane covers the surface of the organs. Since the word "parietal" (pah-ri′e-tal) refers to a wall, the serous membrane attached to the wall of a cavity or sac is known as the **parietal** layer. There is, for example, parietal pleura lining the chest wall, and parietal pericardium lining the sac that encloses the heart. Because organs are called **viscera** (vis′er-ah), the membrane attached to the organs is the **visceral** (vis′er-al) layer. On the surface of the heart is visceral pericardium, while each lung surface is made of visceral pleura.

CONNECTIVE TISSUE MEMBRANES

Compared with epithelial membranes, connective tissue membranes are static, serving chiefly as retaining and supporting structures. These membranes, as has been mentioned, are divided into 2 subgroups, fascial and skeletal membranes.

FASCIAL MEMBRANES

The word "fascia" means "band"; hence fascial membranes are bands or sheets the purpose of which is to support the organs and hold them in place. An example of a fascial membrane is the continuous sheet of tissue which underlies the skin. This contains fat (adipose tissue or "padding") and is called the **superficial fascia.** "Superficial" refers to a surface; so the superficial fascia is closer than any other kind to the surface of the body.

As we penetrate more deeply into the body, we find examples of the **deep fascia,** which contains no fat and has many different purposes. Fascial membranes enclose the glands and the viscera; these envelopes are called **capsules.** Deep fascia covers and protects the muscle tissue; and these coverings are known as **muscle sheaths.** The blood vessels and the nerves also are sheathed with fascia; the brain and the spinal cord are encased in a multilayered covering called the **meninges** (me-nin'jez). Fascia serves also to anchor muscle tissue to structures such as the bones.

SKELETAL MEMBRANES

Skeletal membranes are those which cover bones and cartilage. That which covers the bones is known as **periosteum** (per-e-os'te-um), and the membrane which covers cartilage is called **perichondrium** (per-e-kon'dre-um).

The cavities of the joints are lined with a membrane which sometimes is given a special classification among connective tissue membranes. This type is called the **synovial** (si-no've-al) membranes, and their particular purpose is to secrete a lubricating fluid which reduces the friction between the ends of bones, thus permitting free movement of the joints.

With this we conclude our brief introduction to membranes. As we study each system in turn, other membranes will be uncovered. They may have unfamiliar names, but they will be either epithelial or connective tissue membranes; and we shall be familiar also with their general locations. In short, they will be easy to recognize and remember.

MEMBRANES AND DISEASE

We all are familiar with a number of diseases which directly affect membranes. These range all the way from the common cold, which is an inflammation of the mucosa of the nasal passages, to the sometimes fatal condition known as peritonitis, an infection of the peritoneum, which can follow the rupture of the appendix. More of these diseases of membranes will be covered in due course.

Membranes can act as pathways along which disease can spread. In general, epithelial membranes seem to have more resistance to infections than do those layers made of connective tissue. However, lowered resistance may allow the transmission of infection along any membrane. For example, infections may travel along the lining of the reproductive system tubes and into the urinary system. Sometimes connective tissue membranes form planes of division extending in such a way that infection in one area is prevented from reaching another space. In other cases a vertical plane which separates 2 areas may seem to encourage the travel of bacteria either upward or downward. An infection of the tonsils, for example, may travel down to the chest.

SUMMARY

1. **Characteristics of membranes.**
   A. Simplest combinations of tissue.

B. Thin, skinlike layers of tissue.

C. Secrete substances, line cavities, support organs.

2. **Kinds of membranes.**

    A. Epithelial: outer surface is epithelium; deep surface is connective tissue.

    B. Connective tissue: composed entirely of connective tissue.

3. **Epithelial membranes.**

    A. Mucous membranes: secrete mucus, line passages which communicate with the outside of the body.

    B. Serous membranes.

    (1) Characteristics: covered with mesothelium, line body cavities, are lubricated thinly, have parietal and visceral layers.

    (2) Three serous membranes: pleurae (line lung cavities); pericardium (heart sac); peritoneum (lines abdominal cavity).

4. **Connective tissue membranes.**

    A. Characteristics: static; retaining and supporting structures.

    B. Kinds.

    (1) Fascial membranes: superficial fascia has fat, is bottom layer of skin; deep fascia forms capsules, muscle sheaths; sheaths for nerves and blood vessels; anchors muscle fibers to bones.

    (2) Skeletal membranes: cover bones and cartilage. Periosteum (bone covering); perichondrium (cartilage covering). Synovial membranes line joint cavities and secrete joint lubricant.

5. **Membranes and disease.**

    A. Membrane inflammations: common cold, peritonitis.

    B. Can be pathways along which disease spreads. Also can block off spaces from infection.

QUESTIONS AND PROBLEMS

1. What does the word "membrane" mean, generally speaking?
2. What is the general name for the membranes with which this chapter deals?
3. Name some general characteristics of membranes.
4. What are the 2 broad categories of membranes?
5. What are some general characteristics of epithelial membranes?
6. Name the 2 subgroups of epithelial membranes.
7. Give some characteristics of mucous membranes and name 2 examples of them.
8. Name some characteristics of serous membranes.
9. Name the 3 serous membranes and locate each.
10. What is the name for the kind of epithelium that covers serous membranes?
11. Name the 2 layers of serous membranes and tell what each means.
12. Give some general characteristics of connective tissue membranes.
13. Name the 2 subgroups of connective tissue membranes.
14. What are the main purposes of fascial membranes?
15. Name 2 kinds of fascia.
16. Give 3 examples of deep fascia.

17. What are the main purposes of skeletal membranes?
18. Name 3 examples of skeletal membranes.
19. Name 2 diseases of membranes.
20. How do membranes figure in the penetration and progress of disease organisms within the body?

CHAPTER 6

THE BLOOD

The purposes of blood ▪ Blood constituents and what they do ▪ Blood typing and transfusions ▪ Blood derivatives ▪ Anemia, leukemia and other blood disorders ▪ Ways in which blood is studied.

PURPOSES OF THE BLOOD

It was noted in Chapter 4 that the blood sometimes is classified as a tissue, since nearly half of it is made up of cells. However, since blood has so many unique functions, it deserves to be studied by itself. But the blood should be thought of as being akin to the tissues in that it is one of the primary materials of the body; and without some acquaintance with the composition and the functions of the blood, we could not understand the workings of the body's organ systems.

Blood is a thick (viscous) fluid which varies in color from bright scarlet to a darker brownish red, depending upon how much oxygen it is carrying. The average adult has about 6 quarts of blood in his body.

The blood has 2 main purposes. These are:

1. **Transportation.** Oxygen from the air that is breathed into the lungs is absorbed by the blood through the thin lung tissue and carried to all the tissues of the body. Carbon dioxide, a waste product of cell metabolism, is carried by the blood from the tissues to the lungs, where it is breathed out. The blood carries food materials from the intestine to all the body tissues, and waste products are transported by the blood to the kidneys for excretion. Special secretions called hormones, whose purpose it is to regulate the body's growth, development and normal functions, are transported by the blood from their organs of origin to their various destinations. The blood also transmits heat that is generated in the muscles to other parts of the body, thus aiding in the regulation of body temperature. The blood transports certain mineral salts which maintain what is called the acid-base balance of the body (this will be explained later), build up bones, etc.

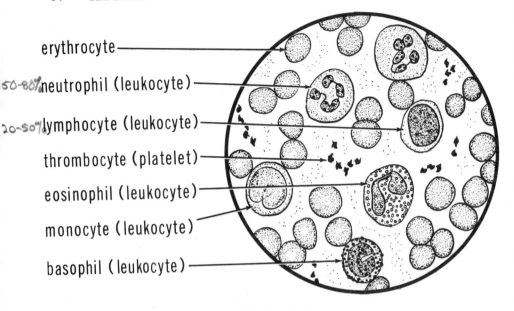

erythrocyte

50-80% neutrophil (leukocyte)

20-50% lymphocyte (leukocyte)

thrombocyte (platelet)

eosinophil (leukocyte)

monocyte (leukocyte)

basophil (leukocyte)

FIG. 20. Blood cells.

2. To Combat Infections. Certain materials in the blood are one of the body's great defenses against pathogenic invasions; other blood constituents are concerned with maintaining the body's immunity to disease.

BLOOD CONSTITUENTS

The blood is composed of 2 prime elements. These are:
1. The liquid element, called **plasma.**
2. The so-called **formed elements,** which are cells and products of cells. The formed elements also are called **corpuscles** (kor'pus-ls) and are grouped as follows:
   A. **Erythrocytes** (e-rith'ro-sites)—red blood cells (*erythro*-red). carry O₂
   B. **Leukocytes** (lu'ko-sites)—white blood cells (*leuko*-white).
   C. **Platelets** (plate'lets)—particles that bring about the process of clotting. These are probably not cells, but cell products. Platelets are called by another name also: **thrombocytes** (throm'bo-sites).

BLOOD PLASMA

Well over half of the total volume of blood is plasma; and plasma itself is approximately 90 per cent water. The remaining part of plasma contains around 100 different substances dissolved or suspended in this water. The plasma content varies somewhat, since the blood carries substances to and from organs which use some and add others. However, in the case of many substances there is a tendency to maintain a certain constant level. Glucose (simple sugar), for example, is kept at an average of about one-tenth of 1 per cent solution (or about one part in a thousand). This is possible partly because glucose is stored in certain cells, especially those of the liver and muscles, and later released as it is used by the tissues to generate energy.

After water, the next largest percentage of material of which the plasma is composed is called **protein.** Proteins are chemical compounds which are the principal constituents of protoplasm; they are essential to the growth and the rebuilding of body tissues—hence their importance. The proteins include such substances as:

1. Digested proteins from foods. These usually are described as protein building blocks.

2. Such vital compounds as antibodies that combat infection.

3. Certain proteins that figure in blood clotting.

Another substance in plasma belongs to a group with the collective name of **carbohydrates** (kar-bo-hi'drates). The principal form of carbohydrate found in the plasma is glucose, which as we saw is stored up as reserve food or released to supply energy.

Lipids (lip'ids) also constitute a small percentage of the blood plasma. Lipids are substances which include fats, among other things. Some lipids also are stored (in the form of fat) or carried to the tissues to supply energy.

Another important ingredient of plasma is the group known as **mineral salts.** Mineral salts include calcium and sodium compounds, various carbonates and phosphates, and potassium and magnesium salts. All these salts are very important to the functioning of the cells (see Chap. 3). Some mineral salts are essential to the formation of bones (calcium and phosphorus). Other mineral salts are essential to the production of hormones in certain glands (e.g., iodine in the thyroid gland). Iron, another mineral of this group, is necessary for the transportation of gases (oxygen and carbon dioxide) by the red cells. Still other salts serve to maintain the body's acid-base balance as has been indicated in Chapter 3.

Other materials in the blood plasma include waste products, hormones and gases.

The Formed Elements, or Corpuscles

The word "corpuscle" means "little body." We shall investigate each of the 3 types of corpuscles in turn. 120 day life

Erythrocytes. Erythrocytes, the red cells, are tiny disk-shaped bodies with a central area that is thinner than the edges. They are different from other cells in that the mature form found in the circulating blood does not have a nucleus. These

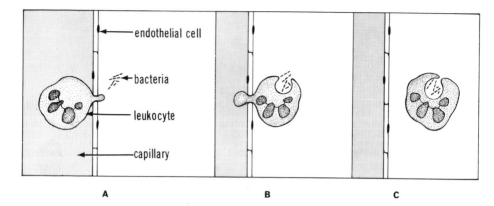

FIG. 21. (A) A white blood cell squeezing itself through a capillary wall, in the region of an infection. (B) and (C) The white cell engulfing the bacteria, part of the body's process of fighting infection.

cells live a much shorter time than most other cells of the body, some of which last a lifetime. One purpose of the red cells is to carry oxygen from the lungs to the tissues. This is accomplished through the main ingredient of the red cells, which is called **hemoglobin** (he-mo-glo′bin). It is the hemoglobin which absorbs this gas and gives the blood its characteristic red color. The more oxygen that is carried by the hemoglobin, the brighter the red color of the blood. Therefore, the blood that goes from the lungs, through the arteries, to the tissues is bright red because it carries a brand-new supply of oxygen. On the other hand, the blood that returns from the tissues, via the veins, and back to the lungs is a much darker red, since it has given up much of its oxygen. The red blood cells also carry the carbon dioxide.

The erythrocytes are by far the most numerous of the corpuscles, averaging from 4.5 to 5 million per cubic millimeter of blood.

Leukocytes. The leukocytes, or white blood cells, are very different from the erythrocytes both in appearance, quantity and function. They contain nuclei of varying shapes and sizes, and the cell itself is shaped like a ball. Leukocytes are outnumbered by red cells by 700 to 1. Whereas the red cells have a definite color, the leukocytes tend to be colorless. The white cells have many different divisions, but for the moment it is sufficient for us to know that the most important function of leukocytes is to destroy certain pathogens. At any time that pathogens enter the tissues, as through a wound, the white blood cells are attracted to that area. They leave the blood vessels through their walls and proceed by what is called ameboid (ah-me′boid) or amebalike motion to the area of infection. There they engulf so many of the pathogens that very often they themselves die and disintegrate (see Fig. 21). A collection of dead and living bacteria, together with dead as well as living leukocytes, forms pus; and a collection of pus localized in one area is known as an abscess. Note: The combining form "leuko," meaning "white," may also be written "leuco."

Platelets. If it were not for the platelets, or thrombocytes, we would not last very long because the slightest cut would prove fatal; we would bleed to death. The platelets, then, are essential to blood clotting, or coagulation. Platelets are not believed to be in themselves cells, but are probably fragments of cells. When blood is shed, or else comes in contact with any tissue other than that which normally carries blood, the platelets immediately disintegrate and release a chemical which reacts with a plasma protein called **fibrinogen** (fi-brin'o-jen). The fibrinogen changes from a liquid to a solid mass called **fibrin,** which forms the clot. (The process by which soluble fibrinogen is changed to insoluble fibrin is complex, involving the enzyme thrombin, calcium ions and other substances).

ORIGIN OF THE CORPUSCLES

The erythrocytes are formed in the red bone marrow, which is the connective tissue found inside the numerous small spaces of the spongy part of all bones. However, the red marrow in which the blood corpuscles are formed should not be confused with the yellow fatty kind which all of us have seen in soup bones, and which has its counterpart in the central cavities of the long bones of humans. Red marrow is found only in the ends of the long bones and in the mass of others.

As has been mentioned, the red cell as it normally appears in the blood has no nucleus. It was not always thus; oddly enough, when red cells are being formed in the marrow, they have nuclei. However, the red cell must lose its nucleus before it is considered mature and ready to be released into the bloodstream. Therefore, if a routine blood examination is performed and some nucleated erythrocytes are seen floating about, we know that something is wrong. And indeed it is; this may be a sign of a certain type of anemia, a disorder which will be discussed shortly.

The leukocytes are for the most part born in the bone marrow, as the red cells are. However, we have noted that there are many different kinds of leukocytes, and some have another origin. One group of leukocytes, known as **lymphocytes** (lim'fo-sites), originate not in the marrow but in the lymph nodes and other lymphoid tissues. A discussion of lymph tissues will be reserved for a later chapter.

We have seen that when any pathogen enters the tissues, the leukocytes are attracted to the site. At the same time the leukocyte-forming tissue goes into emergency war production, so to speak, with the result that the number of leukocytes in the blood is enormously increased. Therefore, if in the course of a blood examination an abnormally large number of white cells are seen to be present, this sometimes is indicative of an infection somewhere. We shall see also that an abnormally small number of white cells is a characteristic sign of a different category of disease.

The platelets are believed to originate in the red marrow, as are nearly all the other corpuscles. They are fragments of certain giant cells, called **megakaryocytes** (meg-ah-kar'e-o-sites), which are formed in the marrow.

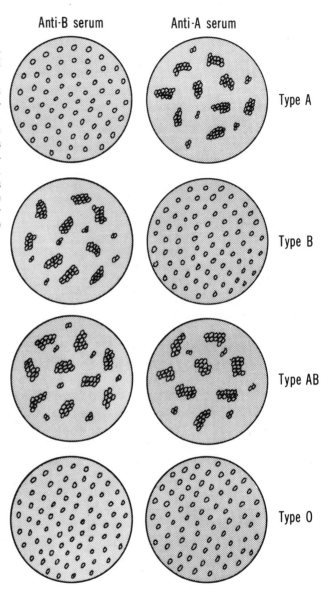

FIG. 22. Blood typing. Red cells in type A blood are clumped (agglutinated) by anti-A serum, those in type B blood are agglutinated by anti-B serum. Type AB blood cells are clumped by both serums and type O blood is not agglutinated by either serum. (Blood serum is defined as the watery part of the blood that remains after the clot has been removed.)

BLOOD TYPING AND TRANSFUSIONS

BLOOD GROUPS

If for some reason the amount of blood in the body is severely reduced, through **hemorrhage** (hem'or-ij), which means copious bleeding, or through disease, the body cells suffer from lack of food and oxygen. The obvious measure to take in such an emergency is the injection of blood from another person into the veins of the patient, which is called a **transfusion.** However, before other aspects of blood transfusion are discussed, it should be pointed out that not just anybody will do as a blood donor.

The blood of some persons is not compatible with that of others. The plasma of one person may contain substances that will damage the red blood cells of another. The red cells of the donor's blood may become clumped or held together in bunches, a process called **agglutination** (ah-gloo-ti-na'shun), by a substance in the patient's blood. It may happen also that the cells of the donor are dissolved or go into solution; they then are said to be **hemolyzed** (he'mo-lizd), a most dangerous condition. These reactions are determined largely by the type of protein in the red cell. Four blood types have thus been recognized and are referred to as the A, B, AB, and O types. The AB person has 2 proteins which may be agglutinated, while the O type has neither of these particular proteins. Because of the lack of these particular proteins, the O type person is known as a universal donor, that is, he may safely give blood to anyone. About 40 per cent of people have type O blood (see Fig. 22). Whatever the type of blood a person may have, he can usually give blood safely to another with the same blood type. In all cases, before a transfusion is given, determination of the blood type and a further check for incompatibility always should be made.

THE RH FACTOR

About 85 per cent of the population have another red cell protein called the **Rh factor.** Such individuals are said to be **Rh positive.** A minority of about 15 per cent lack this protein and are said to be **Rh negative.** If Rh positive blood is given (say by transfusion) to an Rh negative person, he may become **sensitized** to the protein of Rh positive blood. That is, the blood of this person may produce counteracting substances called **antibodies** which in turn will destroy the erythrocytes contained in the "foreign" Rh positive blood. A mother who is Rh negative may become sensitized by proteins from an Rh positive baby (this factor having been inherited from the father), if such proteins find their way into the mother's circulation before or during childbirth. During a later pregnancy the mother's antibodies may pass from her blood into the blood of this second or third infant and there cause destruction of red cells. This results in a condition called **erythroblastosis** (e-rith-ro-blas-to'sis) **fetalis** (fe-ta'lis). The child may be born dead (stillborn). If the infant is alive, replacement transfusions are begun at once. Rh negative blood from a female donor seems to give the best results.

DETERMINATION OF PARENTHOOD

Blood grouping is inherited in a way that is somewhat like the inheritance of eye and hair color, following what is known as Mendelian (men-de'le-an) laws after

Mendel, who first formulated the laws of heredity. Therefore, in certain cases, where the identity of the father is sought, blood group studies of the child and the possible father are made. Unfortunately they provide only negative types of evidence, since such findings tend to prove who could not have been the father, and who might be; but they do not prove conclusively which one actually is the father.

BLOOD BANKS

Blood can be bottled and be kept available for emergencies in blood banks. In order to keep the blood from clotting, sodium citrate (sit'rate or si'trate) in solution is added. This blood may then be stored for a number of days, usually not more than 1 to a maximum of 3 weeks. Such blood storage is especially important in times of disaster and during wartime. The supplies of blood in the bank are dated, and these dates are noted before the transfusion is given to avoid giving blood in which red cells may have disintegrated. Since, as we saw, about 40 per cent of persons have type O blood, and since this type may be used for all types of patients (in an emergency), it is especially important to have larger supplies of this type in the blood bank. In any case, the patient's blood must be crossmatched with the blood to be used before the transfusion is begun.

TYPICAL CONDITIONS REQUIRING TRANSFUSION

The transfer of whole human blood from a healthy person to a patient is often a lifesaving process. A blood transfusion may be indicated for a variety of reasons. For example:

1. For treatment of hemorrhage from serious mechanical injuries, such as cuts or other wounds.

2. In the treatment of anemia from hemorrhaging ulcers, tuberculous lungs with blood loss, and other disorders in which there may be internal bleeding. "Anemia" here means "an insufficiency of blood."

3. In the treatment of erythroblastosis fetalis.

4. In cases of shock, blood poisoning (sepsis), pneumonias, and nephritis (kidney disease).

5. In hemorrhagic diseases such as hemophilia and other blood disorders.

6. As a preoperative procedure, or even during an operation in cases in which there may be considerable blood loss, or if the patient is in a weakened condition.

7. After operations as an aid in combating anemia and shock, and as a help in the recovery process.

USES OF BLOOD DERIVATIVES

Blood is capable of being broken down into its various components and the substances derived from it used for a number of purposes. One of the more common of these processes is to separate the blood plasma from the formed elements. This is accomplished by means of a **centrifuge** (sen'tre-fuge), which is a machine that spins a quantity of blood around in a circle at high speed. If you imagine a weight tied to the end of a string, and think of spinning the weight around in a circle, you will understand how a centrifuge works. There is a force which tends to pull the weight outward. When the container of blood is spun rapidly, that same force will "pull" all the formed elements of the blood into a clump at the bottom of the container, separating them from the plasma, which can be simply poured off.

The blood plasma thus derived is a very useful substance. It may be given as an emergency measure to combat shock and to replace blood volume. The water can be removed, leaving the solids which can be stored in the dry state for a considerable length of time. Later sterile distilled water may be added in order to reconstitute the plasma; it then can be given to treat an injured person, as, for example, in situations that do not make blood typing and the use of whole blood possible (on battlefields or in mass disasters). Since the red cells have been removed, there can be no incompatibility problems; plasma can be given to anyone.

Serum is another blood derivative. We all have observed that if a blood clot is removed (from a cut, for example) a watery fluid remains. This watery fluid is serum, and it is nothing more than plasma from which fibrinogen has been removed through the process of clotting. Serum may be derived from the blood of specially treated animals, and then injected into humans in order to produce an immunity to certain diseases. Further discussion of this subject will be found in Chapter 20.

Other blood fractions used for treatment purposes include the cells which are left after the plasma has been removed. These cells are made into a paste that is used to aid in the healing of ulcers, burns and other injuries. **Gamma globulin** (gam'mah glob'u-lin) is a valuable protein substance obtained from human plasma. It is used for preventing measles and infectious hepatitis (both virus diseases), especially in infants or others who have been exposed to the contagion and are in a debilitated (weakened) condition.

BLOOD DISORDERS

Abnormalities involving the blood depend on several factors and may be divided into 3 groups:

1. The **anemias.** The word "anemia" (ah-ne'me-ah) means "a general condition in which the blood is lacking either in its normal number of red cells or in its overall quantity." This definition suggests the 2 types of anemia:

A. **Primary anemias.** These are characterized by a disturbance of the red-cell-forming mechanism which results in a lowered number of red cells.

B. **Secondary anemias.** These are due to simple loss of blood, or else to a defective formation of hemoglobin due to other diseases.

2. **Neoplastic diseases** of the blood and the blood-forming organs. The word "neoplastic" means "pertaining to a new growth." Therefore, these diseases are

cancerlike. They include the **leukemias** (lu-ke'me-ahs), a group of diseases charac-terized by an increase in the number of white blood cells.

3. **Hemorrhagic disorders.** These include a group of disorders characterized by an abnormal tendency of the body to bleed, caused by a breakdown in the blood's clotting mechanism.

THE ANEMIAS

Primary Anemias. The most important of the primary anemias is **pernicious** (per-nish'us) **anemia.** Its initial cause is apparently a permanent deficiency of a certain factor in the stomach juice which is responsible for the absorption of vitamin B_{12}. This vitamin is essential to the proper formation of red cells. The result is that immature red cells tend to accumulate in the bone marrow in large quantities. The red cell count might go as low as 20 per cent of normal; and a blood examination also reveals the presence of immature red cells in the blood-stream (as was mentioned earlier in this chapter). Neglected cases of pernicious anemia can bring about conditions of deterioration in the nervous system, causing difficulty in walking, weakness and stiffness in the extremities, mental changes, and permanent damage to the spinal cord. Early treatment, including the use of the appropriate vitamin (B_{12}) in large doses and attention to diet, as prescribed by a physician, now assures an excellent outlook. This treatment must be kept up for the rest of the patient's life if continuous good health is to be maintained.

Another type of primary anemia is called **aplastic** (ah-plas'tik) **anemia,** which is a type of marrow failure usually caused by certain poisonous agents. Chemical substances that discourage the production of cells in the morrow include benzene, arsenic, nitrogen mustard, and gold compounds. Physical agents that may injure the marrow include x-rays, atomic radiation, radium and radioactive phosphorus. The bone marrow fails to produce either red or white cells, so that anemia is accompanied by **leukopenia** (lu-ko-pe'ne-ah), which means a drop in the number of white cells. Removal of the toxic agent and transfusions until the marrow is able to resume its activity may result in complete recovery.

Some anemias are brought about by excessive destruction of the red cells. Normally an organ called the spleen destroys the older red blood cells. Occasionally this destruction proceeds at too rapid a pace so that an anemia is the result. More commonly infections and infestations are the cause of blood cell loss. The action of the malarial organism is an interesting example of this. When a man is bitten by the mosquito, the malarial parasite is injected into his bloodstream. Each parasite enters a red cell, where it multiplies until the red cell bursts; that cell is now destroyed. The parasites, now freed, attack other red cells in the same manner. The result is an anemia. Certain bacteria, particularly streptococci, cause dissolving or a so-called **hemolysis** (he-mol'i-sis) and are therefore described as **hemolytic** (he-mo-lit'ik) bacteria. Less common types of anemia in which red cells are hemolyzed (he'mo-lizd) include the so-called sickle cell anemia (most common in the colored race) and the hemolysis occurring in infants as a result of antibodies from an Rh negative mother, a condition mentioned earlier in this chapter.

Secondary Anemias. As we know, the average adult has about 6 quarts of blood. If he loses as much as 2 quarts suddenly, death usually results. On the other hand, if the loss is gradual, over a period of days to weeks, the body can withstand the loss of as much as 4 or 5 quarts. Then it may take 6 months to restore the blood to normal. In the meantime this gradual loss of blood, or chronic bleeding, may cause a severe secondary anemia.

In chronic bleeding it is important to locate and remedy the cause. Repeated hemorrhages from piles (hemorrhoids), excessive menstrual flow, and various types of ulceration in the stomach or bowel all can be causes of this. Sometimes parasites can rob a human of much of his blood. For example, the hookworm (a common infestation of the inhabitants of southern United States) fastens itself to the inside of the intestine and lives on the blood of its host, causing a secondary anemia.

Other causes of this type of anemia include malignancies, infections, cirrhosis of the liver, thyroid deficiency, and chronic kidney disease (nephritis). The person who has a secondary anemia will need frequent blood checks and continued advice and treatment not only for the cause of the secondary anemia but also for the purpose of restoring the condition of his blood to normal.

NEOPLASTIC BLOOD DISEASE

This group of diseases is characterized by an enormous increase in the number of white cells, owing to a cancer of the tissues which produce these cells. We noted that the white cells have 2 main sources: the red marrow and the lymph tissue. If this wild proliferation of white cells stems from a tumor of the marrow, the condition is given the name of **myelogenous** (mi-e-loj′e-nus) **leukemia.** If the majority of the white cells happen to be lymphocytes, the condition is called **lymphatic leukemia.**

At the present time the cause of leukemia is unknown. It has been suggested that there may be inherent factors, and various environmental agents have also been implicated. Chief among these are certain chemicals such as benzene, and excessive exposure to x-rays or to radioactive substances.

The patient with leukemia exhibits the general symptoms of anemia. In addition, he has a tendency to bleed easily. The spleen is greatly enlarged, and several other organs may be increased in size because of the accumulation of white cells within them. X-ray treatments along with drugs are given in cases of leukemia; but because of the malignant character of the disease, it can be considered ultimately fatal.

HEMORRHAGIC DISORDERS

A characteristic that these diseases have in common is a disruption of the coagulation process which brings about abnormal bleeding. A rare but interesting example of this group is a disease called **hemophilia** (he-mo-fil'e-ah), which was made famous by its occurrence in some of the royal families of Russia and Western Europe. Hemophilia is characterized by failure of the blood to clot, so that the victim must use extreme caution to avoid trauma of any kind. Severe bleeding can result from a small cut or skin abrasion, and a fatal hemorrhage can occur from some injuries or surgical procedures. The treatment consists of treating the bleeding as it occurs with transfusions and by other means. The most common kind of hemophilia is a hereditary disease transmitted only by females and only to males.

Another type of "bleeding" disease is **purpura** (pur'pu-rah), in which hemorrhages occur in the skin and the mucous membranes. The abnormal bleeding in this disease is sometimes caused by a reduction in the number of platelets in the blood. There probably are a number of reasons for the low platelet count; one of them is a cancer which destroys the bone marrow in which the platelets originate.

ROUTINE BLOOD STUDIES

Many different kinds of studies may be made of the blood. A few of these have become a standard part of a routine physical examination. The following is a typical list of studies with their objectives and methods.

AMOUNT OF HEMOGLOBIN

It is very important to know that a person has an adequate amount of hemoglobin so that the tissues are assured a sufficient supply of oxygen. This is determined by means of a **hemometer** (he-mom'e-ter), also known as a **hemoglobinometer** (he-mo-glo-bi-nom'e-ter). These devices vary in design, but in general the principle is that a comparison is made between the blood and a standard color scale. The normal amount of hemoglobin varies from about 14 to 16 grams per 100 cc of blood. Too little hemoglobin is a factor in anemia. Because of the rather high percentage of the element iron in hemoglobin, it is important that the diet contain sufficient amounts of available iron, as found in oatmeal, eggs, molasses, and animal organs (heart, kidneys, and liver).

BLOOD CELL COUNTS

An apparatus for counting the number of blood cells is called a **hemocytometer** (he-mo-si-tom'e-ter) and is illustrated in Figure 23. It consists essentially of 2 tubes, one for red cells and the other for white cells, and an accurately ruled glass slide for viewing the blood samples under a microscope; the purpose of the gridiron rulings is to provide a fixed area in which the cells can be counted. The normal count for red cells varies from about 4.5 to 5.5 million cells per cubic millimeter

Fig. 23. Parts of a hemo-
cytometer.

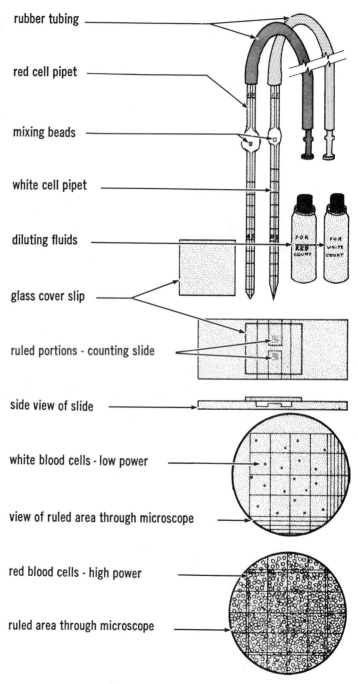

rubber tubing

red cell pipet

mixing beads

white cell pipet

diluting fluids

glass cover slip

ruled portions - counting slide

side view of slide

white blood cells - low power

view of ruled area through microscope

red blood cells - high power

ruled area through microscope

(a cubic millimeter is a very tiny drop of blood). The leukocyte count varies from 5000 to 9000 per cubic millimeter.

Leukopenia (lu-ko-pe'ne-ah) means that the white count is below 5000. It is characteristic of a few infections such as malaria and measles, as well as certain disorders of the blood-forming organs.

Leukocytosis (lu-ko-si-to'sis) means that the white blood count is in excess of 9000 or 10,000 per cubic millimeter. It is particularly characteristic of most infections. It may occur also after hemorrhage and in gout and uremia, a result of kidney disease.

THE BLOOD SLIDE (OR SMEAR)

A drop of blood is spread very thinly and carefully over a glass slide. A special stain is applied to differentiate the otherwise colorless white cells, and then this slide is studied under the microscope. Abnormal red cells which are characteristic of certain anemias may be noted, and malarial or other parasites may be found. Abnormalities in the white cells also are observed. In addition, the **differential white count** (i.e., an estimation of the percentage of each type of white cell) is done using the same stained blood slide. Such a count is an important aid to the physician in making a diagnosis.

SOME LESS COMMON BLOOD TESTS

PLATELET COUNT

A count of the thrombocytes is done occasionally, but it is difficult to do accurately. Normal counts are said to vary from 250,000 to 500,000 in each cubic millimeter. However, numbers as low as 100,000 may not indicate abnormality. In some disorders in which there is a great tendency to hemorrhage, the count may go as low as 10,000.

BLOOD SUGAR TEST

The blood is sometimes analyzed to determine the amount of sugar dissolved in the plasma. The presence of more than the normal amount is called **hyperglycemia** (hi-per-gli-se'me-ah) and is found most frequently in the diabetic person. Sometimes several evaluations of sugar content are done following the giving of a known amount of glucose. This procedure is called the **glucose tolerance test** and usually is given along with another test which determines the amount of sugar in the urine. This combination of tests can indicate faulty cell metabolism.

CLOTTING TIME

Nature prevents excessive loss of blood from small vessels by the formation of a clot. Preceding surgery and under some other circumstances, it is important to know that the time required for coagulation to take place is not too long. Since clotting is a rather complex process involving many elements, a delay may be due to a number of different factors, including lack of certain hormonelike substances, calcium salts, and vitamin K.

BLEEDING TIME

In this test the blood is blotted at half-minute intervals after a cut is made in the ear lobe or finger. A piece of absorbent paper is touched to the drop repeatedly; after 1 to 3 minutes no more drops should form. Since platelets aid in closing spaces in blood vessels, a long bleeding time suggests the possibility of an insufficient number or some abnormality of these tiny bodies.

BLOOD CHEMISTRY TESTS

In addition to tests to determine the amount of glucose in the blood plasma, other analyses are done to aid in evaluating kidney function. These include tests for determining the concentration of urea (u-re'ah), which is a product of the decomposition of proteins in the body and other substances in the blood which eventually are excreted in the urine. Tests and analyses for amounts of certain salts and hormones in the blood are done also when necessary to aid in the diagnosis of illnesses.

STERNAL PUNCTURE

A special needle usually is employed to obtain a sample of red marrow from the spongy bone of the upper sternum (breast bone). This procedure is called a **sternal puncture.** A smear on a glass slide is prepared in much the same way that the blood slide for the differential white count is made. Examination by a trained person will give much valuable diagnostic information concerning the red marrow, useful in the finding of such diseases as leukemia.

SUMMARY

1. **General characteristics of blood.**
   A. Can be considered a tissue.

B. Thick fluid of varying red color.

C. Quantity: about 6 quarts in average adult.

2. **Main purposes of blood.**

A. Transportation (including heat exchange).

B. Defend body against disease.

3. **Prime elements of blood.**

A. Plasma (liquid element).

B. Formed elements (cell and cell-derived elements).

(1) Erythrocytes (red cells).

(2) Leukocytes (white cells).

(3) Platelets (cellular fragments that cause clotting).

4. **Plasma.**

A. Ninety per cent water.

B. Remainder: proteins, carbohydrates, lipids, salts.

5. **Formed elements (corpuscles)**—characteristics.

A. Erythrocytes: carry oxygen; main constituent is hemoglobin, which absorbs the gases; nonnucleated; most numerous of corpuscles.

B. Leukocytes: combat disease; nucleated; several different forms.

C. Platelets: fragments of cells; dissolve and combine with fibrinogen to form the clot (fibrin).

6. **Origin of corpuscles.**

A. Erythrocytes: formed in red marrow; immature cells nucleated; mature cells lose nucleus before going to bloodstream.

B. Leukocytes: formed mostly in red marrow; one form (lymphocytes) originate in lymph tissue.

C. Platelets: formed in red marrow from giant cells.

7. **Blood groups.**

A. Not all blood types compatible.

B. Blood types (A, B, AB, O).

C. Mixing of incompatible bloods may result in agglutination of red cells or hemolysis.

8. **Rh factor.**

A. Most people have special red cell protein; are Rh positive.

B. Minority lack it; are Rh negative.

C. Rh negative mother may have Rh positive baby (factor inherited from father). Mother's blood may cause destruction of baby's red cells.

D. Above condition called erythroblastosis fetalis.

9. **Determination of parenthood:** blood grouping inherited. Blood typing can prove who is not the father and who possibly is, but not *definitely* who is.

10. **Blood banks:** blood bottled and stored for emergencies. Type O—most commonly used (is universal donor).

11. **Transfusions given** in following conditions: hemorrhage, anemia, erythroblastosis fetalis, shock, hemorrhagic diseases, preoperatively and postoperatively.

12. **Blood derivatives.**
    A. Plasma: separated, dried, stored, reactivated, used in emergencies.
    B. Serum: taken from animals, produces immunity.
    C. Others: paste of blood cells; gamma globulin.
13. **Blood disorders—kinds.**
    A. Anemias.
        (1) Primary: disturbance of erythrocyte-forming tissue resulting in lowered count.
        (2) Secondary: due to hemorrhage and defective hemoglobin formation.
    B. Neoplastic diseases: include leukemias.
    C. Hemorrhagic diseases: caused by faulty clotting.
14. **Primary anemias.**
    A. Pernicious anemia: lack of erythrocyte-producing factor in stomach juice. Treated by vitamin B_{12} and diet.
    B. Aplastic anemia: marrow failure caused by poisonous agents.
    C. Destruction of red cells: overactivity of spleen; parasites (malaria); hemolytic bacteria.
15. **Secondary anemias.**
    A. Chronic bleeding (ulcers, hemorrhoids, etc.).
    B. Parasites (hookworm).
16. **Neoplastic diseases.**
    A. Main group: leukemia (myelogenous and lymphatic).
    B. Caused by malignancy in white-cell-producing tissue.
    C. Characterized by greatly increased leukocyte count.
    D. Generally fatal.
17. **Hemorrhagic disorders.**
    A. Characterized by disruption of clotting process.
    B. Examples: hemophilia, purpura.
18. **Routine blood studies.**
    A. Hemoglobin amount estimated, using hemometer.
    B. Total red and white blood counts
        (1) Apparatus used called hemocytometer.
        (2) Too few white cells is called leukopenia.
        (3) More than normal number of white cells is known as leukocytosis.
    C. Examine blood slide for parasites; used also for differential white count.
    D. Differential white count.
19. **Less common blood tests.**
    A. Platelet count.
    B. Blood sugar (glucose).
    C. Clotting time and bleeding time.
    D. Blood chemistry tests.
    E. Sternal puncture.

QUESTIONS AND PROBLEMS

1. How does the color of blood vary with the amount of oxygenation?
2. Name the 2 main purposes of the blood.
3. Name the 2 prime elements of the blood.
4. Name and describe the 3 main groups of cellular structures in blood.
5. Name 4 main ingredients of blood plasma. What are their purposes?
6. What is the main function of erythrocytes? leukocytes? platelets? Where does each originate?
7. What are the names usually given to the 4 main blood groups? What are the factors that are the reason for the different groupings?
8. What is the Rh factor? What proportion of people possess this factor? In what situations is this factor of medical importance? Why?
9. Are blood groups inherited? How is this fact made use of in paternity cases?
10. What are the advantages of blood banks? Are there any disadvantages? If so what are they, and is there a way of counteracting these disadvantages?
11. What are some of the conditions for which blood transfusions are useful?
12. What precautions should always be taken before a transfusion is given?
13. What substances obtained from the blood may be useful in the treatment of the sick, and in what way is each of these blood derivatives used?
14. Name the 3 general categories of blood disorders.
15. Differentiate between the 2 types of anemia and give an example of each.
16. Name 2 kinds of leukemia. What is the chief symptom of leukemia, and what is the reason for it?
17. Name the main characteristic of hemorrhagic disorders and give an example of these.
18. Name 3 common blood tests.

CHAPTER 7

BODY TEMPERATURE
AND ITS REGULATION

Homeostasis ▪ Heat production and loss ▪ The "thermostat" of the body ▪ Normal and abnormal temperature ▪ Effects of heat and cold.

BODY TEMPERATURE AND HOMEOSTASIS

In an earlier chapter it was pointed out that heat is an important by-product of the many chemical activities constantly going on in the tissues all over the body. Simultaneously, heat is always being lost through a variety of outlets. Yet, by virtue of a number of regulatory devices the body temperature remains constant within quite narrow limits under normal conditions. The maintenance of a constant temperature in spite of both internal and external influences is one phase of the important concept known as **homeostasis** (ho-me-o-sta'sis), the tendency of the body processes to maintain a normal state despite forces that tend to alter them. Other examples of the maintenance of homeostasis are the heart rate, respiratory rate and blood pressure, which all tend to remain within the so-called normal limits. In addition to these more obvious types of homeostasis there are many important examples that involve the composition of body fluids. As was mentioned in Chapter 3, electrolytes (compounds that form ions when in solution) must be kept at a certain level at all times if the body cells are to function normally.

HEAT PRODUCTION

Heat is produced when oxygen combines with food products in the body cells. The amount of heat produced by a given organ varies with the kind of tissue and with its activity. While at rest muscles may produce as little as 25 per cent of the total body heat, but when numbers of muscles contract, the heat production may be multiplied hundreds of times. Under basal conditions (rest) the abdominal organs, particularly the liver, produce about one half of the body heat; but during vigorous

81

muscular activity this ratio is greatly changed. While the body is at rest, the brain may produce 15 per cent of the body heat, but an increase in activity in nerve tissue produces very little increase in heat production. The largest amount of heat, therefore, is produced in the muscles and the glands. It would seem from this description that some parts of the body would tend to become much warmer than others. The circulating blood, however, distributes heat fairly evenly throughout the entire body.

The rate at which heat is produced is affected by a number of factors. When the body is at complete rest (basal condition), the glandular organs such as the liver continue to add some heat constantly with but slight variations. But the amount of heat produced in muscles during activity is hundreds of times as great as during rest. In addition to these causes of variation, certain hormones, such as thyroxine from the thyroid gland and epinephrine (adrenaline) from the medulla of the adrenal gland, may increase the rate of heat production. The intake of food also is accompanied by increased heat production. The reasons are not entirely clear. More fuel is poured into the blood and is therefore more readily available for cellular "combustion." The glandular structures and the muscles of the digestive system generate additional heat as they set to work. This does not account for all the increase, however, nor does it account for the much greater increase in metabolism following a meal containing large amounts of protein. Whatever the reasons, the intake of food definitely increases the chemical activities that go on in the body and thus adds to heat production.

HEAT LOSS

More than 80 per cent of heat loss occurs through the skin (see Chap. 8). The remaining 15 to 20 per cent is dissipated via the respiratory system and with the urine and feces. Networks of blood vessels in the deeper part (corium, or dermis) of the skin are capable of bringing considerable quantities of blood near the surface so that heat can be dissipated to the outside. This can occur in several ways. Heat can be transferred to the surrounding air (conduction). Heat also travels from its source in the form of heat waves or rays (radiation). If the air is moving so that the layer of heated air next to the body is constantly being carried away and replaced with cooler air (as by an electric fan), the process is known as convection. Finally, heat loss may be produced by evaporation. Any liquid uses heat during the process of changing to the vapor state. Rub some alcohol on your arm; it evaporates rapidly, and in so doing uses so much heat, taking it from the skin, that your arm feels cold. Perspiration does the same thing, though not so quickly. The rate of heat loss through evaporation depends upon the humidity of the surrounding air. When this exceeds 60 per cent or so, perspiration will not evaporate so readily; and one feels generally miserable unless some other means such as convection (by a fan) can be resorted to.

If the temperature of the surrounding air is lower than that of the body, excessive heat loss is prevented by both natural and artificial means. Clothing checks heat loss by trapping "dead air" both in its material and its layers. This noncirculating air is a good insulator. An effective natural insulation against cold is the layer of fat under the skin. Even though the skin temperature may be low, this fatty tissue prevents the deeper tissues from losing too much heat. This layer is on the average slightly thicker in the female than in the male. Naturally there are individual variations, but as a rule the degree of insulation depends on the thickness of this layer of subcutaneous fat.

Other factors that play a part in heat loss include the volume of tissue compared with the amount of skin surface. Just as a child loses heat more rapidly than an adult, so such parts as the fingers and the toes are affected more by exposure to cold because in each case there is a greater amount of skin compared with total tissue volume.

TEMPERATURE REGULATION

Since the body temperature remains almost constant in spite of the wide variations in the rate of heat production or loss, obviously there must be a temperature regulator. Actually, many areas of the body take part in this process, but the most important heat regulating center is a section inside the brain, located just above the pituitary gland, called the **hypothalamus** (hi-po-thal'ah-mus). Some of the cells in the hypothalamus control the production of heat in the body tissues, while another group of cells controls heat loss. This control comes about in response to the heat brought to the brain by the blood as well as to nerve impulses from the temperature receptors in the skin. If these 2 factors indicate that too much heat is being lost, impulses are sent quickly from the brain to the involuntary (autonomic) nervous system which in turn causes constriction of the skin blood vessels in order to reduce heat loss. Other impulses are sent to the muscles to cause shivering, a rhythmic contraction of many body muscles, which results in increased heat production. The output of epinephrine may be increased, also, if conditions call for it. The smooth muscle about the hair roots contracts, forming "gooseflesh."

If, on the other hand, there is danger of overheating, the hypothalamus will transmit impulses which stimulate the sweat glands to increased activity and also dilate the blood vessels in the skin so that there is increased blood flow with a correspondingly greater loss of heat. The hypothalamus also may encourage relaxation of muscles and thus minimize the production of heat in these organs (see Chap. 10).

Muscles are especially important in temperature regulation because variations in the amount of activity of these large masses of tissue can readily increase or decrease the total amounts of heat produced according to the needs of the body. Since muscles form roughly one third of the bulk of the body, either an involuntary or a purposeful increase in the activity of this big group of organs can form enough heat to offset considerable decrease in the temperature of the environment.

NORMAL BODY TEMPERATURE

The normal temperature range as obtained by the usual thermometers may extend from 97° to 100°F. Temperature of the body varies with the time of the day. Usually it is lower in the early morning, since the muscles have been relaxed and no food has been taken in for several hours. Temperature usually is higher in the late afternoon and evening because one has been physically active and has had food.

Normal temperature also varies with the part of the body. Skin temperature as obtained in the armpit (axilla) is lower than mouth temperature, and mouth temperature is a degree or so lower than rectal temperature. If it were possible to place a thermometer inside the liver, it is believed that it would register a degree or more higher than the rectal temperature. The temperature within a muscle might be even higher during its activity.

ABNORMAL BODY TEMPERATURE

FEVER

Fever is a condition in which the body temperature is higher than normal. Usually the presence of fever is due to an infection, though there can be many other causes such as malignancies, brain injuries, toxic reactions, reactions to vaccines, and diseases involving the central nervous system. Sometimes emotional bouts can bring on a fever.

Curiously enough, fever usually is preceded by a chill—that is, a violent attack of shivering and a sensation of cold that such measures as blankets and hot water bottles seem unable to relieve. At the same time heat is being generated and stored in the body; and when the chill subsides, the body temperature is elevated.

The old adage that a fever should be starved is completely wrong. During a fever there is an increase in metabolism that is usually proportional to the amount of fever. In addition to the use of available sugar and fat there is an increase in the use of protein, and during the first week or so of a fever there is definite evidence of destruction of body protein. A high calorie diet with plenty of protein is therefore desirable.

When a fever ends, sometimes the drop in temperature to normal occurs very rapidly. This sudden fall in temperature is called the **crisis,** and usually is accompanied by symptoms indicating rapid heat loss: profuse perspiration, muscular relaxation and dilated blood vessels in the skin. A gradual drop in temperature, on the other hand, is known as **lysis.**

The mechanism of fever production is not completely understood, but we might think of the hypothalamus as a thermostat which is set higher at this time. This change in the heat-regulating mechanism often follows the injection of a foreign protein or the entrance into the bloodstream of bacteria or their toxins. Up to a point fever may be beneficial because it steps up **phagocytosis** (fag-o-si-to'sis), the process by which white blood cells surround, engulf and digest bacteria and other foreign bodies (see Chap. 20); inhibits the growth of certain organisms (such as the spirochete of syphilis); and probably encourages the production of antibodies. Sometimes fever is induced on purpose as a form of treatment, particularly for syphilis of the nervous system.

The body cannot endure temperatures beyond about the 112° level because at that point tissues are irreversibly damaged and death occurs.

It is extremely important that the nurse keep accurate daily temperature records of patients, since a knowledge of the temperature level and its fluctuations is invaluable in the doctor's diagnosis. The temperature chart is a "picture" which tells a lot to the practiced eye.

EFFECTS OF EXTREME OUTSIDE TEMPERATURES

The body's heat-regulating devices are efficient, but there is a limit to what they can accomplish. If the outside temperature is too high, one may perspire so much that dehydration and **heat exhaustion** can result. Heat exhaustion is a condition caused by excessive salt loss, and its symptoms include muscle cramps, dizziness, vomiting and fainting. This condition usually can be forestalled by taking salt tablets in hot weather.

Sunstroke (sometimes called **heat stroke)** also is caused by high outside temperatures. It differs from heat exhaustion in that one of the heat regulators is affected; namely, the sweat glands. Dehydration begins a chain of events which terminates in decreased blood supply to the skin and diminished secretion of perspiration. As a consequence, the body temperature rockets up to a level that can be fatal. The victim of sunstroke exhibits many of the symptoms of heat exhaustion (i.e., dizziness, fainting) but with this significant difference: there is an absence of perspiration; the skin is dry and flushed. Sunstroke is an extremely serious emergency. The most important first-aid measure is to lower the temperature; otherwise permanent brain damage can result. Cooling of the body is accomplished by immersing the victim in cool water or else by spraying him with it. Ice should be applied to the head, and cold drinks administered if the patient is conscious.

The body is no more capable of coping with prolonged exposure to cold than to heat. If, for example, the body is immersed in cold water for a time, the water (a better heat conductor than air) removes more heat from the body than can be replaced, and the body temperature falls. This can happen too, of course, in cold air—particularly when clothing is inadequate. An excessively low body temperature is termed **hypothermia** (hi-po-ther'me-ah), and its main effects are lowered respiratory rate and blood pressure and a feeling of drowsiness finally ending in coma and perhaps death. Hypothermia, the opposite of fever, is caused mainly by prolonged exposure to cold, rarely by abnormal conditions within the body.

Exposure to cold, particularly to moist cold, can cause permanent local tissue damage. The areas most likely to be affected by cold are the face, the ears and the extremities. The usual reason for these injuries is that the cold causes a spasm of the smooth muscle of the arteriole walls, diminishing the blood supply to the area. This condition causes interference with cell nutrition and metabolism; and necrosis of the tissues with gangrene can result. Examples of cold damage are **chilblains** (localized itching and painful red areas on the skin), **frostbite** and immersion foot or trench foot. The very young, the very old, and those who suffer from disease of the circulatory system are particularly susceptible to cold injuries.

A frostbitten area should *never* be rubbed, but should be thawed by wrapping in blankets or by immersion in warm water. The affected area should be treated gently; if the feet are frostbitten, the victim should not be permitted to walk.

Hypothermia is employed in certain types of surgery. In such cases the hypothalamus is depressed by drugs and the body temperature may be reduced to below 90° with no apparent harm. The heart may be stopped for several minutes during hypothermia; heart surgery has been accomplished successfully on these patients.

SUMMARY

1. **Body temperature and homeostasis.**
   A. Homeostasis: tendency of body processes to maintain normal state.
   B. Body temperature regulation a phase of homeostasis.
2. **Heat production.**
   A. Produced constantly in metabolic processes.
   B. Muscles and glands produce most heat.
   C. Heat distributed through body by blood.
   D. Heat production rate determined by muscle and glandular activity, food intake, external temperature.
3. **Heat loss.**
   A. Outlets: chiefly skin; also respiratory system, urine, feces.
   B. Heat loss from skin: conduction, radiation, convection, evaporation.
   C. Excess heat loss prevented by artificial means (clothing), natural means (subcutaneous fat).
4. **Temperature regulation.**
   A. Chief center is hypothalamus.
   B. Information reaches it via blood and also nerves from temperature receptors.
   C. Hypothalamus causes either increased heat production (blood vessel constriction in skin, shivering, "gooseflesh," possibly increased epinephrine) or increased heat loss (activation of sweat glands, blood vessel dilation, muscular relaxation).
5. **Normal body temperature.**
   A. Normal range 97°–100°F.
   B. Varies with time of day, part of body.

6. **Abnormal body temperature.**
    A. Fever.
        (1) Abnormally high body temperature, usually caused by infection.
        (2) Preceded by chill; terminates in crisis or lysis.
        (3) Causes destruction of some body protein; increases phagocytosis and possibly antibody production.
    B. Extremes in outside temperature.
        (1) Heat: can cause heat exhaustion or sunstroke.
        (2) Cold: can cause hypothermia (sometimes but rarely of pathological origin); cold injuries (chilblains, frostbite, immersion foot, trench foot).

QUESTIONS AND PROBLEMS
1. What is homeostasis? Name 4 aspects of it.
2. How is heat produced in the body? What structures produce the most heat during increased activity?
3. Name 4 factors affecting heat production.
4. By what channels is heat lost from the body?
5. Name 4 ways in which heat escapes to the environment.
6. In what ways is heat kept in the body?
7. Name the main temperature regulator and describe what it does when the body is too hot and when it is too cold. What part do muscles play?
8. What is the normal body temperature range? How does it vary with respect to the time of day and the part of the body?
9. Define fever, name some aspects of its course, and list some of its beneficial and detrimental effects.
10. Name and describe 2 consequences of excessive outside heat. Why do these conditions occur?
11. What is the prime emergency measure for sunstroke?
12. What is hypothermia? Under what circumstances does it usually occur? List some of its effects.
13. Name and describe 2 common cold injuries. What happens in the body to bring these conditions about?

CHAPTER 8

THE SKIN IN HEALTH AND DISEASE

What is the skin? ▪ How is the skin constructed? ▪ Important functions of the skin ▪ What can the skin tell you? ▪ Diseases of the skin ▪ What is the best skin care?.

Is the skin merely a body covering, is it an organ, or is it a composite of parts that make it properly a system? Actually, it has some properties of each of these, and so may be classified in 3 different ways, namely:

1. It may be called an **enveloping membrane** because it is a rather thin layer of tissue covering the entire body.

2. It may be referred to as an **organ** (the largest one, in fact) because it contains several kinds of tissue, including epithelial, connective, and nerve tissues.

3. The skin is also known as the **integumentary system,** "integument" (in-teg'u-ment) meaning "covering," because it includes sweat and oil glands as well as other parts that work together as a body system.

STRUCTURE OF THE SKIN

Layers Enveloping the Body

The surface of the body is covered by 3 main layers of tissue, each different from the other in structure and function. These are:

1. The **epidermis** (ep-e-der'mis), or outermost layer, which is subdivided into strata (stra'tah), or layers, and is made entirely of epithelial cells with no blood vessels.

2. The **dermis,** or true skin, which has a framework of connective tissue, and contains many blood vessels, nerve endings and glands.

3. The **subcutaneous** (sub-ku-ta'ne-us), or under-the-skin layer, which is a combination of elastic and fibrous tissue as well as deposits of fat (adipose tissue). This layer sometimes is referred to as the **superficial fascia** (see Chap. 5) and

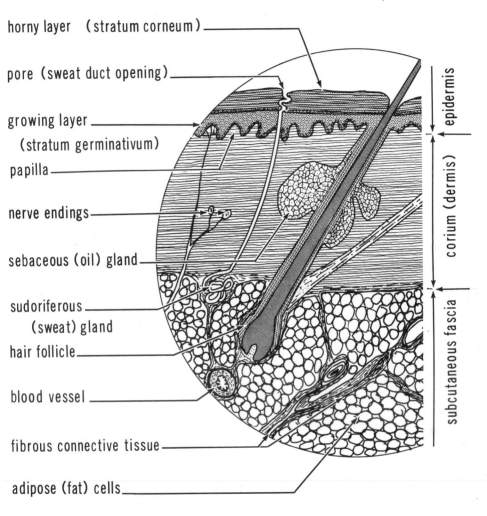

horny layer (stratum corneum)

pore (sweat duct opening)

growing layer
(stratum germinativum)

papilla

nerve endings

sebaceous (oil) gland

sudoriferous
(sweat) gland

hair follicle

blood vessel

fibrous connective tissue

adipose (fat) cells

epidermis

corium (dermis)

subcutaneous fascia

FIG. 24. Cross section of the skin.

actually is a means of connecting the skin proper to the surface muscles. The fat in this sheet of tissue serves as insulation as well as a reserve store for energy.

THE EPIDERMIS

The outer cells of the epidermis are flat and horny. They are constantly being shed, and additional cells are pushed outward from the deeper layers of the epidermis. Since there are no blood vessels in this part of the skin, nutrition and fluids reach all the epidermal cells by means of the tissue fluid. This fluid seeps or filters out of the blood vessels in the deeper dermis and flows slowly toward the surface between the layers of skin cells. The epidermis undergoes constant change as the germinating cells of the deeper strata produce new daughter cells. The pigment granules called **melanin** (mel'ah-nin), which give the skin its color, also are found in the germinating part of the epidermis. The ridges in the epidermis can be seen in fingerprints. These are due to elevations and depressions in the epidermis and the dermis. The deep surface of the epidermis is accurately molded upon the outer part of the dermis, which has raised and depressed areas.

THE DERMIS, OR CORIUM

The dermis, or corium (ko're-um), the so-called true skin, has a framework of elastic connective tissue and is well supplied with blood vessels and nerves. Involuntary muscle fibers also are found in the dermis, particularly where there are hairs. The thickness of the dermis as well as that of the epidermis varies so that some areas such as the soles of the feet and the palms of the hands are covered with very thick layers of skin, while the skin of the eyelids is very thin and delicate. Most of the appendages of the skin, including the sweat and oil glands, the nails and the hairs, extend into the dermis and often deeper into the subcutaneous layer.

GLANDS OF THE SKIN

The sweat, or **sudoriferous** (su-dor-if'er-us), **glands** are coiled tubelike structures located mainly in the dermis, though sometimes in the subcutaneous tissue. Each gland has an excretory tube that extends to the surface and opens at a pore. Contrary to a popular notion, these pores do not open and close like a mouth, since there is no muscle tissue connected with them. The wax, or **ceruminous** (se-ru'min-us), **glands** in the ear canal and the **ciliary** (sil'e-er-e) **glands** on the eyelid edges are modifications of sweat glands.

The **sebaceous** (se-ba'shus), or **oil, glands** are saclike or alveolar (al-ve'o-lar) in structure, and their oil secretion helps to keep the hair from becoming brittle. Their ducts open most often into the hair follicles, but in some situations they open onto the skin surface. Before the baby is born, these glands produce a covering like cream cheese. This secretion is called the **vernix caseosa** (ver'niks ka-se-o'sah).

Blackheads are formed of a mixture of dirt and oily secretion that may collect at the openings of the sebaceous glands. If these glands become infected, pimples result. If sebaceous glands of the scalp become closed, a sac of secretion may form and gradually become larger and larger. These cysts (i.e., sacs containing a liquid or a semisolid) usually are referred to as **wens.** Usually it is not too difficult to remove such tumorlike cysts by surgery.

FUNCTIONS OF THE SKIN

Although the skin has several functions, the 3 which are by far the most important are:

1. Protection of deeper tissues against drying and against invasion by pathogenic organisms or their toxins.

2. Regulation of body temperature by dissipating heat to the surrounding air.

3. Obtaining information about the environment by means of the nerve endings which are so profusely distributed in the skin.

The intact skin is incapable of defense against sharp objects, but it is an able defender against pathogens, toxins, and the process of evaporation. A break in the continuity of the skin by trauma (traw'mah), that is, a wound or injury of any kind, may be followed by serious infection. The care of wounds involves to a large extent the prevention of the entrance of pathogens and toxins into the deeper tissues and body fluids.

The regulation of body temperature is also a very important function of the skin. The normal temperature may vary slightly, but we think of 98.6°F. (37°C) as the standard when a thermometer is placed in the mouth for 3 to 5 minutes. The body temperature reading may be expected to be somewhat less if taken in the axilla (ak-sil'ah), and somewhat more if taken in the rectum. The skin forms a large surface for radiating body heat to the air. When the blood vessels enlarge (dilate), more blood is brought to the surface so that heat can be dissipated into the air. The evaporation of sweat from the surface of the body also helps to cool the body. As is the case with so many body functions, the matter of temperature regulation is complex and involves several parts of the body, including certain centers in the brain.

A child loses heat faster than does an adult since a higher proportion of the body is skin surface, and thus relatively more area is exposed. Therefore, it is important to prevent undue exposure to the elements in the case of infants and small children. The elderly do not produce heat in the body so easily nor to so great an extent; therefore they also should be protected against cold.

A most important function of the skin is in obtaining information from the environment. Because of the many receptors (nerve endings) for pain, touch, pressure and temperature, which are located mostly in the dermis, the skin may be regarded as one of the chief sensory organs of the body. Many of the reflexes which make it possible for the human being to adjust himself to the environment begin as sensory impulses from the skin. Here, too, the skin works in cooperation with the brain and the spinal cord to make these important functions possible.

The functions of absorption and excretion are minimal as far as the skin is concerned. The absorbing power of the skin is very limited. Ointments containing mercury have in the past been used in the treatment of syphilis; but much more effective and less harmful drugs now are given by mouth or by injection. Oil of wintergreen (methyl salicylate) also may be absorbed from the skin, but its dosage in this way is very indefinite. Excretion by the skin is limited to water and salt in perspiration; and from the point of view of removing waste products from the body the skin's excretory function is also negligible.

The human skin does not "breathe." The pores of the epidermis serve only as outlets for perspiration and oil from the glands. The public is bombarded with misinformation about the skin, sometimes merely for the purpose of selling lotions, potions and all sorts of supposedly magical preparations. Breathing is a function of the respiratory system and not of the skin. Beware of cosmetics that purportedly aid in skin breathing!

OBSERVATION OF THE SKIN

What can the skin tell you? What do its color, texture and other attributes indicate? Much can be learned by the astute observer.

The color of the skin is dependent upon a number of factors, including:

1. The amount of pigment in the epidermis.
2. The quantity of blood circulating in the surface blood vessels.
3. The concentration of hemoglobin in the blood.
4. The presence or absence of oxygen in the blood.
5. The existence of such substances as bile, silver compounds or other chemicals in the blood.

PIGMENT OF THE SKIN

The pigment of the skin is called **melanin** (mel'ah-nin). It is found also in the hair, the middle coat of the eyeball, the iris of the eye and in certain tumors. Melanin is common to all races, but the darker people have a much larger quantity of it distributed in these tissues. A normal increase in this skin pigment occurs as a result of exposure to the sun. Abnormal increases in the quantity of melanin may occur either in localized areas or throughout the entire body surface. Diffuse spots of pigmentation may be characteristic of some endocrine disorders.

DISCOLORATION OF THE SKIN

A yellowish discoloration of the skin may be due to the presence of bile in the blood. Such a condition is called **jaundice** (jawn'dis) and may be a symptom of a number of disorders such as:

1. A tumor pressing on the common bile duct or a stone within the duct, either of which would obstruct the flow of bile into the small intestine.
2. Inflammation of the liver (hepatitis).
3. Certain diseases of the blood in which red corpuscles are rapidly destroyed.

Another cause of a yellowish discoloration of the skin is the excessive intake of carrots and other deeply colored vegetables. This condition is known as **carotinemia** (kar-o-te-ne'me-ah).

Chronic poisonings may cause grayish or brown discoloration of the skin. In most cases a bluish color will indicate cyanosis. A peculiar bronze color is present in Addison's disease (malfunction of the adrenal gland). So many other disorders cause discoloration of the skin that an entire chapter could be written on this topic alone.

Skin Injuries

A wound or local injury is called a **lesion** (le'zhun). Lesions of the skin which should be noted by those who care for the sick include:

1. **Excoriations** (eks-ko-re-a'shuns) which may be evidence of scratching.
2. **Ulcers** or other breaks in the skin.
3. Areas of redness, called **erythema** (er-e-the'mah), as well as other discoloration.
4. Spots of any kind.

Skin Eruptions

A skin rash (eruption) may be localized as in a diaper rash, or it may be generalized as in measles and other systemic infections. Some terms often used to describe skin eruptions are:

1. **Macules** (mak'ules) or macular (mak'u-lar) rash, in which the spots are neither raised nor depressed, typical of measles and also descriptive of freckles.
2. **Papules** (pap'ules) or a papular (pap'u-lar) rash, in which there are firm raised areas, as in some stages of chickenpox and in the second stage of syphilis. Characteristic of pimples.
3. **Vesicles** (ves'e-kals) or vesicular (ve-sik'u-lar) eruptions, in which blisters or small sacs are full of fluid, such as may be found in some of the eruptions of smallpox and chickenpox.
4. **Pustules** (pus'tules) or pustular (pus'tu-lar) lesions, which may follow the vesicular stage of chickenpox and smallpox.
5. **Crusts,** which are made of dried pus and blood and are commonly referred to by laymen as scabs.

SKIN DISEASES

Dermatitis

Inflammation of the skin is called **dermatitis** (der-mah-ti'tis). It may be due to many kinds of irritants, such as the oil of poison oak or poison ivy plants, detergents, and strong acids or alkalies or other chemicals. Prompt removal of the irritant is the most effective prevention and treatment. A thorough soap-and-water bath as soon as possible after contact with plant oils may prevent the development of the itching eruptions.

Sunburn and Its Complications

Sunlight may cause chemical and biological changes in the skin. The skin first becomes reddened (erythematous) and then may become swollen and blistered. Some people suffer from severe burns and become seriously ill. There is considerable evidence to support a theory that continued excessive exposure to the sun is an important cause of skin cancer. The current fad for tanning requires the skin to protect itself by producing considerably more than usual amounts of melanin. This increase in pigmentation may have the effect of reducing the ability of the body to profit from the desirable smaller amounts of sun available during some parts of the year. A moderate amount of exposure to the sun enables the skin to convert certain substances into vitamin D, the so-called sunshine vitamin.

Eczema

Eczema (ek′ze-mah) is an unpleasant disease which may be found in all age groups and in both sexes. However, it is more common in the very young and in the elderly. Eczema may affect any and all parts of the skin surface. It is a non-contagious disease which may manifest itself by redness (erythema), blisters (vesicles), and pimplelike (papular) lesions. There also may be scaling and crusting of the skin surface. Eczema may be a manifestation of an allergy to certain foods, detergents, soaps and other chemicals. Psychological and emotional disturbances may precipitate or aggravate an attack of eczema just as they bring on bouts of asthma and other allergic responses. There may be a hereditary predisposition to allergic disorders; therefore some individuals must give more than average attention to diet as well as to proper physical and mental hygiene.

Acne

Acne (ak′ne) is a disease of the oil glands of the skin. Common acne, or **acne vulgaris,** is found most often in individuals between the ages of 14 and 25. The infection of the oil glands takes the form of pimples which usually surround blackheads. Acne is usually most severe at adolescence because certain glands in the body which control the secretions of the sebaceous glands are then particularly active. Frequent, thorough cleansing of the skin with warm soap and water may be effective treatment in some cases. Changes of diet, along with applications of antiseptic ointment, sometimes help. Occasionally more radical procedures, including x-ray therapy, may be required.

Impetigo

Impetigo (im-pe-ti'go) is an acute contagious disease of a staphylococcal or streptococcal origin that may be serious enough to cause the death of newborn infants. It takes the form of blisterlike lesions which become filled with pus and contain millions of virulent bacteria. It is found most frequently among poor and undernourished children. A child may reinfect himself or infect others. Sometimes the infection is spread by contaminated linen or dishes. In a nursery, for example, utmost care in handling infants in order to prevent the spread from baby to baby is extremely important. Despite ordinary precautions, fatalities from impetigo have occurred at various times in the United States. Impetigo is so contagious that children who develop the disease should not be permitted to return to school until a physician writes a statement that the condition is cured.

Baldness (Alopecia)

Alopecia (al-o-pe'she-ah) may be due to infection as well as to a number of other factors. It may be inherited, particularly in males. Baldness may be an expression of aging, in which case it usually begins at the crown of the head and is associated with atrophy of the structures of the scalp. It may be the result of such systemic diseases as syphilis and myxedema. A severe infection such as scarlet fever may cause the loss of hair, but in such cases recovery from the disease usually is accompanied by the regrowth of the hair. A chronic fungous infection which involves the oil glands and hair follicles may result in alopecia. In these cases frequent shampooing and constant attention to skin hygiene may prevent balding. Dandruff is often due to fungous disease of the scalp, and the assistance of a physician should be sought if one is to prevent alopecia.

Athlete's Foot

Fungi are the usual cause of athlete's foot, also known as **epidermophytosis** (ep-e-der-mo-fi-to'sis). The disease involves the toes and the soles of the feet most commonly, but occasionally it may affect the fingers, the palms of the hands and the groin region. In acute cases the lesions may include vesicles, fissures and ulcers. Predisposition to fungous infection varies. Some individuals may be exposed to pathogenic fungi with no ill effects, while in other people a mild exposure will cause a severe skin infection. Those who perspire a great deal are particularly susceptible to athlete's foot. Frequent changing of hose and of shoes together with thorough drying of the feet, with particular attention to the spaces between the toes, will discourage infection. Dusting powders in the shoes and on the feet will also deter fungous growth. Most patent medicines are relatively ineffective. It would be better to see a physician and then follow his instructions.

OTHER DISORDERS OF THE SKIN

In addition to those disorders which have been discussed, common skin diseases include:

1. **Shingles,** known also as **herpes zoster** (her'pez zos'ter), in which groups of blisters form along the course of certain nerves.

2. **Boils,** or **furuncles** (fu'rung-kls), caused by bacteria which enter hair follicles or sebaceous glands.

3. **Psoriasis** (so-ri'ah-sis), in which a variety of lesions appear, including scaly red patches with definite outlines (circumscribed areas).

4. **Carbuncles,** infected areas which tend to involve the deeper parts of the skin, and may extend into the fascia, sometimes with fatal results.

CARE OF THE SKIN AND ITS APPENDAGES

COSMETICS, QUACKERY AND SKIN CARE

It is rather ironic that more money is spent on skin, hair and nail care than on a combination of all types of medical and health services. Yet authorities agree that the one most important factor in keeping the skin and the hair attractive is good general health. The person with even a slightly underactive thyroid gland (Chap. 18) will have dry skin and hair, and no amount of creams could begin to take the place of taking thyroid extract tablets in proper amounts. The pallor of the anemia victim could be remedied much more effectively by appropriate medical care than by any amount of cosmetics.

The normal skin secretions are slightly acid. Quacks have taken advantage of this fact by applying testing material (such as litmus paper) to the skin and then calling attention to the acid reaction by the warning that this "acid condition" should be corrected. Naturally they are selling the pills or potions for that purpose at a handsome profit. Actually the body protects itself against pathogens by producing this acid secretion. As the acid stomach juice kills bacteria in the food we eat, so the skin secretions tend to destroy or at least inhibit bacterial growth. Dirt and dead skin cells, however, dilute this acid; hence cleanliness is important too.

The cleansing soap-and-water bath or shower is an important part of good grooming and health. Here the individual should know himself and his peculiar personal needs. Those who have dry skins need to replace some of the oil that is removed by bathing if general health measures fail to remedy the dryness. For those who have very active sweat and oil glands, soap and water twice a day or more may be advisable, and creams and oily applications should be avoided. For most persons the so-called cleansing cream is not a proper substitute for soap and water.

Exposure to the elements, particularly to wind and sun, may call for applications of zinc ointment or some other fatty protective substance. Many sunburn lotions are of dubious value. A layer of an opaque ointment on the nose and other exposed surfaces will keep too many ultraviolet rays from reaching the skin, and may help to prevent undue drying.

Nails and Their Care

The nails are made of translucent (i.e., partly transparent) cells that originate from the outer part of the epidermis. Bacteria tend to collect under the nails and the cuticle, which should be kept pushed back. Hangnails should be removed after applying antiseptic. A clean manicure scissors should be used. Care should be taken to keep bacteria out of the deeper tissues and the blood vessels which are located in the root or nail bed. Toenails will have less tendency to become ingrown if they are cut straight across. Nails of both the toes and the fingers are affected by the general health. They may become discolored, dry and cracked in chronic diseases of the nervous system and of the skin, and in conditions accompanied by prolonged fever.

Wanted and Unwanted Hair

Hair, like the nails, is an appendage of the skin. It collects dirt easily and usually requires shampooing at least once a week in order to be kept clean and healthy.

People seem to have formed a definite ideal as far as hair distribution is concerned, hence the universal concern over the vagaries of hair growth (or nongrowth). Much time and money are spent by men to check the relentless progress of baldness, and by women to correct an unfortunate superfluity of hair in the wrong places. Most of these expenditures are futile. Contrary to popular belief, shaving does not cause the hair to grow in more thickly, nor does it become coarser. Hair can be removed safely and effectively by electrolysis, one hair at a time, provided that it is done by an expert. It is an expensive and slow process. For the present it would seem advisable for women to shave if they wish to remove unwanted hair; and perhaps men can learn to accept baldness or wear an appropriate hairpiece.

SUMMARY

1. **Ways in which the skin can be classified.**
   A. An enveloping membrane.
   B. The largest organ.
   C. A body system (integumentary).
2. **Structure of the skin.**
   A. Layers.
       (1) Epidermis.
           (a) Outermost layer of skin, stratified.
           (c) Made of epithelial cells with no blood vessels.
           (c) Undergoes constant cellular change.
           (d) Contains pigment (melanin).
       (2) Dermis.
           (a) True skin, connective tissue framework.
           (b) Contains blood vessels, nerves and glands.
       (3) Subcutaneous layer.
           (a) Called superficial fascia.
           (b) Fat deposits are a reserve energy store.
   B. Glands of the skin (in dermis).
       (1) Sudoriferous: sweat glands.
       (2) Sebaceous: oil glands.
       (3) Ciliary and ceruminous: modified sweat glands.
3. **Functions of the skin.**
   A. Protection against pathogens, toxins, and drying of under tissues.
   B. Regulation of body temperature.
   C. Sensory organ for pain, touch, heat, cold and pressure.
   D. Excretory function: limited to water and salt.
4. **Observation of the skin.**
   A. Pigmentation (melanin content).
       (1) Melanin content varies with race.
       (2) Sunlight causes increased pigmentation.
       (3) Abnormal melanin content or distribution can be a sign of disease.
   B. Discoloration.
       (1) Yellowish discoloration (jaundice): bile in the blood.
       (2) Bluish discoloration: cyanosis.
       (3) Bronze discoloration: Addison's disease.
       (4) Grayish or brownish discoloration: chronic poisoning.
   C. Skin injuries: excoriations, ulcers, erythema, spots.
   D. Skin eruptions: macules, papules, vesicles, pustules, crusts.
5. **Skin disorders.**
   A. Dermatitis (inflammation of the skin): chemical irritants.
   B. Sunburn and complications.

(1) Severe burns.

(2) A possible cause of cancer.

(3) Pigmentation increase precludes benefit of small amounts of sunlight at other times.

C. Eczema.

(1) Found mostly in the young and the aged.

(2) Erythema, blisters, papular lesions.

(3) Noncontagious.

D. Acne.

(1) Most common at adolescence.

(2) Pimples and blackheads.

E. Impetigo.

(1) Common in poor and malnourished children.

(2) Blisterlike lesions filled with pus and bacteria.

(3) Highly contagious.

F. Baldness.

(1) May be inherited.

(2) Can be caused by disease. Hair may grow back after a fever.

G. Athlete's foot: a fungous infection.

H. Other skin disorders: shingles, boils, psoriasis, carbuncles and others.

6. **Care of the skin and its appendages.**

A. Cosmetics are of no value when the condition to be corrected is of pathologic origin.

B. Nails must be kept free of bacteria.

C. Most measures to check baldness or to remove unwanted hair are impractical or useless.

QUESTIONS AND PROBLEMS

1. What characteristics of the skin classify it as a membrane, as an organ, and as a system? What term do you think fits it best and why?

2. Of what type of cells is the epidermis composed?

3. Explain how nutrients and oxygen reach the cells of the epidermis.

4. What kind of tissue forms the framework of the dermis?

5. What glands are found in the dermis, and how do their secretions reach the surface? What is the function of the skin pores?

6. What is the subcutaneous tissue made of, and what is another name for it?

7. Explain the 3 most important functions of the skin.

8. What are the facts about the skin as an organ of respiration and excretion?

9. What are the most important contributors to the color of the skin, normally?

10. What do you think of the claims made for some cosmetics? Give examples.

11. What are some examples of disorders that affect the skin at the same time as they upset the entire body chemistry?

12. What are some examples of irritants that frequently cause a dermatitis?

13. What are the values of exposure to the sun, and what precautions need to be considered? What are some complications that may follow sunburn?
14. What is eczema? Name the most important causes.
15. At what ages are impetigo patients in the most danger, and what are some of the precautions that need to be taken?
16. What are the most common causes of baldness?
17. What are the best measures to take to prevent and to control athlete's foot?
18. Define psoriasis, herpes zoster and carbuncles.
19. Name some instances in which cosmetics are ineffective in remedying a basic defect. Why are they ineffective?
20. What is the value of the acid secretion of the skin?

CHAPTER 9

BONES, JOINTS AND MUSCLES

Relationships ▪ Bone tissue ▪ The skeleton ▪ Landmarks on bones ▪ Bone disorders ▪ Movable and immovable joints ▪ Arthritis and other joint disorders ▪ Muscles as organs ▪ Some skeletal muscles ▪ Muscle disorders.

THE MUSCULOSKELETAL SYSTEM

The bones are the framework around which the body is constructed. The muscles might be considered its motive power. The joints, where the bones come together, allow the bones, powered by the muscles, a great variety and range of motion. The combination of bones, joints, muscles, and related connective tissues is known as the **musculoskeletal system.**

THE BONES

BONE STRUCTURE

In an earlier chapter we saw that the bones are composed chiefly of bone tissue, known as **osseous** tissue. It should be understood at the outset that a bone is anything but lifeless. Even though the spaces between the cells of bone tissue are permeated with stony deposits of calcium, these cells themselves are very much alive. Bones are organs, with their own system of blood and lymphatic vessels and nerves.

In the embryo (the early development stage of a baby) most of the bones-to-be are cartilage. During the second and third months following conception calcium compounds begin to be deposited in the skeleton. The process of depositing these hard calcium salts continues throughout life, more rapidly at some times than at others. In children the bones are relatively pliable because they contain a larger proportion of cartilage and a smaller amount of the firm calcium salts than those of the adult. In the elderly person there is much less of the softer tissues such as cartilage and a high proportion of calcium salts; therefore, the bones are brittle. Fractures of bones in older people heal with difficulty mainly because of this relatively high proportion of inert material and the small amount of the more vascular softer tissues.

There are 2 kinds of marrow: **red marrow,** found in certain parts of all bones, which manufactures most of the blood cells; and **yellow marrow** of the "soup bone" type, found chiefly in the central cavities of the long bones. Yellow marrow is largely fat.

Bones are covered on the outside (except at the joint region) by a membrane called **periosteum** (per-e-os'te-um). The central cavity of the long bones is lined with a thinner membrane known as **endosteum** (en-dos'te-um).

These bone membranes contain blood and lymph vessels as well as nerves—which latter make their presence felt if, for instance, one suffers a blow on the shin. The chief functions of endosteum and periosteum are to produce bone during the period of the individual's growth, and to aid in repair following an injury such as a fracture.

MAIN FUNCTIONS OF BONES

Bones have a number of functions, many of which are not at all obvious. Some of these are:

1. To serve as a firm framework for the entire body.
2. To protect such delicate structures as the brain and the spinal cord.
3. To serve as levers, which are actuated by the muscles that are attached to them.
4. To serve as a storehouse for calcium, which may be removed and become a part of the blood if there is not enough calcium in the diet.
5. To produce blood cells.

DIVISIONS OF THE SKELETON

The complete bony framework of the body is known as the **skeleton,** and it may be divided into 2 main groups of bones:

1. The **axial** (ak'se-al) **skeleton,** which includes the bony framework of the head and the trunk.
2. The **appendicular** (ap-en-dik'u-lar) **skeleton,** which forms the framework for those parts usually referred to as the arms and legs, but called the **extremities** by the biologists.

The Framework of the Head. The bony framework of the head is called the skull, and it is subdivided into 2 parts, namely;

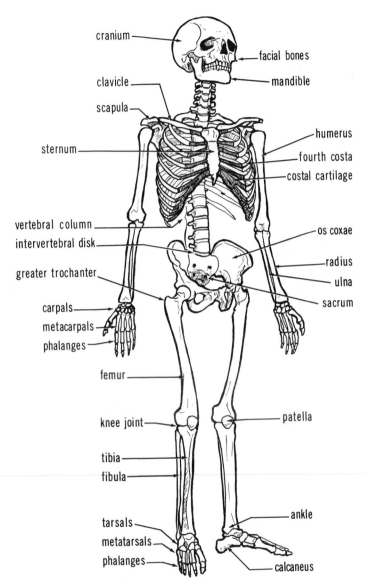

Fɪɢ. 25.
The skeleton.

cranium
facial bones
mandible
clavicle
scapula
humerus
sternum
fourth costa
costal cartilage
vertebral column
intervertebral disk
os coxae
radius
greater trochanter
ulna
sacrum
carpals
metacarpals
phalanges
femur
knee joint
patella
tibia
fibula
tarsals
metatarsals
phalanges
ankle
calcaneus

1. The **cranium,** which is a rounded box that encloses the brain and is made of 8 distinct cranial bones.

2. The **facial portion** of the skull, composed of 14 separate bones.

The bones that form the cranium are:

1. The **frontal bone,** which forms the framework for the forehead, the roof between the eyeballs and the frontal parts of the cerebrum, and contains 2 air spaces (sinuses).

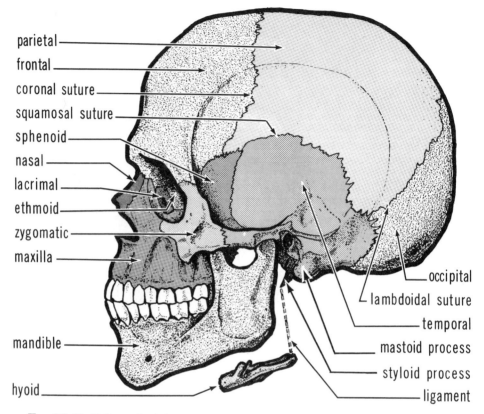

FIG. 26. Skull from the left. Note the hyoid bone, normally suspended by a ligament from the temporal bone's styloid process.

2. The 2 **parietal** (pah-ri'e-tal) **bones,** which form the larger part of the upper and side walls of the cranium.

3. The 2 **temporal bones,** which form the lower sides and part of the base of the central areas of the skull, and which contain the mastoid sinuses as well as the parts of the ear.

4. The single **ethmoid** (eth'moid), which is a delicate, spongy bone located between the eyes and forming a part of the cranial floor between the frontal lobes of the brain and the upper nasal cavities.

5. The **sphenoid** (sfe'noid) **bone,** which is a bat-shaped bone that extends behind the eyes and forms a part of the base of the skull in this region.

6. The single **occipital** (ok-sip'i-tal) **bone** which is located at the back of the skull and includes most of the base of the skull. It extends at the base to meet with the sphenoid medially and the temporal and parietal at the sides.

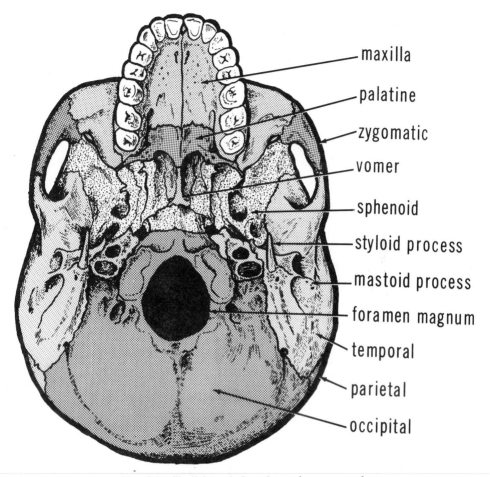

FIG. 27. Skull from below, lower jaw removed.

The places at which the cranial bones join are called **sutures.**

The facial bones include:

1. The **mandible** or lower jaw bone, which is the only movable bone of the skull.

2. The **maxillae** (mak-sil′e), which form the upper jaw. Each maxilla contains a rather large air space called the **maxillary sinus.**

3. The **zygomatic** (zi-go-mat′ik) **bones,** one on each side, which form the higher portion of the cheek.

4. Smaller bones of the face, which include the 2 **lacrimal bones,** one at the corner of each eye; the single **vomer** (vo′mer) that forms the lower part of the nasal septum; the paired **palatine bones** at the back of the hard palate; the slender **nasal**

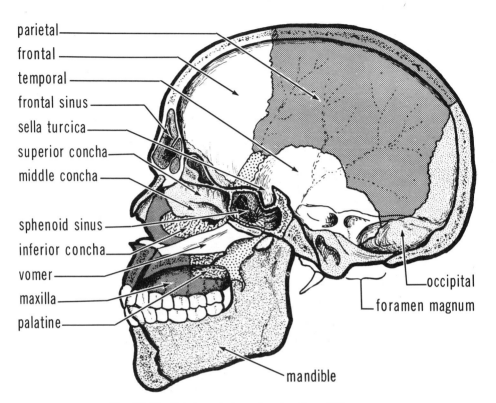

parietal

frontal

temporal

frontal sinus

sella turcica

superior concha

middle concha

sphenoid sinus

inferior concha

vomer

maxilla

palatine

occipital

foramen magnum

mandible

FIG. 28. Skull, internal view, showing the midline vomer
and the lateral nasal conchae.

bones, supporting the bridge of the nose; and the paired inferior **nasal conchae** (kong′ke). The paired superior and middle nasal conchae are all part of the ethmoid, one of the cranial bones.

In addition to the bones of the cranium and the facial bones there are 6 tiny bones or **ossicles** (3 pairs) in the middle ear (Chap. 11) and a single horseshoe- or U-shaped bone that lies just below the skull proper, called the **hyoid** (hi′oid) **bone,** to which the tongue is attached. Actually, the hyoid bone may be thought of as forming the boundary between some of the head structures and those of the neck. It is suspended by a ligament on each side from the temporal bones and can be felt near the mandible or lower jaw bone in the upper neck region (see Fig. 26).

Openings in the base of the skull provide spaces for the entrance and exit of many blood vessels, nerves, and other structures. Projections and slightly elevated portions of the bones provide for the attachment of muscles and sometimes contain delicate structures, as, for example, the part that encloses the middle and internal parts of the ear. Air spaces called sinuses provide lightness and serve as resonating chambers for the voice.

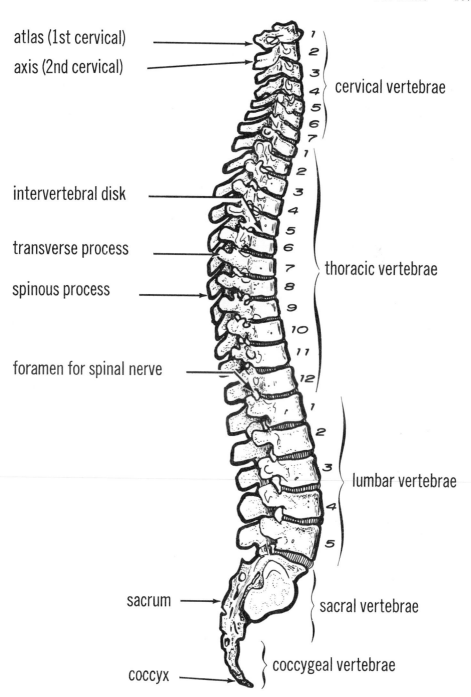

atlas (1st cervical)

axis (2nd cervical)

cervical vertebrae

intervertebral disk

transverse process

spinous process

thoracic vertebrae

foramen for spinal nerve

lumbar vertebrae

sacrum

sacral vertebrae

coccygeal vertebrae

coccyx

FIG. 29. Vertebral column.

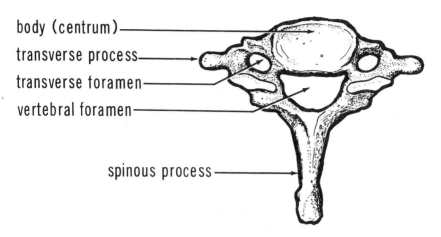

body (centrum)

transverse process

transverse foramen

vertebral foramen

spinous process

FIG. 30. Seventh cervical vertebra, from above.

The Framework of the Trunk. The bones of the trunk include the **vertebral** (ver'te-bral) **column** and **rib cage.** The vertebral column is made of a series of irregularly shaped bones, numbering 33 or 34 in the child; but because of unions that occur later in the lower part of the spine, there usually are 26 separate bones in the adult column. Each of these vertebrae (ver'te-bre) has a body at the front, an opening for the spinal cord toward the back, and a group of projections extending from the arch that encircles the canal, or opening, for the spinal cord. Between the vertebrae are plates of cartilage that absorb shocks and make for flexibility. The spinal column is divided into 5 regions, as follows:

1. The **cervical** (ser've-kal) section, made of 7 vertebrae which form the main framework of the neck.

2. The **thoracic** region, which contains 12 bones, and has a distinct outward or convex curve. It differs from all other parts of the column in that here are attached 12 pairs of ribs.

3. The **lumbar** area, which contains 5 somewhat larger vertebrae than are found in the first 2 sections. It is usually curved inward (concave). Abnormal curvature of the lumbar area is called **lordosis.**

4. The **sacral** (sa'kral) portion of the column, which is made of 5 vertebrae in the child, but which undergoes union of bones so that the adult has one **sacrum** (sa'krum). This serves to complete the framework of the pelvic girdle at the back.

5. The **coccygeal** (kok-sij'e-al) or tail part, made of 4 or 5 bones in the child, but which fuses to form a single coccyx (kok'siks) in the adult.

The rib cage is made of 24 ribs attached to the vertebral column at the back (dorsally) and to the breast bone or **sternum** (ster'num) in front. It serves to support the chest and protect the heart, the lungs, and other organs. Each rib is a slender, somewhat flattened bone that curves and is slightly twisted. The variation

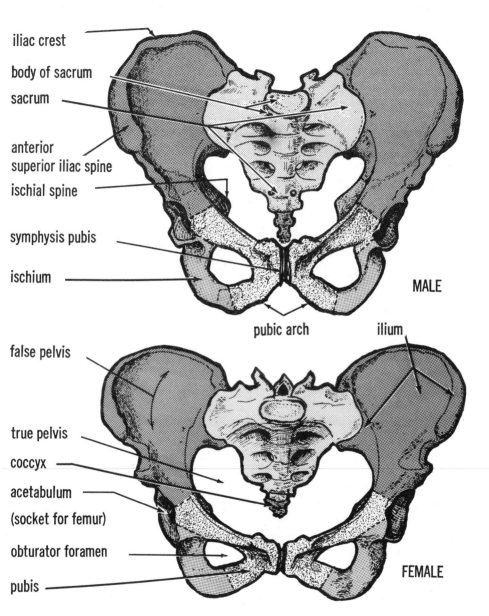

iliac crest

body of sacrum

sacrum

anterior
superior iliac spine

ischial spine

symphysis pubis

ischium

MALE

pubic arch

ilium

false pelvis

true pelvis

coccyx

acetabulum

(socket for femur)

obturator foramen

pubis

FEMALE

Fig. 31. The pelvis. *(Top)* Male pelvis. *(Bottom)* Female pelvis. Note the more rectangular shape and the larger outlet of the female pelvis. The landmarks are the same for both.

in the anterior attachment to the sternum has led to the following grouping of the ribs, or **costae** (kos′te):

1. **True ribs,** which are the first 7 pairs. These are attached directly to the sternum by means of individual extensions called **costal** (kos′tal) **cartilages.**

2. **False costae,** which include the remaining 5 pairs of ribs. Of these, the eighth, ninth and tenth pairs attach to the cartilage of the rib above. The final 2 pairs attach to nothing at all in front and are called **floating ribs.** These last 2 ribs are relatively short and so do not extend around to the front of the body.

The Bones of the Extremities. The framework of the extremities includes the longest bones in the body. Long bones contain a special central canal not found in any other bones. This **medullary** (med′u-lar-e) **canal** or marrow cavity is filled with soft tissue, largely fat, which gives the bone lightness and provides a reservoir for storage of fuel in case of need. This bone structure can be compared with a bamboo stick in its relative lightness and strength. Other bones of the extremities are flat, irregular, or short; and like bones elsewhere in the body, contain red marrow.

The extremities are considered as having 2 divisions: upper and lower. The upper extremities include the shoulders, the arms (between shoulders and elbows), the forearms (between the elbows and the wrists), the wrists, the hands, and the fingers. The lower extremities include the hips (pelvic girdle), the thighs (between the hips and the knees), the legs (between the knees and the ankles), the ankles, the feet, and the toes.

The bones of the upper extremities are grouped as follows:

1. The shoulder or **pectoral** (pek′to-ral) **girdle,** which contains the collar bone, or **clavicle** (klav′i-kle), and the shoulder blade, or **scapula** (skap′u-lah).

2. The bone of the arm proper, the **humerus** (hu′mer-us), which connects at the top with the scapula and with the 2 forearm bones at the elbow.

3. The forearm bones, which are the **ulna** (ul′nah) on the little-finger (medial) side, and the **radius** (ra′de-us) on the thumbside, which is lateral when the palm is directed forward.

4. The **carpal** (kar′pal) **bones** of the wrist, which number 8 for each side, all different and with individual names.

5. The **metacarpal bones** of the palm of the hand, which are 5 in number on either side. Their distal ends form the knuckles.

6. The **phalanges** (fa-lan′jez), which are the bones forming the framework of the fingers, numbering 14 for either side. Each of these bones is called a **phalanx** (fa′lanks), and exact identification may be made by using the words "distal" for the tips, "middle" for the next group, and "proximal" for those connected with the metacarpal bones. Each finger has 3 phalanges; the thumb has but 2.

The bones of the lower extremities are grouped in a similar fashion:

1. The **pelvic girdle** of the hip region, which includes an **os coxae** (kok′se) on each side, articulating (joining) with the sacrum at the back. The pelvis proper is

the lower part of the body cavity, and its boundaries comprise the inner edges of the 2 ossa (os'ah) coxae, the sacrum and the coccyx. The pelvis of the female is broader and lighter than that of the male, and has a greater capacity, all of which differences are an adaptation to pregnancy and childbirth.

2. The thigh bone, called the **femur** (fe'mer). This is the longest bone in the body.

3. The **patella** (pah-tel'lah), commonly called the kneecap. This is an example of a **sesamoid** (ses'ah-moid) **bone,** a type usually encased in connective tissue cords (tendons) and designed to minimize friction. The patella is the largest sesamoid bone in the body; smaller examples of this type are found in both the upper and the lower extremities.

4. The 2 leg bones, which include the larger, weight-bearing bone called the **tibia** (shin bone) and the slender **fibula** (fib'u-lah), which does not extend up as high as the knee joint and is not weight-bearing.

5. Ankle and foot bones, which include the 7 **tarsus bones** (of the ankle) and the 5 **metatarsus** (or instep) **bones,** on either side. The heel bone, or **calcaneus** (kal-ka'ne-us), is the largest of these.

6. The **phalanges** of the toes, which are counterparts of those in the fingers. There are 3 of these in each toe except for the great toe, which has but 2.

Landmarks of Bones. The contour of bones resembles the topography of an interesting and varied landscape with its hills and valleys. The projections often serve as regions for muscle attachments. There are hundreds of these prominences or **processes** with different names. Some are very important points of reference, as for example:

1. The **olecranon** (o-lek'rah-non) **process** which is the upper part of the ulna and forms the point of the elbow.

2. The **iliac** (il'e-ak) **spine,** which refers particularly to the pointed upper front part of the hip bone, or os coxae. There actually are 3 other iliac spines on each side, but this is the most important of these and is often used as a landmark, or reference point, in diagnosis and treatment.

3. The **ischial** (is'ke-al) **spine** at the back of the pelvic outlet, which is used as a point of reference during childbirth to indicate the progress of the presenting part (usually the baby's head) down the birth canal.

4. The greater **trochanters** (tro-kan'ters), which are large rounded projections located at the upper and lateral (side) portions of the femur.

Some bones are divided into areas based on the parts that were separated from each other by cartilage during childhood. An important example of this regional division is found in the pelvic girdle where the os coxae is divided into 3 areas:

1. The **ilium,** which forms the upper wing-shaped part on each side.

2. The **ischium** (is'ki-um), which includes a part on which we sit called the **ischial tuberosity** as well as the spine mentioned in the previous paragraph.

3. The **pubis,** which forms the front portion of the os coxae and includes the

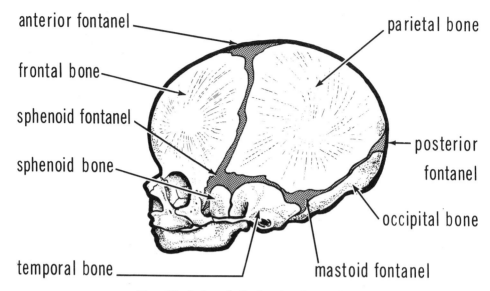

anterior fontanel

frontal bone

sphenoid fontanel

sphenoid bone

temporal bone

parietal bone

posterior fontanel

occipital bone

mastoid fontanel

FIG. 32. Infant skull, showing fontanels.

region of union of the 2 ossa coxae in the center front to form the joint known as the **symphysis** (sim'fi-sis) **pubis.**

The skull of the infant has areas in which the bone formation is incomplete, leaving so-called soft spots. Although there are a number of these, the largest and best known is near the front at the junction of the two parietal bones with the frontal bone. It is called the **anterior fontanel** (fon-tah-nel'), and it does not usually close until the child is about 18 months old (see Fig. 32).

Holes that extend into or through bones are called **foramina** (fo-ram'i-nah). Numerous foramina permit the passage of blood vessels to and from the bone tissue and the marrow cavities. Larger foramina in the base of the skull and in other locations allow for the passage of cranial nerves, blood vessels, and other structures that connect with the brain. The largest such opening in the skull is called the **foramen** (fo-ra'men) **magnum,** which contains the spinal cord and related parts. The largest foramina in the entire body are found in the pelvic girdle, near the front of each os coxae, one on each side of the symphysis pubis. These are called the **obturator** (ob'tu-ra-tor) **foramina,** and are partially covered by a membrane.

Valleylike depressions on a bone surface are called **fossae** (fos'se), the singular form being **fossa** (fos'sah). Some of these are filled with muscle tissue, as is the case with the large fossae of the two scapulae. Other depressions are narrow elongated areas called **grooves.** They may allow for the passage of blood vessels or nerves as in the case of the ribs, where grooves contain intercostal nerves and vessels.

DISORDERS OF BONE

Osteomyelitis (os″te-o-mi-e-li′tis) is an infection of the bone, often also involving the marrow, caused by pus-producing bacteria. These pathogens may reach the bone through the bloodstream or by way of an injury in which the skin has been broken. Further, an injury without a break in the skin may make the bone more susceptible to blood-borne infection. Before the advent of antibiotic drugs, bone infection was very resistant to treatment and the outlook was poor. Now there are fewer cases in the first place because many of the bloodstream infections are prevented or treated early enough so that bone infection is less common. If those that do appear are treated promptly, the chance of a cure is usually excellent.

Tuberculosis may involve bone tissue notably in the spinal column, the pelvis, the hands, and the knees. In the spine destruction of the bodies of the vertebrae may cause collapse of the front portion of the column, often in the thoracic region. This causes an increase in the curvature and the hunchback appearance, called **kyphosis** (ki-fo′sis). Tuberculosis of the spine has a special name: **Pott's disease.**

Tumors in bone tissue may originate there, or cancer cells may be carried to the bone and form metastases. Those tumors that start in the osseous tissue may be benign as in the case of certain cysts, or they may be malignant. These tumors are somewhat more common in younger persons than are the cancers that originate from epithelium.

Severe violence is capable of causing **fractures** in almost any bone. The word "fracture" means "a break or rupture in a bone," and such injuries may be classified as follows:

1. **Compound** fractures, which include those in which the skin and other soft tissues are torn and the bone protrudes through the skin.

2. **Simple** fractures, which are those in which the break in the bone is not accompanied by a break in the skin.

3. **Greenstick** fractures, incomplete breaks in which the bone splits in much the same way as a piece of green wood might. These are most common in children.

4. **Impacted** fractures, which are those in which the broken ends of the bone are jammed into each other.

5. **Comminuted** (kom′i-noot-ed) fractures, those in which there is more than one fracture line with several fragments resulting.

6. **Spiral** fractures, in which the bone has been twisted apart. These are relatively common in skiing accidents.

The most important first-aid care of fractures is prevention of movement of the affected parts. Protection by simple splinting after careful evaluation of the situation, leaving as much as possible "as is," and a call for expert help is usually safest. Those who have back injuries may be spared serious spinal cord damage if careful moving on a firm board or door can be done correctly. If a doctor or ambulance can reach the scene, a "hands off" rule for the untrained is to be strongly recommended. If there is no external bleeding, covering the victim

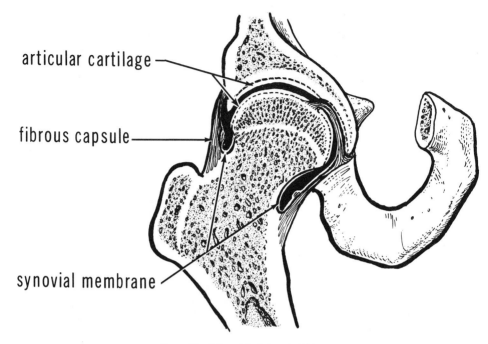

articular cartilage

fibrous capsule

synovial membrane

FIG. 33. Movable joint (of hip).

with blankets may help combat shock. First aid should always first be directed toward the control of hemorrhage.

Abnormal body chemistry involving calcium may cause certain bone disorders. One of these is called Paget's disease, or **osteitis deformans** (os-te-i'tis de-for'mans). The bones undergo periods of calcium loss followed by times of excessive deposition of calcium salts. The bones become deformed. Cause and cure are not known at the present time. The bones also can become decalcified owing to the effect of a tumor of the parathyroid gland (see Chap. 18).

Rickets is primarily a disease of children, and is characterized by a hampering of growth and the failure of the bones to calcify sufficiently. The main cause of rickets is a deficiency of calcium and phosphorus. This can result directly from not having enough of these minerals in the diet. It also can result indirectly through a deficiency of vitamin D, a fat-soluble vitamin which is necessary in order that calcium and phosphorus may be absorbed by the body. Consequently, unless foods containing vitamin D are provided, the body will not be able to utilize these minerals, no matter how great the quantities of them taken in with the food. Insufficient sunlight can be another predisposing factor in rickets, since the ultraviolet rays of the sun act on the skin to manufacture vitamin D. Rickets is most prevalent among children who grow up in the murk of city slums.

The failure of the bones to calcify keeps them soft and easily bent. Certain deformities are a consequence, notably bowlegs.

JOINTS

KINDS OF JOINTS

Joints, or more scientifically, **articulations,** may be defined as the region of union of 2 or more bones. Classification depends on the structure in the region of this union and the functions of the joints. A simplified version of usual classifications follows:

1. Freely movable joints, which are called **diarthroses** (di-ar-thro'ses), all of which contain a lubricating fluid inside a joint cavity that is lined with **synovial** (si-no've-al) **membrane.**

2. Immovable and relatively fixed joints, which occasionally allow slight motion. These do not have a distinct cavity containing fluid.

JOINT STRUCTURE

Connective tissue bands, called **ligaments,** hold the bones together and are found in connection with all the freely movable joints and many of the less movable articulations. In some cases these completely enclose the joint and are called **capsular** (kap'su-lar) **ligaments.** Additional ligaments reinforce and help to stabilize the joints at various points. The contacting surfaces of each joint are covered by a smooth layer of gristle called the **articular** (ar-tik'u-lar) **cartilage.** Inside the joint space is the rather thick, colorless synovial fluid, which has been named after its resemblance to egg white.

The slightly movable and immovable joints form continuous structures in which either cartilage or fibrous connective tissue fills the gap between the bones. These soft tissue areas are larger in the child, become smaller in the adult, and may become completely filled by bone in later life. The joints between the vertebrae in the lower part of the spinal column and those between the 3 sections of each of the ossa coxae are examples of immovable joints that completely disappear rather early in life. The skull joints, or sutures, are held together by fibrous connective tissue aided by the dovetailing of the rather irregular sawtooth type of bone edges.

JOINT FUNCTION

The chief function of the freely movable joints is to allow for changes of position and so provide for motion. These movements are given names to describe the nature of the change in position of the body parts. Examples of some names of movements are:

1. **Flexion** (flek'shun), which is a bending motion, decreasing the angle between 2 parts.

2. **Extension,** which is a straightening or stretching: the reverse of flexion.

3. **Abduction,** which means motion *away from* the midline of the body. Raising the arm away from the body (as when reaching for something up on a high shelf) involves abduction of the upper extremity.

4. **Adduction,** which means motion *toward* the midline. The scissors kick used in swimming is an example of adduction of the lower extremities.

5. **Rotation,** which means motion around a central axis, as in swinging the head in saying "No."

DISORDERS OF JOINTS

Joints are subject to certain disorders of a mechanical nature, examples of which are **dislocations** and **sprains.** A dislocation is a derangement of the parts of the joint. A sprain is the name for the wrenching of a joint with rupture or tearing of the ligaments.

The most common type of joint infection is **arthritis,** meaning "inflammation of the joints." There are many different kinds of arthritis, a familiar form of it being **rheumatoid arthritis.** This condition is a crippling one, characterized by swelling of the joints of the hands, the feet and other parts of the body as a result of inflammation and overgrowth of the synovial membrane and other joint tissues. The articular cartilage is gradually destroyed, and the joint cavity develops adhesions—that is, the surfaces tend to stick together—so that the joints stiffen and are ultimately rendered useless. The cause of rheumatoid arthritis is still unknown, though some types of streptococci are suspected. The administration of ACTH or cortisone is often an effective treatment, particularly in the early acute stages.

Arthritis also can be brought on by such infections as rheumatic fever and gonorrhea.

The joints as well as the bones proper are subject to attack by the tuberculosis organism, and the result may be a gradual destruction of parts of the bone near the joint. The organism is carried by the blood stream, usually from a focus in the lungs or lymph nodes, and may cause considerable damage before it is discovered. The bodies of several vertebrae sometimes are affected; or one hip or other single joint may be diseased. The patient may complain only of difficulty in walking, and diagnosis is difficult unless an accompanying lung tuberculosis has been found. This disorder is more common in children.

Degenerative joint diseases are a group which usually occur in older people. Sometimes such factors as obesity and repeated traumata can help to bring them about. Degenerative diseases occur mostly in joints involving weight-bearing.

Various degenerative changes in the joints include the formation of spurs at the edges of the articular surfaces, thickening of the synovial membrane, atrophy of the cartilages, or calcification of the ligaments.

Gout is a kind of arthritis basically caused by a disturbance of metabolism. One of the products of metabolism is uric acid, which normally is excreted in the urine. If there happens to be an overproduction of uric acid, or for some reason not enough is excreted, the accumulated uric acid forms crystals which are deposited as masses about the joints and other parts of the body. The joints become inflamed and extremely painful. Any joint can be involved, but the one most commonly affected by gout is the great toe. Most victims of gout are men past middle life.

Backache is a common complaint. Some of the causes are:

1. Diseases of the vertebrae, such as infections or tumors; and in older people, degenerative arthritis or atrophy (wasting away) of the bone following long illnesses.

2. Disorders of the intervertebral disks, especially those in the lower lumbar region. Pain may be very severe, with muscle spasm and extension of symptoms along the course of the sciatic nerve (back of the thigh).

3. Abnormalities of the lower vertebrae or of the ligaments and other supporting structures.

4. Disorders involving organs of the pelvis or those in the retroperitoneal space (as the pancreas). Variations in the position of the uterus are seldom a cause.

5. Strains on the **lumbosacral** joint (where the lumbar region joins the sacrum) or strains on the **sacroiliac** joint (where the sacrum joins the ilium of the pelvis).

MUSCLES

CHARACTERISTICS OF SKELETAL MUSCLE

As was indicated in Chapter 4, there are 3 basic kinds of muscle tissue: skeletal, smooth, and cardiac muscle. This chapter will be concerned only with skeletal muscle, which is attached to the bones, and which is also known as voluntary muscle because normally it is under the control of the will.

Skeletal muscles may be regarded as organs since they are made of a combination of muscle and connective tissue. When stimulated by nerve impulses, the long and threadlike muscle cells (fibers) become shorter and thicker, resulting in muscle contraction. Muscle fibers are arranged in bundles that are held together by connective tissue. Groups of these bundles are held together by additional connective tissue, and the entire muscle is encased in a tough connective tissue sheath called the **epimysium** (ep-i-mis'e-um).

Most muscles have 2 or more attachments to the skeleton. The method of attachment varies. In some instances the connective tissue within the muscle ties directly to the periosteum of the bone. In other cases the connective tissue sheath and partitions within the muscle all extend to form specialized structures that aid in attaching the muscle to bones. Such an extension may take the form of a cord, in which case it is called a **tendon.** In other cases a sheet called an **aponeurosis** (ap-o-nu-ro′sis), or else **fascia** (which has been discussed previously), may attach muscles to bones.

Whatever the nature of the muscle attachment, the principle remains the same: to furnish a means of harnessing the power of the muscle contractions. A muscle might be compared with a hoisting winch: in order that the winch may work at all, it must be firmly anchored somewhere while its cable handles the load. A muscle must be anchored also, usually to a relatively fixed structure. This fixed attachment of a muscle is known as its **origin,** while the end that exerts the power and movement (like the end of the cable of the winch) is called the **insertion.** The actual movement of the muscle is its **action.**

Within the muscle sheath are found the blood and lymphatic vessels as well as nerve fibers. Muscles receive an abundant blood supply because of the large amount of oxygen consumed by their cells, along with sugar, to generate power and heat.

Nerve fibers carry impulses to the muscles, each fiber supplying from a few up to more than a hundred individual muscle cells. The endings of the motor nerve fibers are called **myoneural** (mi-o-nu′ral) **junctions** or **motor end plates** (see Chap. 10).

Muscle tone refers to a partially contracted state of the muscles which is normal even though the muscles may not be in use at the time. The maintenance of this tension is due to the action of the nervous system, and the effect of it is to keep the muscles in a constant state of readiness for action. Muscles that are little used soon become flabby, weak and out of tone. If a person's muscle tone is poor, his general state of health is considered "below par."

SOME INDIVIDUAL SKELETAL MUSCLES

The human body contains more than 400 skeletal muscles, constituting between 35 and 40 per cent of body weight. A large number of the skeletal muscles are arranged in pairs. A movement is initiated by one muscle or set of muscles called the **prime mover.** When an opposite movement is to be made, another muscle or set of muscles, known as the **antagonist** (an-tag′o-nist), takes over. In this way body movements are coordinated, and a large number of complicated movements are carried out without the necessity of planning in advance the means of performing them. At first, however, any new complicated movement must be learned. Think of a child learning to walk or to write, and consider the number of muscles which he uses unnecessarily or forgets to use when the situation calls for them.

Muscles of the Head. The principal muscles of the head are those of facial expression and those of chewing (mastication).

The muscles of facial expression include the vaguely circular ones around the eyes and the lips. They are called the **orbicularis** (or-bik-u-la′ris) **muscles** because of their shape (think of "orbit"). The muscle surrounding each eye is called the

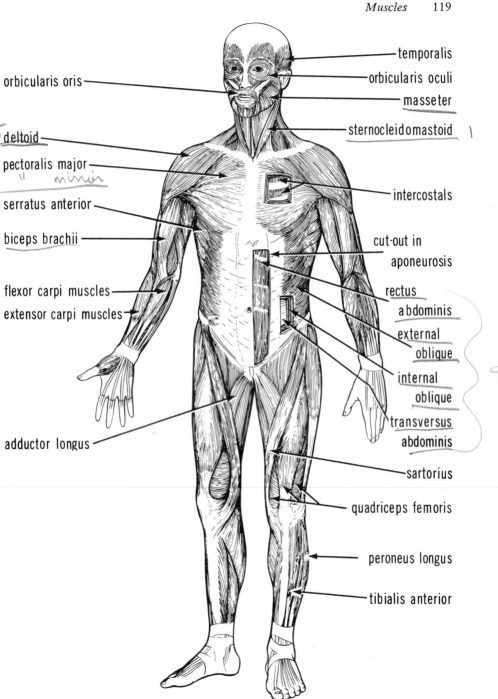

FIG. 34. Principal muscles (anterior view).

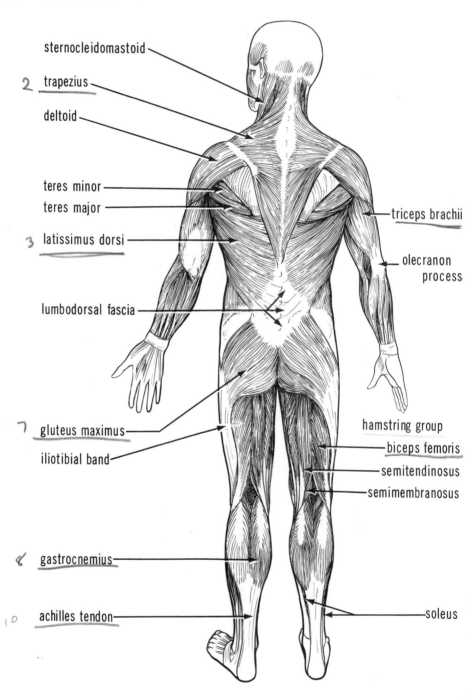

FIG. 35. Principal muscles (posterior view).

orbicularis oculi (ok'u-li), while the muscle of the lips is the **orbicularis oris.** These muscles, of course, are all provided with antagonists.

One of the largest muscles of expression forms the fleshy part of the cheek and is called the **buccinator** (buk'se-na-tor). It is used in whistling or blowing and is sometimes referred to as the trumpeter's muscle. You can readily think of other muscles of facial expression: for instance, the antagonists of the orbicularis oris which can produce a smile, a sneer, or a grimace. There are a number of scalp muscles by means of which the eyebrows are lifted or else drawn together into a frown.

There are 4 pairs of muscles of chewing, all of which insert on the mandible and move it. The largest are the **temporal** (tem'po-ral) **muscles,** located above and near the ear, and the **masseter** (mas-se'ter) **muscles** at the angle of the jaw.

The tongue has 2 groups of muscles. The first group, called the **intrinsic muscles,** are located entirely within the tongue. The second group, the **extrinsic muscles,** originate outside the tongue. It is because of these many muscles that the tongue has such remarkable flexibility and can perform so many different functions. Consider the intricate tongue motions involved in speaking, chewing and swallowing.

Muscles of the Neck. The neck muscles tend to be ribbonlike and extend up and down or obliquely in several layers and in a complex manner. The 2 pairs you will hear of the most frequently are the **trapezius** (trah-pe'ze-us) **muscles,** which extend into the upper back, and the **sternocleidomastoid** (ster-no-kli'do-mas'toid), sometimes referred to simply as the **sternomastoid.** The latter muscle extends along the side of the neck. It may be injured or for other reasons be shortened, resulting in a condition called wryneck **(torticollis).** Both of these muscles help to hold the head erect. The upper part of the trapezius also assists in moving the head to one side or the other.

Muscles of the Upper Extremities. The muscles that produce finger movements are the several **flexor digitorum** (dij-e-to'rum) and the **extensor digitorum muscles.** The thumb has a special muscle for flexion; and this appendage, incidentally, by virtue of its position and freedom of movement, has been one of the most marvelously useful endowments of man. Many movements of the wrist are produced by the **flexor carpi** and the **extensor carpi muscles.** The muscles of the fingers, the thumb and the wrist are located in the forearm with tendons extending into the wrist, hand, and fingers except for the smaller and less powerful muscles forming the few fleshy parts of the hands and fingers.

In the upper arm is the **biceps brachii** (bra'ke-i), the muscle almost invariably displayed by small boys as proof of their strength. On the opposite side of the upper arm is the **triceps brachii,** or boxer's muscle, which straightens the elbow when a blow is delivered.

The muscular cap of the shoulder is the **deltoid muscle,** an upside-down triangle that abducts the arm. The deltoid is often used as an injection site.

Muscles of the Chest and the Back. On either side of the chest, high up in the breast region, is the large **pectoralis** (pek-to-ra'lis) **major.** This muscle begins at the sternum, the upper ribs and the clavicle, and forms the anterior "wall" of the armpit. It ends at the humerus and serves to flex the arm across the chest.

Below the armpit, on the side of the chest, is the **serratus** (ser-ra'tus) **anterior.** It originates on the upper 8 or 9 ribs on the side and the front of the thorax and inserts in the scapula on the side toward the vertebrae. The serratus anterior muscle moves the scapula forward when, for example, one is pushing something.

In the spaces between the ribs are inserted the **intercostal muscles.** These are particularly important in respiration, serving to enlarge the thoracic cavity upon inspiration.

If we move around to the back of the body, the first important muscle to be encountered is the **trapezius,** part of which we already have seen in the neck. The trapezius is a large muscle which comes down from the neck and fans out like a pointed cape over the back of the shoulders. One purpose of the trapezius is to maintain the position of the shoulders. If you raise your shoulders and throw them back, the trapezius is the chief muscle used.

The other superficial muscle is the **latissimus** (lah-tis'i-mus) **dorsi,** originating in the lower half of the spine and covering the lower half of the thoracic region. This is the principal muscle used in bringing the arm down forcibly, as, for example, in swimming. The muscles which act on the vertebral column itself are thick vertical masses that lie under the relatively flat trapezius and latissimus dorsi.

Muscles of the Abdomen. The abdominal muscles serve a number of purposes. One is to assist indirectly in the process of respiration, relaxing when the diaphragm contracts and vice versa. They also are compressors of internal organs, aiding in the acts of defecation, urination, childbirth and other processes. Another function of the abdominal muscles is to bend the trunk in various directions.

The lateral walls of the abdomen have 3 main muscles arranged in layers: the **external oblique** on the outside, the **internal oblique** in the middle, and the innermost layer called the **transversus abdominis.** The fibers of these 3 muscles all run in different directions. With these layers "glued" together, the total effect is like that of a piece of plywood; the result is a very strong abdominal wall. The front of the abdomen is closed in by the long, narrow **rectus abdominis,** which originates at the pubis and ends at the ribs. It is surrounded by connective tissue layers from the other 3 muscles.

Within the ventral body cavity, forming the partition between the abdominal cavity and the thoracic cavity, is the **diaphragm,** the dome-shaped muscle used in breathing.

The pelvic floor, or **perineum** (per-i-ne'um), has its own form of diaphragm, shaped somewhat like a shallow dish. One of the principal muscles of this pelvic diaphragm is the **levator ani** (le-va'tor a'ni), which acts on the rectum and thus aids in defecation.

Muscles of the Lower Extremities. The muscles in the lower extremities are among the largest and strongest in the body and are specialized for locomotion and balance. The **gluteus maximus** (gloo'te-us mak'si-mus), which forms much of the fleshy part of the hips and the buttocks, is relatively large in the human being because of its function in standing in the erect position. This muscle extends the hip and is very important in walking and running. It also is used frequently as a site for injections, particularly if the quantity of the medication is large.

The **sartorius** is a long, narrow muscle that begins at the iliac spine, winds downward and inward across the entire thigh, and ends on the upper medial surface of the tibia. It is called the tailor's muscle because it is used in crossing the legs.

On the front of the thigh is a large 4-part muscle called the **quadriceps femoris** (kwod're-seps fem'or-is). This muscle extends the knee as in kicking a football. Charleyhorse is a spasm, or soreness and stiffness, which may involve any muscle, but this term is used most often in connection with the quadriceps femoris. Sometimes this muscle is used as an injection site.

A short double muscle located high up on the thigh is the powerful **iliopsoas** (il-e-o-so'as). This muscle extends from the lumbar vertebrae and the ilium to the top part of the femur. It is a flexor of the thigh and also helps to keep the trunk from falling backward when the body is standing erect.

On the inside (medial part) of the thigh are the **adductors,** which serve to press the thighs together. Anyone who rides horseback uses these muscles more than any others.

The posterior thigh muscles are called the **hamstring group,** and their tendons can be felt behind the knee on either side. They serve to bend the leg backward toward the thigh.

The **gastrocnemius** (gas-trok-ne'me-us) is the chief muscle of the calf of the leg. It has been called the toe dancer's muscle because it is necessary in order to stand on tiptoe. It ends near the heel in a prominent cord called the **Achilles tendon,** which then attaches to the calcaneus (heel bone). The Achilles tendon is the largest tendon in the body.

Another leg muscle which acts on the foot is the **tibialis** (tib-e-a'lis) **anterior,** located on the front of the leg. This muscle performs the opposite function of the gastrocnemius. Anyone who feels inclined to walk on his heels will use the tibialis anterior to raise the rest of the foot off the ground.

The ankle joint is not constructed exactly like that of the hand; it does not have quite the freedom of movement of the latter. The ankle does have a small amount of "side play" (i.e., medial and lateral rotation). These movements have special names: **inversion** (to bend the ankle so that the sole of the foot is facing the opposite foot) and **eversion** (bending the ankle in the opposite direction so that the sole of the foot is facing outward, away from the body). The principal muscle of inversion is the tibialis anterior, just discussed; the muscle of eversion is the **peroneus** (per-o-ne'us) **longus,** located on the outside of the leg (i.e., laterally).

The toes, like the fingers, are provided with a set of muscles likewise called the **flexor digitorum** and the **extensor digitorum muscles.** The former originate both at the tarsus and at the posterior surface of the tibia, and pass through the sole of the foot to the toes. The latter arise both from the tarsus and the anterior surface of the fibula, and pass over the top of the foot to the toes.

MUSCULAR DISORDERS

Myalgia (mi-al'je-ah) means "muscular pain," whereas **myositis** (mi-o-si'tis) is a term that indicates actual inflammation of muscle tissue. **Fibrositis** (fi-bro-si'tis) means "inflammation of connective tissues," particularly those connected with muscles and joints. Usually a combination disorder called **fibromyositis** is present. Such a condition is commonly referred to as rheumatism, lumbago, or charley-horse. The disorder may be acute with severe pain on motion, or it may be chronic. Sometimes the application of heat together with massage and rest will relieve the symptoms.

Bursitis is inflammation of a **bursa,** a bursa being a cavity or sac filled with synovial fluid. The purpose of a bursa is to minimize friction. Some communicate with joints; others are closely related to muscles. Sometimes bursae develop spontaneously in response to prolonged friction.

Bursitis can be very painful, with swelling and limitation of motion. Some examples of bursitis are:

1. **Students' elbow,** in which the bursa over the point of the elbow (olecranon) is inflamed, due to long hours of leaning on the elbow while studying.

2. **Ischial bursitis,** said to be common in those who must sit a great deal, such as taxicab drivers and truckers.

3. **Housemaid's knee,** in which the bursa in front of the patella is inflamed. This form of bursitis is found in those who must be on their knees a great deal.

4. **Subdeltoid bursitis** in the shoulder region, a fairly common and unpleasant form. In some cases a local anesthetic is injected to relieve the pain.

Bunions are enlargements commonly found at the base and medial side of the great toe. Usually prolonged pressure has caused the development of a bursa, which then has become inflamed. Special shoes may be necessary if surgery is not done.

Flatfoot is a common disorder in which the **arch** of the foot, the normally raised portion of the sole, breaks down so that the entire sole rests on the ground. This condition may be congenital, in which case it usually gives little trouble. However, flatfoot can result from a progressive weakening of the muscles that support the arch, and usually this condition is accompanied by a great deal of pain. Incorrect use of the muscles that support the arch (such as toeing out when walking), or lack of exercise, are thought to bring about flatfoot. Walking with the toes pointed straight forward, in properly fitted shoes, is one of the best ways of preventing flatfoot and other painful foot disorders. Other exercises, under the supervision of a trained person (preferably an orthopedic physician) can be helpful in strengthening the muscles that help maintain the foot arches.

Strains and **sprains** are typical injuries that often affect muscles. Severe and excessive exertion can cause detachment of muscles from bones or tearing of some of the muscle cells. Sprains can involve damage to other structures besides the ligaments, namely blood vessels, nerves and muscles. Much of the pain and swelling accompanying a sprain can be prevented by the immediate application of ice packs, which will constrict some of the smaller blood vessels and reduce internal bleeding.

Two diseases that affect muscles are **muscular dystrophy** (dis'tro-fe) and **myasthenia gravis** (mi-as-the'ne-ah gra'vis). The cause and cure of these afflictions are not yet known but are the subject of intensive research. Muscular dystrophy appears most often in male children and is a progressive disorder ending in complete helplessness. Myasthenia gravis is characterized by chronic muscular fatigue brought on by the slightest exertion. It affects adults and begins with the muscles of the head. Drooping of the eyelids **(ptosis)** is a common early symptom.

SUMMARY

1. **Bones.**
    A. Specific bones.
        (1) Head.
            (a) Cranial: frontal, 2 parietal, 2 temporal, ethmoid, sphenoid, occipital.
            (b) Facial: mandible, 2 maxillae, 2 zygomatic, 2 lacrimal, vomer, 2 palatine, 2 nasal conchae, 2 nasal bones, ossicles (of ear), hyoid.
        (2) Trunk.
            (a) Vertebral column. Regions: cervical, thoracic, lumbar, sacral, coccygeal.
            (b) Ribs: true ribs (first 7), false costae (5 including floating ribs).
        (3) Extremities.
            (a) Upper: pectoral girdle (clavicle, scapula), humerus, radius, ulna, 8 carpal bones, 5 metacarpal, phalanges.
            (b) Lower: pelvic girdle (2 ossa coxae), femur, patella (largest sesamoid), tibia, fibula, 7 tarsal, 5 metatarsal (calcaneus etc.), phalanges.
    B. Landmarks of bones.
        (1) Prominences: olecranon, iliac spine, ischial spine, trochanters.
        (2) Pelvic divisions: ilium, ischium, pubis.
        (3) Anterior fontanel (and others) in infants.
        (4) Foramina: foramen magnum, obturator foramina.
        (5) Fossae and grooves.
    C. Disorders: osteomyelitis, tuberculosis, fractures, osteitis deformans, rickets.
2. **Joints.**
    A. Types: movable, immovable.
    B. Structure: held together with ligaments; surfaces covered with articular cartilage, lubricated with synovial fluid.

C. Movements: flexion, extension, abduction, adduction, rotation.

D. Disorders: dislocations, sprains, arthritis, tuberculosis, degenerative diseases, gout, backache.

3. **Muscles.**

A. Characteristics: bundles of fibers covered with epimysium; attached by tendons or aponeuroses (or fascia); fixed attachment (origin), movable attachment (insertion); nerve fibers end at motor end plates; muscle tone maintained by nervous system.

B. Individual muscles.

   (1) Head.

      (a) Face: orbicularis oculi, orbicularis oris, buccinator, scalp muscles (some).

      (b) Mastication: temporal, masseter.

      (c) Tongue: intrinsic, extrinsic.

   (2) Neck: trapezius, sternocleidomastoid.

   (3) Upper extremities: flexor digitorum and extensor digitorum muscles; flexor carpi and extensor carpi muscles; biceps brachii, triceps brachii, deltoid.

   (4) Chest and back: pectoralis major, serratus anterior, intercostals, trapezius, latissimus dorsi.

   (5) Abdomen: external oblique, internal oblique, transversus abdominis, rectus abdominis, diaphragm, pelvic floor muscles (including levator ani).

   (6) Lower extremities: gluteus maximus, sartorius, quadriceps femoris, iliopsoas, adductors, hamstring group, gastrocnemius, tibialis anterior, peroneus longus, flexor digitorum and extensor digitorum muscles.

C. Disorders: myalgia, myositis, fibrositis, fibromyositis, bursitis, flatfoot, strains, sprains, muscular dystrophy, myasthenia gravis.

QUESTIONS AND PROBLEMS

1. Give a general description of a bone with respect to its tissues, membranes, vessels, etc.
2. Name 5 general functions of bones.
3. What are the main cranial and facial bones?
4. What are the main divisions of the vertebral column? The ribs?
5. Name the bones of the upper and lower extremities.
6. Name: 4 bone prominences; 3 divisions of the pelvic girdle; the largest fontanel; 2 prominent foramina.
7. Name and describe 3 bone diseases and 5 types of fractures.
8. What are the 2 kinds of joints?
9. Describe joint structure and describe 5 kinds of joint movements.
10. Describe 3 different joint diseases.

11. Give a general description of skeletal muscle with respect to its structure, function, attachments and nerve connections.
12. Name the main muscles of the head and define each. What are the 2 principal neck muscles?
13. Name and define the principal muscles of the upper extremities; the chest and the back.
14. Name the main muscles of the abdominal wall and give the reason for their especially light and strong construction.
15. Name and locate the main lower extremity muscles.
16. Describe briefly: bursitis, flatfoot (include some cause in both cases).

CHAPTER 10

THE BRAIN, SPINAL CORD, AND NERVES

The nervous system and its parts ▪ Nerves and nerve cells ▪ The brain and its subdivisions ▪ Lobes and areas in the cerebral hemispheres ▪ Functions of various parts of the brain ▪ Speech centers and the process of learning ▪ Sleeping sickness and other brain infections ▪ Strokes, brain tumors, and epilepsy ▪ The structure and functions of the spinal cord ▪ Coverings of the brain and spinal cord ▪ Cranial nerves, spinal nerves, and their disorders ▪ The autonomic nervous system.

Once a number of the body systems have been surveyed, it should become fairly obvious that not one of these systems is capable of functioning alone. All are interdependent, and all must work together as one unit in order that the normal conditions within the body may prevail. The agency that insures the coordination of the organs and organ systems is the nervous system. Conditions both within and outside the body are constantly changing; and one purpose of the nervous system is to respond to these internal and external changes (known as **stimuli**) and so cause the body to adapt itself to the new conditions.

The nervous system has been very aptly compared with a telephone exchange in which the brain and the spinal cord act as centers and the nerve trunks serve as cables and wires for carrying messages to and from various parts of these centers.

THE NERVOUS SYSTEM AS A WHOLE

The parts of the nervous system may be grouped according to how they are made (structure) or else on the basis of what the parts do (function).

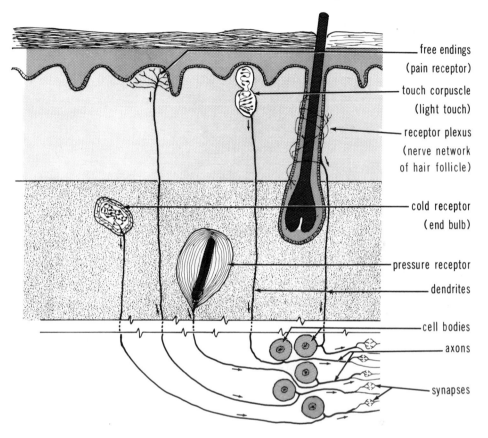

free endings
(pain receptor)

touch corpuscle
(light touch)

receptor plexus
(nerve network
of hair follicle)

cold receptor
(end bulb)

pressure receptor

dendrites

cell bodies

axons

synapses

FIG. 36. Diagram of sensory neurons and their receptors in the skin.

STRUCTURAL (ANATOMIC) CLASSIFICATION

The structure of the nervous system serves as the basis for the more commonly used grouping of the parts of the nervous system, as follows:

1. The **central** nervous system, which includes the brain and the spinal cord.

2. The **peripheral** (pe-rif′er-al) nervous system, which is made up of **cranial** and **spinal** nerves. Cranial nerves are those which carry impulses to and from the brain. Spinal nerves are those which carry messages to and from the spinal cord.

From the standpoint of structure, the central and peripheral nervous systems together include most of the nerve tissue in the body. However, certain peripheral nerves have a special function, and for this reason are grouped together under the name **autonomic** (aw-to-nom′ik) nervous system. The reason for this separate classification is that the autonomic nervous system has to do largely with activities

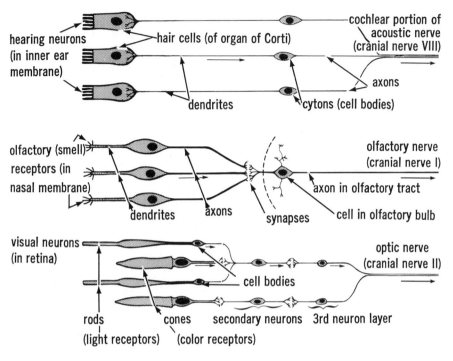

FIG. 37. Diagram of neurons for receiving special senses.

which go on more or less automatically. This system carries impulses from the central nervous system to the glands, the involuntary muscles found in the walls of tubes and hollow organs, and the heart. The autonomic nervous system is subdivided into the **sympathetic** and **parasympathetic** nervous systems, both of which will be explained later in this chapter.

Some of the nerves that carry autonomic nervous system impulses are cranial, and others are spinal.

ON NERVES IN GENERAL

The basic nerve cell is called a **neuron.** Neurons are composed of a **cell body,** containing the nucleus, with the addition of threadlike projections of the cytoplasm known as **nerve fibers.** The nerve fibers are of 2 kinds: **dendrites** (den'drites), which conduct impulses *to* the cell body; and **axons,** which conduct impulses *away from* the cell body. The dendrites of sensory neurons are very different from those of other neurons. They are usually single and they may be very long (as much as 3 feet) or they may be short; but in any case, they do not have the treelike appearance so typical of other dendrites. Each sensory nerve fiber (dendrite) has a special

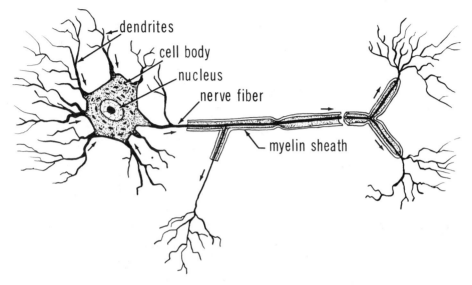

Fɪɢ. 38. Diagram of a motor neuron.

structure called the **receptor,** or **end organ,** where the stimulus is received and the sensory impulse begins. Sensations such as pain, touch, hearing, and seeing which involve these sensory neurons will be discussed in the next chapter (see Figs 36, 37 and 38).

A **nerve** is a bundle of nerve fibers, located *outside* the central nervous system, which conducts impulses from one place to another. A nerve can be compared with a telephone cable made up of many wires. In the case of nerves the "wires," or nerve fibers are bound together with connective tissue.

Nerve fibers that are connected with receptors (for receiving stimuli) conduct impulses *to* the brain and cord, and when grouped together form **afferent** nerves. Those fibers that carry impulses *from* the centers out to the muscles and glands form **efferent** nerves. Some nerves contain a mixture of afferent and efferent nerve fibers and are often referred to as **mixed nerves.**

THE CENTRAL NERVOUS SYSTEM

THE BRAIN

Main Parts of the Brain. The largest part of the brain is the **cerebrum** (ser′e-brum), which is divided into the 2 **cerebral** (ser′e-bral) **hemispheres,** a right and a left one. The **brainstem** includes the deeper parts that comprise the interbrain (thalamus, etc.) that cannot be seen unless the brain is sectioned, and a series of

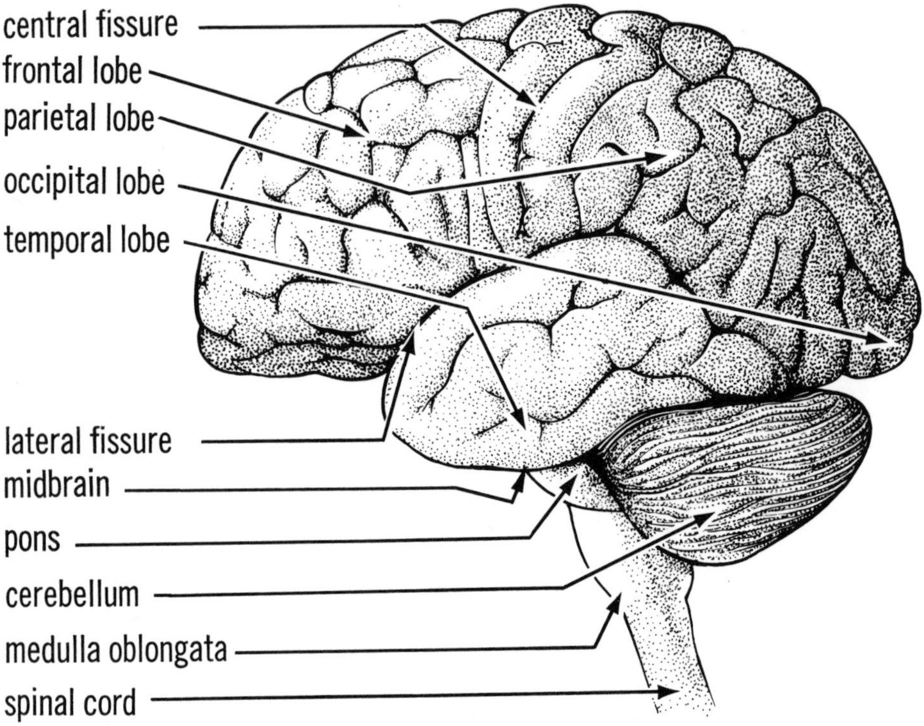

central fissure

frontal lobe

parietal lobe

occipital lobe

temporal lobe

lateral fissure

midbrain

pons

cerebellum

medulla oblongata

spinal cord

FIG. 39. The external surface of the brain showing the main parts and some of the lobes and fissures (sulci) of the cerebrum.

smaller parts that extend downward. Starting at the upper part of this series, we may see a small part of the **midbrain.** Below it and plainly visible from the under view of the brain are the **pons** (ponz), and the **medulla oblongata** (me-dul'lah ob'long-ga'tah), which connects with the spinal cord through a large opening in the base of the skull. The pons connects the midbrain and the medulla. Next to the cerebral hemispheres in size is the **cerebellum** (ser-e-bel'um), a word meaning "little brain." It is located immediately below the back part of the cerebral hemispheres and is connected with the other parts of the brain only by means of the bridgelike pons.

Structure of the Cerebral Hemispheres. The outer nerve tissue of the cerebral hemispheres is gray matter and is called the **cerebral cortex.** This gray cortex is arranged in folds forming elevated portions known as **convolutions** (kon-vo-lu'shuns), separated by depressions or grooves called **fissures,** or **sulci** (sul'si). Internally the cerebral hemispheres are made largely of white matter and a few islands of gray matter. Inside the hemispheres are 2 spaces extending in a somewhat irregular fashion. These are the **lateral ventricles,** which are filled with a watery fluid common to both the brain and the spinal cord called **cerebrospinal** (ser-e-bro-spi'nal) **fluid,** to be discussed later on.

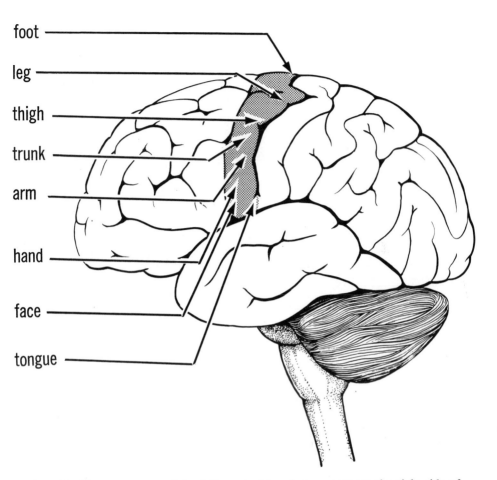

foot

leg

thigh

trunk

arm

hand

face

tongue

Fig. 40. The motor area of the left cerebral hemisphere governs the right side of the body, and the upper part of the brain governs the muscles of the lower part of the body.

Although there are many fissures (sulci), a few are especially important landmarks. These include the:

1. **Longitudinal fissure,** which is a deep groove that separates the upper parts of the cerebral hemispheres from each other.

2. **Central fissure,** which extends from the top of the brain near the center downward along the side at right angles to the longitudinal fissure.

3. **Lateral fissure,** which curves somewhat along the side of the brain and separates the temporal lobe from the rest of the cerebral hemisphere (see Fig. 40).

Let us examine the cerebral cortex, the layer of gray matter which forms the surface of each cerebral hemisphere. It is within the cerebral cortex that all impulses

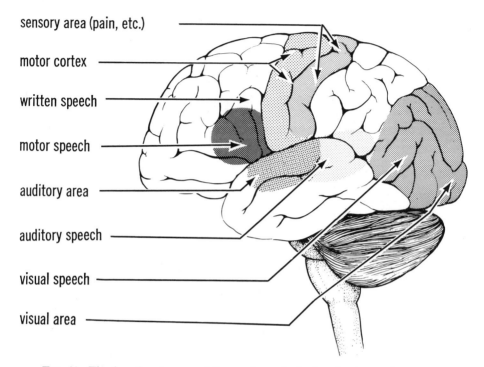

sensory area (pain, etc.)

motor cortex

written speech

motor speech

auditory area

auditory speech

visual speech

visual area

FIG. 41. The functional areas of the cerebrum including the 4 speech centers.

are received and analyzed. These form the basis of knowledge; the brain "stores" knowledge, much of which can be produced on demand by means of the phenomenon which we call memory. It is in the cerebral cortex that all thought takes place, all association and judgment and discrimination. It is from the cerebral cortex, too, that the orders originating from conscious deliberation emanate; that is, the voluntary movements are controlled here.

Division and Functions of the Cerebral Cortex. The cerebral cortex of each hemisphere is divided into 4 **lobes,** areas named from the overlying cranial bones. It has been found that each area controls a certain category of functions. The 4 lobes, with some of their characteristic functions, are as follows:

1. The **frontal lobe,** which is relatively much larger in the human being than in any other organism. This contains the **motor cortex** which controls the voluntary muscles. The left side of the brain governs the right side of the body and the right side of the brain governs the left side of the body. The upper portion of the center controls the lower parts of the body. The frontal lobe also contains 2 areas used in speech (the speech centers will be covered in a later discussion).

2. The **parietal** (pah-ri'e-tal) **lobe,** which occupies the upper part of each hem-

isphere, just behind the central fissure. This contains the **sensory area,** in which the general senses such as pain, touch, and temperature are interpreted. Also, such interpretations as the determination of distances, sizes and shapes take place here.

3. The **temporal lobe,** which is lateral (at the side) and folds under the hemispheres on each side. This contains the **auditory center** for interpreting impulses from the ear.

4. The **occipital** (ok-sip'i-tal) lobe, which is the most posterior, and extends over the cerebellum. This contains the **visual area** for interpreting messages from the retina of the eye.

Speech Centers. The speech areas are among the most interesting groups of centers in the cerebral hemispheres. The development and the use of these areas are closely connected with the processes of learning. These areas are called the:

1. **Auditory speech center,** located in the temporal lobe near the auditory center. While the auditory center enables a person to interpret sounds, it does not have anything to do with the understanding of words. Such an understanding of language requires the development of the auditory speech center. Often this is the first of the speech centers to be developed in the child. Babies often seem to understand what is being said long before they do any talking themselves. It is usually several years before children learn to read or write the words. In many parts of the world people never learn to read or write their language.

2. **Visual speech center,** which is somewhat above and in front of the visual center. In this area the ability to read with understanding is developed. You may see the writing in the Japanese language, for example, but this would involve only the visual center in the occipital lobe unless you could read the words.

3. **Motor speech center,** located just in front of the lowest part of the motor cortex in the frontal lobe. Since the lower part of the motor cortex controls the muscles of the head and the neck, it seems logical to think of the speech area as an extension forward to make possible the control of the muscles of speech in the tongue, the soft palate, and the larynx.

4. **Written speech center,** located above the motor speech center, and in front of the cortical area that controls the muscles of the arm and the hand. Again this center is an extension forward from the motor cortex. The ability to write words usually is one of the last phases in the development of learning words and their meaning, although occasionally a person may write words more readily than he can vocalize them.

Other Parts of the Cerebral Hemispheres. Beneath the gray matter of the cerebral cortex is the white matter, consisting of nerve fibers which connect the cortical areas with each other and with other parts of the nervous system. Among the most important of these large collections of nerve fibers is the **internal capsule,** a crowded strip of white matter where any injury is apt to cause extensive damage. At the base of each hemisphere are the nerve cell groups called **basal ganglia** (gang'gle-ah), which regulate the body movements originating in the cerebral cortex.

On the underside of each cerebral hemisphere is the **olfactory** (ol-fak'to-re) **area,** concerned with the sense of smell, which is stimulated by the impulses arising in the nerve receptors of the nose.

The Interbrain. The interbrain, or **diencephalon** (di-en-sef'ah-lon), can be seen only by cutting into the central section of the brain. It includes the **thalamus** and the **hypothalamus.** The 2 masses of gray matter that form the thalamus are relay centers and act to monitor sensory stimuli, suppressing some and magnifying others. The hypothalamus is located in the midline area below the thalamus and contains cells that control body temperature, water balance, sleep, appetite and some of our emotions, such as fear and pleasure. Both divisions of the autonomic nervous system are under the control of the hypothalamus. Thus it influences the heart's beating, the contractions of the walls of the bladder and other vital body functions.

The Midbrain. The midbrain is located just below the center of the cerebrum. It forms one of the forward parts of the brainstem. Four rounded masses of gray matter that are hidden by the cerebral hemispheres form the upper part of the midbrain. These four bodies, the **corpora quadrigemina** (kor'po-rah kwod-ri-jem'i-nah), act as relay centers for certain eye and ear reflexes. The ventral white matter of the midbrain conducts impulses between the higher centers of the cerebrum and the lower centers in the pons, cerebellum, medulla and spinal cord.

The Cerebellum. The cerebellum is made of 3 parts: the middle portion, called the **vermis** (meaning "wormlike"), and 2 lateral hemispheres at the sides. As in the case of the cerebral hemispheres, the cerebellum has an outer area of gray matter and an inner portion that is largely white matter. The functions of the cerebellum are:

1. To aid in the coordination of voluntary muscles so that they will function smoothly and in an orderly fashion. Disease of the cerebellum causes muscular jerkiness and tremors.

2. To help maintain balance in standing, walking, and sitting, as well as during more strenuous activities. Messages from the internal ear and from the tendon and muscle sensory end organs aid the cerebellum.

3. To aid in maintaining muscle tone so that all muscle fibers are slightly tensed and ready to produce necessary changes in position as quickly as may be necessary.

The Pons. The pons is white in color because it is made largely of myelinated nerve fibers. These fibers in the pons carry messages from one side of the cerebellum to the other, from the cerebellum to the higher centers in the cerebrum and midbrain, and from the cerebellum to the lower centers, including the medulla and the spinal cord. Not only is the pons an important connecting link between the cerebellum and the rest of the nervous system, but it also contains connections with 4 pairs of cranial nerves. Further it contains nerve fibers that carry impulses to and from the centers located above and below it. Certain reflex (involuntary) actions are controlled in the pons; namely, some occurring in respiration.

The Medulla Oblongata. The medulla of the brain is located between the pons and the spinal cord. It appears white externally because, like the pons, it contains

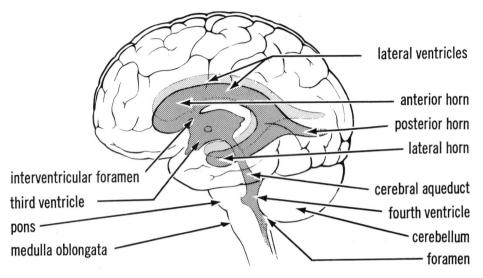

lateral ventricles

anterior horn

posterior horn

lateral horn

interventricular foramen

third ventricle

pons

medulla oblongata

cerebral aqueduct

fourth ventricle

cerebellum

foramen

FIG. 42. Diagram to show the brain ventricles.

many covered (myelinated) nerve fibers. Internally it contains collections of cell bodies (gray matter), which are called **centers** or **nuclei.** Among these are the very important vital centers including:

1. The **respiratory center,** which controls the muscles of respiration in response to chemical and other stimuli.

2. The **cardiac center,** which tends to slow the heart rate so that it will not beat too rapidly to be effective.

3. The **vasomotor** (vas-o-mo′tor) **center,** which affects the muscles in the blood vessel walls and hence helps to determine blood pressure.

The last 4 pairs of cranial nerves are connected with the medulla. The nerve fibers that carry messages up through the spinal cord to the brain continue through the medulla also, as do similar descending or **motor fibers.** These groups of nerve fibers form tracts (bundles) and are grouped together according to function. The motor fibers from the motor cortex of the cerebral hemispheres extend down through the medulla, and most of them cross from one side to the other (decussate) while going through this part of the brain. It is in the medulla that the shifting of nerve fibers results in the right cerebral hemisphere control of muscles in the left side of the body, and the upper portion of the cortex control of muscles in the lower portions of the person. The medulla is an important reflex center, and it is here that certain neurons end and impulses are relayed to other neurons.

Ventricles of the Brain. Within the brain are four fluid-filled spaces called the ventricles. These extend into the various parts of the brain in a somewhat irregular fashion. We have already mentioned the largest, the lateral ventricles in the 2 cerebral hemispheres. Their extensions into the lobes of the cerebrum are called **horns** (see Fig. 42). These paired ventricles communicate with a midline space, the third ventricle, by means of the openings called **foramina** (fo-ram'i-nah). The third ventricle is bounded on each side by the 2 parts of the thalamus, while the floor is occupied by the hypothalamus. Continuing down from the third ventricle a small canal, called the **cerebral aqueduct,** extends through the midbrain into the fourth ventricle. The latter is continuous with the near microscopic neural, or central, canal of the spinal cord. Do not confuse this tiny canal inside the cord with the much larger vertebral, or spinal, canal that is a part of the dorsal cavity enclosing the entire cord, together with its membranes and surrounding fluid. In the roof of the fourth ventricle are three openings that allow the escape of fluid to the area that surrounds the brain and spinal cord (see Fig. 45). This will be discussed later.

After removal of some of the fluid, air or other substances may be injected, and x-rays called **encephalograms** or **ventriculograms** are taken. Tumors or other brain disorders may sometimes be located by this means.

Brain Waves. The interactions of the billions of nerve cells in the brain give rise to measurable electric currents. These may be recorded by an instrument called the **electroencephalograph,** which was mentioned in Chapter 3. The recorded tracings or brain waves produce an **electroencephalogram,** not to be confused with the encephalogram mentioned in the last paragraph.

Disorders of the Brain. Since the scientific name for the brain is **encephalon** (en-sef'ah-lon), infection of the brain is known as **encephalitis** (en-sef-ah-li'tis). There are many causes of such disease, but the 2 chief pathogens are:

1. Viruses, which cause some of the epidemic types of sleeping sickness sometimes found in the United States and in other parts of the world.

2. Certain one-celled animals (protozoa) called **trypanosoma** (tri-pan-o-so'mah), which cause the so-called African sleeping sickness. These protozoa are carried by a kind of fly (tsetse) and are capable of invading the cerebrospinal fluid of man.

Other infections that may involve the brain and related parts include **abscesses** and **meningitis** (to be explained later on). As in the case of encephalitis a variety of organisms may cause these disorders. Viruses, bacteria, protozoa, and fungi may travel from the centers of infection in the teeth, the sinuses, the tonsils, and in the middle ear.

Stroke, or **cerebral apoplexy** (ap'o-plek-se), is by far the most common kind of brain disorder. Rupture of a blood vessel (with a consequent **cerebral hemorrhage**), thrombosis, or embolism may cause destruction of brain tissue. Such disorders are more frequent in the presence of artery wall disease, and hence are more common after the age of 40. The onset may seem to be sudden and often is referred to as a **cerebrovascular** (ser-e-bro-vas'ku-lar) **accident.** The effects of a stroke will depend on the extent and location of the artery involvement. A hemorrhage into the white matter of the internal capsule in the lower part of the cerebrum may cause extensive paralysis on the side opposite to the affected area. Such a paralysis is called

hemiplegia (hem-e-ple'je-ah), and the person so afflicted is known as a **hemiplegic** (hem-e-ple'jik).

Cerebral palsy (pawl'ze) is a disorder present at birth. It is characterized by diverse disorders of muscles varying in degree from weakness to complete paralysis, and in extent from a slight disorder of the lower extremity muscles to a multiplicity of paralyses involving all 4 extremities and the speech muscles as well. With patient and continuous muscle reeducation, speech training, and other corrective procedures these victims may be helped considerably.

Epilepsy, or so-called falling sickness, is a chronic disorder in which there is abnormality of brain function without apparent changes in the nerve tissues. In most cases the cause is not known. The study of brain waves obtained with the electroencephalograph usually shows abnormalities and is helpful both in diagnosis and treatment. Research is constantly improving and increasing the knowledge concerning the various forms of epilepsy. Many of these sufferers can be helped to live a normal active life if they follow a very careful hygienic regimen and use appropriate medication as outlined by a physician.

Tumors of the brain may develop at any age, but are somewhat more common in young and middle-aged adults. The symptoms produced depend on the location of the growth, its destructiveness, and the amount it compresses the brain tissue. Involvement of the frontal portions of the cerebrum often causes mental symptoms, such as changes in personality, disordered conduct, and drowsiness. Early surgery offers hope of cure in some cases.

Aphasia (ah-fa'ze-ah) is a term that refers to the loss of the ability to speak or write, or the loss of the understanding of written or spoken language. There are several different kinds of aphasia, depending on what part of the brain is affected. Usually damage to a speech center causes more disturbance in the well-educated person than it does in the illiterate. It also has been noted that there is a tendency for the last language to be acquired to be the first to be lost; and conversely, the speech concepts that were obtained first (in childhood) remain the longest. The lesion that causes aphasia is likely to be in the left cerebral hemisphere in the right-handed person. Often much can be done for these people by patient retraining and much understanding. The brain is an organ that has a marvelous capacity for adapting itself to different conditions, and its resources are tremendous. Often some means of communication can be found even though speech areas are damaged.

THE SPINAL CORD

Location of the Spinal Cord. In the embryo the spinal cord occupies the entire spinal canal and so extends down into the tail portion of the vertebral column. However, the column of bone grows much more rapidly than the nerve tissue of the cord, so that the end of the cord soon fails to extend into the lower part of the spinal canal. This disparity in growth increases so that in the adult the cord ends

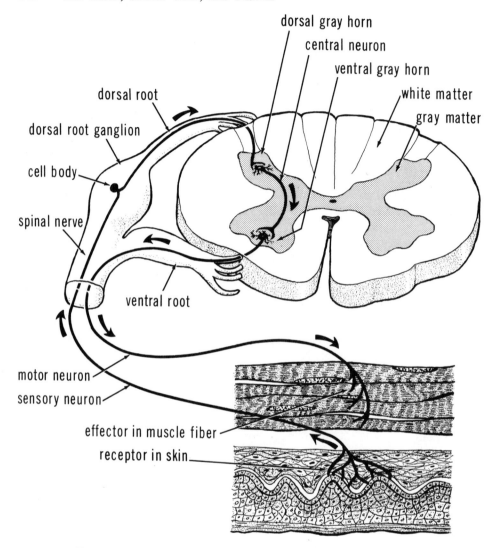

FIG. 43. Reflex arc showing pathway of impulses and cross section
of spinal cord.

in the region just below the area to which the last rib attaches (between the first
and second lumbar vertebrae).

Structure of the Spinal Cord. Examination of the spinal cord reveals that it has
a small irregularly shaped internal section made of gray matter (nerve cell bodies),
and a larger area surrounding this gray part that is made of white matter (nerve
fibers). A cross section of the cord shows that the gray matter is so arranged that

a column of cells extends up and down dorsally, one on each side; another column is found in the ventral region; while a third less conspicuous part is situated on each side. These 3 pairs of columns of gray matter give this cross section an H-shaped appearance (see Fig. 43). The white matter can be seen to be made of thousands of nerve fibers arranged in 3 areas external to the gray matter on each side.

Functions of the Spinal Cord. The functions of the cord may be divided into 3 aspects:

1. Reflex activities, which involve the transfer and integration of messages that enter the cord, so that a sensory (afferent) impulse entering the center will become a motor (efferent) message leaving the cord.

2. A pathway for conducting sensory impulses from afferent nerves upward through ascending tracts to the brain.

3. A pathway for conducting motor (efferent) impulses from the brain down through descending tracts to the nerves that will supply muscles or glands.

The reflex pathway through the spinal cord usually involves 3 or more nerve cells together with their fibers, including:

1. The **sensory neuron,** which has its beginning in a receptor and its nerve fiber in a nerve that leads to the cord (see Fig. 36).

2. One or more **central neurons,** which are entirely within the cord.

3. The **motor neuron,** which receives the impulse from a central neuron and then carries it via its long axon through a nerve to a muscle or a gland (see Fig. 38).

The knee jerk is an example of a spinal reflex. The pathway for the impulses that make this reflex possible includes a sensory neuron which has its receptor in the tendon just below the knee, its sensory nerve fiber in the nerves that extend to the spinal cord, central neurons inside the lower part of the cord, and motor neurons that send processes through nerves from the cord to the effectors in the thigh's kicking muscle.

Disorders Involving the Spinal Cord. An acute virus disease affecting both the spinal cord and the brain is **poliomyelitis,** which is most commonly found in children. The polio virus is spread from the nose and the throat; from here it travels to the central nervous system, possibly by way of the respiratory passages and the blood. The virus may destroy the motor nerve cells in the spinal cord, in which case paralysis of one or more limbs results. The virus also can attack some of the cells of the brain and cause death. Prevention of poliomyelitis by means of the Salk vaccine (or by other recently developed oral vaccines) is one of the many wonderful advances in preventive medicine.

Injuries to the spinal cord occur in traffic accidents in which bones of the spinal column are broken or dislocated. In wars gunshot or shrapnel wounds may damage the cord in varying degrees. Since the nerve tissue of the brain and the cord cannot repair itself, severing the cord causes paralysis below the injury, together with loss of all sensation from this area. Loss of sensation and of motion in the lower part of the body is called **paraplegia** (par-ah-ple′je-ah).

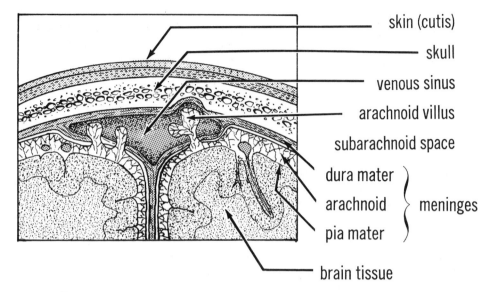

skin (cutis)

skull

venous sinus

arachnoid villus

subarachnoid space

dura mater ⎫

arachnoid ⎬ meninges

pia mater ⎭

brain tissue

FIG. 44. Frontal (coronal) section of top of head to show meninges and related parts.

Spinal Puncture and Anesthesia. Fluid may be removed from the space below the spinal cord. Since the cord is only about 18 inches long and ends some distance above the level of the hip line, a spinal puncture usually is done between the third and fourth lumbar vertebrae, about the level of the top of the hip bone. This cerebrospinal fluid may be studied in the laboratory for evidence of disease or injury.

Anesthetics such as cocaine or its derivatives (procaine) sometimes are dissolved in cerebrospinal fluid and then injected into the space below the cord, thus removing temporarily all sensation from the lower part of the body. In the hands of a trained operator this method of giving an anesthetic may have a number of advantages for certain types of surgery in selected patients. Under this type of anesthetic the patient is "awake" during the operation; but of course feels nothing in his lower body.

COVERINGS OF THE BRAIN AND THE SPINAL CORD

The **meninges** (me-nin'jez) are 3 layers of connective tissue that surround the brain and the spinal cord to form a complete enclosure. The outermost of these membranes is called the **dura mater** (du'rah ma'ter). It is the thickest and toughest of these meninges. Inside the skull, the dura mater splits in certain places to provide channels for the blood coming from the brain tissue. The second layer

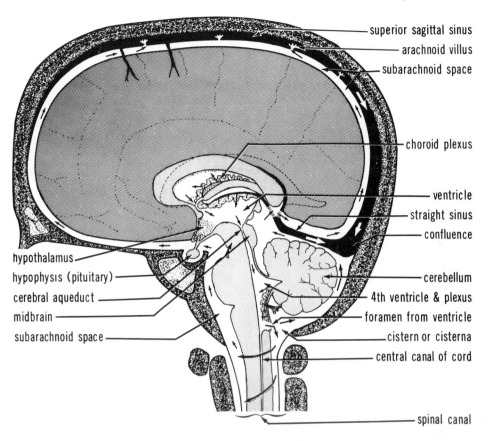

superior sagittal sinus
arachnoid villus
subarachnoid space
choroid plexus
ventricle
straight sinus
confluence
cerebellum
4th ventricle & plexus
foramen from ventricle
cistern or cisterna
central canal of cord
spinal canal

hypothalamus
hypophysis (pituitary)
cerebral aqueduct
midbrain
subarachnoid space

FIG. 45. The flow of cerebrospinal fluid from choroid plexuses back to blood in venous sinuses shown in black arrows, while blood flow is in white arrows.

around the brain and the spinal cord is the **arachnoid** (ah-rak′noid) membrane (so-called because it resembles the webs produced by spiders, which belong to a group of animals called the Arachnida). The arachnoid membrane is loosely attached to the deepest of the meninges by weblike fibers so that a space for fluid is located between the arachnoid and the innermost membrane. The third layer around the brain, the **pia mater** (pi′ah ma′ter), is attached to the nerve tissue of the brain and spinal cord and dips into all the depressions, unlike the other 2 meninges. It is made of a delicate connective tissue in which there are many blood vessels. The blood supply to the brain is carried, to a large extent, by the pia mater (see Fig. 44).

Infection of the Meninges. Meningitis (men-in-ji′tis) is an inflammation of the brain coverings caused by pathogenic bacteria, notably a diplococcus called the

meningococcus (me-ning-go-kok'us). This organism attacks the membranes, only around the cord in spinal meningitis; or it may attack the entire membranous enclosure, in which case it is called **cerebrospinal** (ser-e-bro-spi'nal) **meningitis.** Occasionally other bacteria cause a nonspecific infection. With a greatly lowered resistance, tuberculosis may involve the brain coverings and cause death. In other cases, injury to a pimple or a boil of the face may spread staphylococci or streptococci through veins up to the meninges, causing a serious meningitis.

CEREBROSPINAL FLUID

Fluids may serve to cushion shocks that would otherwise injure delicate organs. This is true of the normal "water on the brain" called cerebrospinal fluid. This fluid is formed inside the ventricles of the brain, mostly by special structures called the **choroid plexuses.** As in the case of other tissue fluids, some may be formed by filtration from the capillaries and may bring nutrients to the cells as well as remove waste products from the cells. This fluid normally flows freely from ventricle to ventricle and finally out into the **subarachnoid space,** which completely encloses the brain and spinal cord. Much of the fluid is returned to the blood in the venous sinuses through projections called the **arachnoid villi** (or granulations) (see Figs. 42 and 45).

Any obstruction to the normal flow of cerebrospinal fluid, as for example an injury to the membranes around the 3 exit openings, may cause the dreaded condition known as **hydrocephalus** (hi-dro-sef'ah-lus). As the fluid accumulates, the mounting pressure can squeeze the brain against the skull and destroy it. Since the bones have not become fused in the infant, the usual victim, the cranium itself can become enormously enlarged. In the adult there is no such cranial enlargement, but the pressure causes brain damage.

A relatively new treatment for hydrocephalus involves the implantation of an artificial brain-drain. A tube of medical silicone (or other suitable material) is brought from the brain ventricle, behind the ear, and down the neck under the skin. The tube is finally spliced into the jugular vein. Here the fluid is drained into the blood stream.

THE PERIPHERAL NERVOUS SYSTEM

CRANIAL NERVES

Location of the Cranial Nerves. There are 12 pairs of cranial nerves in all (henceforth, when a cranial nerve is referred to, a pair really is meant). The first 4 cranial nerves are located near the front of the brain and are attached to the undersurface. The next 4 nerves are related to the pons, and the last 4 are attached to the medulla. All but 2 of these nerves supply nerve fibers to structures in the head. One nerve

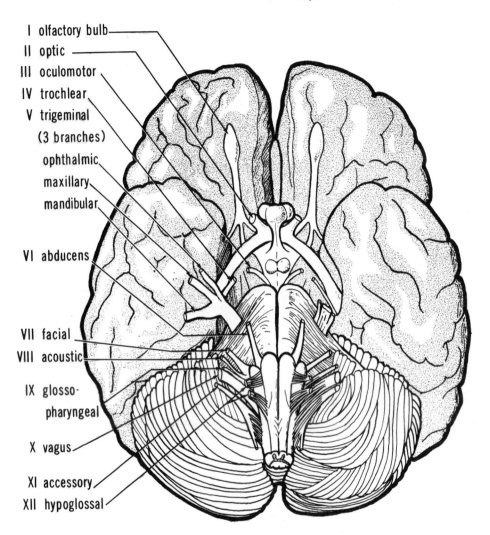

I olfactory bulb
II optic
III oculomotor
IV trochlear
V trigeminal
(3 branches)
ophthalmic
maxillary
mandibular
VI abducens
VII facial
VIII acoustic
IX glosso-
pharyngeal
X vagus
XI accessory
XII hypoglossal

FIG. 46. Base of brain, showing cranial nerves.

extends to muscles in the neck, while another (the longest) cranial nerve sends branches into the thoracic and the abdominal organs.

General Functions of the Cranial Nerves. From a functional point of view we may think of the kinds of messages which the cranial nerves handle as belonging to one of 4 categories:

1. Special sense impulses such as smell, visual, and hearing messages.

2. General sense impulses such as pain, touch, temperature, deep muscle sense, and pressure and vibration senses.

3. Voluntary muscle control or somatic motor impulses.

4. Involuntary control or visceral effector messages to glands and involuntary muscles.

Names and Specific Functions of the Cranial Nerves. The 12 cranial nerves are listed as follows:

1. The **olfactory nerve,** which carries smell impulses to the brain.

2. The **optic nerve,** which is the nerve of vision.

3. The **oculomotor nerve** which is concerned with the contraction of most of the eye muscles.

4. The **trochlear** (trok′le-ar) **nerve,** which supplies one eyeball muscle on each side.

5. The **trigeminal** (tri-jem′i-nal) **nerve,** which is the great sensory nerve of the face and head. It has 3 branches that carry general sense impulses. The third branch is joined by motor fibers to the muscles of chewing (mastication).

6. The **abducens** (ab-du′senz) **nerve** which is another nerve sending controlling impulses to an eyeball muscle.

7. The **facial nerve,** which is largely motor. The muscles of facial expression are all supplied by branches from the facial nerve. This nerve also includes sensory fibers for taste (forward two-thirds of the tongue) and contains secretory fibers to the smaller salivary glands (the submaxillary and sublingual), and to the lacrimal gland.

8. The **acoustic nerve,** which contains special sense fibers for hearing as well as those for balance from the semicircular canals of the internal ear.

9. The **glossopharyngeal** (glos-o-fah-rin′ge-al) **nerve** which contains general sense fibers from the back of the tongue and the pharynx (throat). This nerve contains all the 4 kinds of fibers. These include fibers for taste from the back of the tongue (posterior one-third), those that supply the largest salivary gland (parotid), and motor nerve fibers to control the swallowing muscles (in the pharynx).

10. The **vagus** (va′gus) **nerve,** which is the longest cranial nerve. It supplies most of the organs in the thoracic and abdominal cavities. This nerve also contains secretory fibers to glands that produce digestive juices and other secretions.

11. The **accessory nerve** (formerly called the spinal accessory nerve), which is made up of motor nerve fibers controlling 2 muscles of the neck (trapezius and sternocleidomastoid).

12. The **hypoglossal nerve,** the last of the 12 cranial nerves, which carries impulses controlling the muscles of the tongue.

Disorders Involving the Cranial Nerves. Damage to the optic nerves leading to atrophy (wasting away) is an important cause of blindness. Pressure of the eye fluid, such as occurs in glaucoma; poisons such as wood alcohol; or certain infections, notably syphilis, may cause destruction of optic nerve fibers.

Injury to a nerve that contains motor fibers causes paralysis of the muscles supplied by these fibers. The third cranial (oculomotor) nerve may be damaged by infections, particularly syphilis, or by various poisonous substances. Since this nerve supplies so many muscles connected with the eye, including the lid lifter (levator), its injury will cause a paralysis that usually interferes seriously with eye function. **Bell's palsy** is a facial paralysis due to involvement of the facial nerve, on one side as a rule, with a resulting distortion of the face because of one-sided paralysis of the muscles of facial expression.

Neuralgia (nu-ral'je-ah) means "nerve pain." It is used particularly to refer to a severe spasmodic pain affecting the fifth cranial nerve, and goes by various names, including **trigeminal neuralgia, trifacial neuralgia,** and the French term **tic** (tik) **douloureux** (doo-loo-roo'). At first the pain comes at relatively long intervals; but as time goes on, it is likely to appear at shorter intervals with the attacks of pain of longer duration. Sometimes surgery is required to effect relief.

SPINAL NERVES

Location and Structure of the Spinal Nerves. There are 31 pairs of spinal nerves, and each nerve is attached to the spinal cord by 2 roots: the **dorsal root** and the **ventral root.** To each dorsal root are attached small masses of nerve cell bodies (gray matter) called **dorsal root ganglia** (gang'gle-ah), ganglia being defined as collections of nerve cell bodies usually located *outside* the central nervous system. To these ganglia lead nerve fibers from the sensory receptors of various areas of the body. A sensory receptor is a nerve ending which responds to stimuli. There are 2 categories of receptors: those which are located generally over the body and respond to general sensations as pain, touch, temperature changes, and such. Then there are the receptors of special sensations such as taste, vision, etc., the impulses from which are carried by cranial nerves. These organs of special sense will be taken up in the next chapter.

The ventral roots are a combination of motor (efferent) nerve fibers supplying voluntary muscles, involuntary muscles, and glands. The cell bodies for the voluntary fibers are located in the ventral part of the cord gray matter (anterior or ventral gray horn) while the cell bodies for the involuntary fibers are to be found in the lateral gray horns.

Branches of the Spinal Nerves. Each spinal nerve continues only a very short distance away from the spinal cord and then branches into small posterior divisions and rather large anterior divisions. The larger anterior branches interlace to form networks called **plexuses** (plek'sus-es) which then give off branches to the body parts. The 3 main plexuses are:

1. The **cervical plexus,** which supplies motor impulses to the muscles of the neck and receives sensory impulses from the neck and the back of the head. The cervical plexus also gives off the phrenic nerve, which activates the diaphragm.

2. The **brachial** (bra'ke-al) **plexus,** which sends numerous branches to the shoulder, the arm, the forearm, the wrist, and the hand.

3. The **lumbosacral** (lum-bo-sa'kral) **plexus,** which supplies nerves to the lower

extremities. The largest of these branches is the **sciatic** (si-at'ik) nerve, which leaves the dorsal part of the pelvis and extends down the back of the thigh. At its beginning it is nearly an inch thick, but it soon sends branches to the thigh muscles; and near the knee it divides into 2 subdivisions that supply the leg and the foot.

Disorders of the Spinal Nerves. Neuritis (nu-ri'tis) means "inflammation of a nerve," but the term is also used to refer to degenerative and other disorders that may involve nerves. It may affect a single nerve as a result of blows, bone fractures, or other mechanical injuries. Often the disorder implicates many nerves throughout the body. Nutritional deficiency, as well as various poisons such as alcohol, carbon monoxide, and barbitals, are causative agents. A lack of the B vitamin known as **thiamin** (thi'ah-min) is thought to be important in chronic alcoholism in which neuritis is fairly common. Neuritis is really a symptom rather than a disease, so that thorough physical and laboratory studies may need to be made to discover the cause.

Sciatica (si-at'e-kah) is a form of neuritis characterized by severe pain along the sciatic nerve and its branches. There are many causes of this disorder, but probably the most common are rupture of a disk between the lower lumbar vertebrae and arthritis of the lower part of the spinal column.

Shingles (herpes zoster) is characterized by numerous blisters along the course of certain nerves, most commonly the intercostal nerves, which are branches of the thoracic spinal nerves in the waist area. The cause is believed to be a virus that attacks the sensory cell bodies inside the spinal ganglia. Recovery in a few days is usual, but neuralgic pains may persist for years and be very distressing. This infection also may involve the first branch of the fifth cranial nerve and cause pain in the eyeball and surrounding tissues.

THE AUTONOMIC NERVOUS SYSTEM

PARTS OF THE AUTONOMIC NERVOUS SYSTEM

Although the internal organs such as the heart, the lungs, and the stomach contain sensory nerve endings and nerve fibers for conducting sensory messages to the brain and cord, most of these impulses do not reach consciousness. These sensory impulses from the viscera, as in the case of many from the skin and the muscles, are translated into reflex responses without reaching the higher centers of the brain. The sensory neurons from the organs are grouped with those that come from the skin and voluntary muscles. On the other hand, the efferent neurons that supply the glands and the involuntary muscles are arranged very differently from those that supply the voluntary muscles. This variation in the location and arrangement of the **visceral efferent** neurons has led to classifying them as a part of a separate division called the autonomic nervous system.

The autonomic nervous system has many special parts including ganglia that serve as relay stations. In these ganglia each message is transferred (at a point of

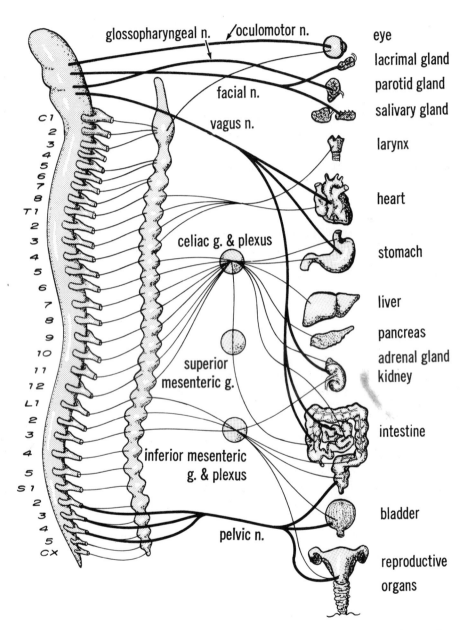

FIG. 47. Autonomic nervous system. The light lines represent nerve pathways for the sympathetic impulses. The heavy lines are nerve pathways for parasympathetic impulses. The circles are ganglia.

contact or **synapse**) from the first neuron to a second one which then carries the impulse to the muscle or gland cell. In the case of voluntary muscle cells each nerve fiber extends all the way from the spinal cord to the muscle with no intervening relay station. The location of parts of the autonomic nervous system is roughly this:

1. The sympathetic pathway begins in the spinal cord with cell bodies of the thoracolumbar (tho-rah-ko-lum′bar) area, which is in the region of the lower neck and chest. From this part of the cord nerve fibers extend to the ganglia of one of the sympathetic trunks. These trunks are 2 cordlike strands that extend up and down on either side of the spinal column from the lower neck to the upper abdominal region. The beadlike enlargements of this trunk are called the **lateral ganglia.** These ganglia contain the cell bodies of the second set of neurons whose fibers then extend to the glands and involuntary muscle tissues.

2. The parasympathetic pathway begins in the cell bodies of the midbrain, medulla, and lower (sacral) part of the spinal cord. From these centers the first set of fibers extends to autonomic ganglia that are usually located near or within the walls of the organs. The pathway then continues along a second set of neurons that stimulate the visceral tissues.

FUNCTIONS OF THE AUTONOMIC NERVOUS SYSTEM

The autonomic nervous system regulates the action of the glands, the smooth muscles of hollow organs, and the heart. These actions are all carried on automatically; and whenever any changes occur which call for a regulatory adjustment, this is done without our being conscious of it. The sympathetic part of the autonomic nervous system tends to act largely as an accelerator, particularly under conditions of stress. If you will think of what happens to a person who is frightened or angry, you can easily remember the effects of impulses from the sympathetic nervous system:

1. Stimulation of the adrenal gland, which produces hormones, including **epinephrine** (ep-e-nef′rin), that prepare the body to meet emergency situations in many ways (see Chap. 18). The sympathetic nerves and hormones from the adrenal reinforce each other.

2. Dilation of the pupil and decrease in focusing ability (for near objects).

3. Increase in the rate and forcefulness of heart contractions.

4. Increase in blood pressure due partly to the more effective heartbeat and partly to constriction of small arteries in the skin and the internal organs.

5. Dilation of the bronchial tubes in order to allow for more oxygen to enter.

6. Inhibition of peristalsis and of secretory activity so that digestion is slowed. If you have tried to eat while you were angry, you may have noted that the saliva was thicker and so small in amount that the food was swallowed with difficulty. Then when the food does reach the stomach, it seems to remain there longer than usual.

Once the crisis has passed, the parasympathetic part of the autonomic nervous system normally acts as a balance for the sympathetic system. The parasympathetic system brings about constriction of the pupil, slowing of the heart rate, and constriction of the bronchial tubes; and, most important to remember, this system stimulates peristalsis and increases the quantity and fluidity of secretions. The saliva, for example, flows more easily and profusely.

DISORDERS OF THE AUTONOMIC NERVOUS SYSTEM

Injuries due to wounds by penetrating objects, or due to tumors, hemorrhage, spinal column dislocations or fractures, may cause damage to the sympathetic trunk. In addition to these rather obvious kinds of disorders, there are a great number of conditions in which symptoms suggest autonomic malfunction but in which the method of operation is not so well understood and about which scientists do not yet entirely agree. These disorders are related to the part that psychological problems play in the functioning of organs supplied by the autonomic nervous system.

SUMMARY

1. **Nervous system as a whole.**
   A. Function: coordinating system of the body.
   B. Divisions.
     (1) Central nervous system: brain, spinal cord.
     (2) Peripheral nervous system: cranial and spinal nerves.
     (3) Autonomic nervous system (functional classification of a certain group of peripheral nerves).
2. **Nerves:** bundles of nerve fibers, carrying impulses. Nerve tissue is made of nerve cells (neurons) whose components are: cell body, nerve fibers (axons, dendrites). Afferent nerves to central nervous system; efferent nerves from central nervous system.
3. **Brain.**
   A. Main parts: cerebrum (2 hemispheres), midbrain, pons, medulla, cerebellum.
   B. Fissures (sulci): longitudinal fissure, central fissure, lateral fissure.
   C. Ventricles filled with cerebrospinal fluid.
   D. Cerebral cortex: highest functions of brain performed here.
     (1) Frontal lobe (motor cortex).
     (2) Parietal lobe (sensory area).
     (3) Temporal lobe (auditory center).
     (4) Occipital lobe (visual area).
   E. Speech centers: auditory, visual, motor, written.
   F. Other parts of cerebral hemispheres: internal capsule, basal ganglia, olfactory area.

G. Interbrain and midbrain.

H. Cerebellum: aids in muscle coordination, balance, muscle tone.

I. Pons: links parts of brain; some reflex action.

J. Medulla: contains respiratory, cardiac, vasomotor centers.

K. Ventricles of the brain.

L. Brain waves.

M. Brain disorders: encephalitis, abscess, stroke, cerebral palsy, epilepsy, tumors, aphasia.

4. **Spinal cord.**

A. Structure: H-shaped gray matter, surrounded by white matter; all inside spinal canal.

B. Function: reflexes, conducts sensory impulses to brain, conducts motor impulses from brain to organs. Reflex pathway: nerve cells are sensory (outside cord in ganglia), central, motor.

C. Disorders: poliomyelitis, injuries (paraplegia).

5. **Coverings of brain and spinal cord.**

A. Meninges: dura mater, arachnoid, pia mater.

B. Disorders: cerebrospinal meningitis.

6. **Cerebrospinal fluid.**

A. Cushions shocks.

B. Accumulation in brain: hydrocephalus.

7. **Cranial nerves.**

A. General functions: special sense impulses, general sense impulses, voluntary muscle control, involuntary control.

B. Names: olfactory, optic, oculomotor, trochlear, trigeminal, abducens, facial, acoustic, glossopharyngeal, vagus, accessory, hypoglossal.

C. Disorders: infections, Bell's palsy, injury, neuralgia.

8. **Spinal nerves.**

A. Attached to spinal cord by dorsal and ventral roots. Dorsal roots receive sensory impulses, ventral roots supply muscles and glands.

B. Branches (plexuses): cervical, brachial, lumbosacral.

C. Disorders: neuritis, sciatica, shingles.

9. **Autonomic nervous system.**

A. Regulates action of glands, smooth muscles, heart.

B. Divisions.

(1) Sympathetic nervous system: origin in thoracolumbar area. Accelerates some body processes.

(2) Parasympathetic nervous system: some originate in cranial, others in spinal (sacral) region. Balances action of sympathetic system.

C. Disorders: some irregularities complicated by psychological influences.

QUESTIONS AND PROBLEMS

1. What is the main function of the nervous system?

2. Name the 3 divisions of the nervous system.

3. Describe a neuron and name its parts.
4. Name and locate the main parts of the brain and briefly describe the main functions of each.
5. Name 4 divisions of the cerebral cortex and state what each does.
6. Name and describe the 4 speech centers.
7. Name and describe 6 typical brain disorders.
8. Locate and describe the spinal cord. Name 3 of its functions.
9. Describe a typical reflex action.
10. Name and describe 2 spinal cord disorders.
11. Name the covering of the brain and the spinal cord and its divisions. What is an infection of this covering called?
12. What is the purpose of the cerebrospinal fluid? Describe hydrocephalus.
13. Name 4 general functions of the cranial nerves.
14. Name and describe the functions of the 12 cranial nerves.
15. Locate the spinal nerves and name 3 main branches of each of them.
16. Name 2 disorders of the spinal nerves.
17. Describe the function of the autonomic nervous system.
18. Name the 2 parts of the autonomic nervous system, and show how they work during and following a moment of extreme fear.

CHAPTER 11

THE SENSORY SYSTEM

More than five senses ▪ The eye and its parts ▪ Pathway for light rays ▪ Eye infections ▪ Eye defects and eyestrain ▪ Blindness ▪ The ear and its disorders ▪ Taste and smell senses and their values ▪ Relationship of hunger and appetite ▪ Pressure, heat, cold, and touch ▪ Importance of pain and methods of pain relief ▪ Position sense and muscle coordination.

SENSES AND SENSORY MECHANISMS

The word "sense" might be defined as "the interpretation, by the specialized areas of the cerebral cortex, of an impulse arising from the receptors which are designed to report changes taking place either within the body or outside of it." These sensory receptors consist of the endings of the dendrites of afferent neurons. Some receptors are designed to respond only to special stimuli (sound waves, light rays) while others respond to such general sensations as pain or pressure.

The senses have been said to number 5. Actually there are more than that. A partial list includes the following:

1. Visual sense from the eye.

2. Hearing sense from the ear.

3. Taste sense from the tongue receptors.

4. Smell sense from the upper nasal cavities.

5. Pressure, heat, cold, pain and touch from the skin.

6. Position and balance sense from the muscles, the joints, and the semicircular canals in the ear.

7. Hunger and thirst senses from various internal parts of the body.

THE EYE

PROTECTION OF THE EYEBALL AND ITS PARTS

In the embryo the eye develops as an outpocketing of the brain. As in the case of the brain, the eye is a delicate organ. Therefore, nature has carefully protected the eye by means of the following:

1. The skull bones that form the eye **orbit** (cavity) serve to protect more than half of the eyeball at the back (dorsally).

2. The lids and the eyelashes aid in protecting the eye at the front part (anteriorly).

3. The tears wash away small foreign objects that may enter the lid area.

4. A sac lined with an epithelial membrane separates the front of the eye from the eyeball proper and aids in the destruction of some of the pathogenic bacteria that may enter from the outside.

COATS OF THE EYEBALL

The eyeball has 3 separate coats or tunics. The outermost layer is called the **sclera** (skle′rah) and is made of firm, tough, connective tissue. It is commonly referred to as the white of the eye. The second tunic of the eyeball is known as the **choroid** (ko′roid) **coat.** It is made of a delicate network of connective tissue containing much dark brown pigment and interlaced with many blood vessels. The innermost coat, called the **retina** (ret′i-nah), includes some 10 different layers of nerve cells, including the end organs commonly called the **rods** and **cones.** These are the receptors for the sense of vision.

PATHWAY OF LIGHT RAYS

Light rays pass through a series of transparent, colorless eye parts. On the way they undergo a process of bending known as **refraction.** This refracting of the light rays makes it possible for light from a very large area to be focused upon a very small surface, the retina, where the receptors are located. The following are, in order from outside in, the transparent refracting parts, or **media,** of the eye:

1. The **cornea** (kor′ne-ah) is a forward continuation of the outer coat, but it is transparent and colorless, whereas the sclera is opaque and white.

2. The **aqueous humor,** a watery fluid which fills much of the eyeball in front of the lens, helps to maintain the slight forward curve in the cornea.

3. The **crystalline lens** is a circular structure made of a jellylike material.

4. The **vitreous body** fills the entire space behind the lens and is necessary to keep the eyeball in its spherical shape.

The cornea is referred to frequently as the "window" of the eye. It bulges forward slightly and is the most important refracting structure. Injuries caused by foreign objects or by infection may result in scar formation in the cornea and a resulting area of opacity through which light rays cannot pass. If such an injury involves the central area in front of the pupil (the hole in the center of the colored part of the eye), blindness may be the result. The cornea may be transplanted; eye banks store corneas obtained from donors immediately after death, or in some cases, before death.

The next light-bending medium is the aqueous humor, followed by the crystalline lens. The lens has two bulging surfaces, so it may be best described as biconvex. During youth the lens is elastic and therefore is an important part of the system of accommodation to near vision. In the process of accommodation the lens becomes thicker and thus bends the light rays a greater amount, as is required for near objects. With aging the lens loses its elasticity, and therefore its ability to adjust by thickening, resulting in what is known as the **old eye,** or presbyopia (pres-be-o'pe-ah).

The last of these transparent refracting parts of the eye is the vitreous body. As in the case of the aqueous humor it is important in maintaining the ball-like shape of the eyeball as well as aiding in refraction. The vitreous body is not replaceable; an injury that causes a loss of an appreciable amount of the jellylike vitreous material will cause collapse of the eyeball. This will require the removal of the eyeball, an operation called **enucleation** (e-nu-kle-a'shun).

MUSCLES OF THE EYE

Certain muscles are inside the eyeball itself, and therefore are described as **intrinsic** (in-trin'sik), while others are attached to bones of the eye orbit as well as to the sclera and are called **extrinsic** (eks-trin'sik) muscles.

The intrinsic muscles are found in 2 circular structures:

1. The **iris,** the colored or pigmented part of the eye, which has a central opening called the pupil. The size of the pupil is governed by the action of 2 sets of muscles, one of which is arranged in a circular fashion, while the other extends in a radial manner resembling the spokes of a wheel.

2. The **ciliary body,** which is shaped somewhat like a flattened ring with a hole that is the size of the outer edge of the iris. This muscle alters the shape of the lens.

The purpose of the iris is to regulate the amount of light entering the eye. If a strong light is flashed in the eye, the circular muscle fibers of the iris, which form a sphincter, contract and thus reduce the size of the pupil. On the other hand, if the light is very dim, the radial involuntary iris muscles, which are attached at the outer edge, contract; the opening is pulled outward and thus enlarged. This pupillary enlargement is known as **dilation** (di-la'shun).

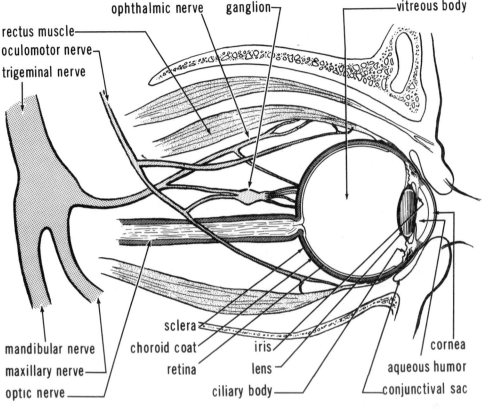

ophthalmic nerve   ganglion⌐   vitreous body

rectus muscle⸺
oculomotor nerve⸺
trigeminal nerve

sclera
choroid coat
retina
iris
lens
ciliary body

mandibular nerve
maxillary nerve⸺
optic nerve⸺

cornea
aqueous humor
conjunctival sac

FIG. 48. The eye and its nerves.

The pupil changes size, too, according to whether one is looking at a near object or a distant one. A near object causes the pupil to become smaller; a far view will cause it to enlarge.

The muscle of the ciliary body is similar in direction and method of action to the radial muscle of the iris. When the ciliary muscle contracts, it removes the tension on the suspensory ligament of the lens. The elastic lens then recoils and becomes thicker in much the same way that a rubber band would thicken if a pull on it were released. This action changes the focus of the lens, and thus adjusts the eye for either long views or close-ups.

The 6 extrinsic muscles connected with each eye are ribbonlike and extend forward from the apex of the orbit behind the eyeball. One end of each muscle is attached to a bone of the skull, while the other end is attached to the white (sclera) of the eye. These muscles pull on the eyeball in a coordinated fashion that causes the 2 eyes to move together in order to center on one visual field. There is another muscle located within the orbit which is attached to the upper eyelid. When this muscle contracts, it keeps the eye open.

NERVE SUPPLY TO THE EYE

The 2 sensory nerves of the eye are:

1. The **optic nerve,** which carries visual impulses received by the rods and cones in the retina to the brain. This, it will be recalled, is the second cranial nerve.

2. The **ophthalmic** (of-thal'mik) **nerve** which carries impulses of pain, touch and temperature from the eye and surrounding parts. It is a branch of the fifth (trigeminal) cranial nerve.

The optic nerve is connected with the eyeball a little toward the medial or nasal side of the eye at the back. At this region there are no rods and cones; and so this part, which is a circular white area, is called the **blind spot,** known also as the **optic disk.** There is a tiny depressed area in the retina called the **fovea centralis** (fo've-ah sen-tra'lis), which is the clearest point of vision.

There are 3 nerves that carry motor fibers to the muscles of the eyeball. The largest is the **oculomotor** nerve, which supplies motor fibers, voluntary and involuntary, to all the muscles but two. The other 2 nerves, the **trochlear** and the **abducens,** supply one voluntary muscle apiece.

THE LACRIMAL APPARATUS AND THE CONJUNCTIVAL SAC

The **lacrimal** gland produces tears and is located above the eye toward one side; that is, it is superior and lateral to the eyeball. Tiny tubes carry the tears to the front surface of the eyeball, where they serve to constantly wash the sac that separates the front part of the eyeball from the larger back portion. This sac is lined with a membrane called the **conjunctiva** (kon-junk-ti'vah). The conjunctiva lines the eyelids and is reflected onto the front of the eyeball. It is kept moist by the tears flowing across the front of the eye. Tears then are carried into tiny openings near the nasal corner of the eye. From these openings tears are carried by tubes that drain into the nose via the nasolacrimal duct. A slight excess of tears, or **lacrimation** (lak-re-ma'shun), causes nose blowing; and a greater overproduction of tears results in an overflow onto the face.

EYE INFECTIONS

Inflammation of the membrane that lines the eyelids and covers the front of the eyeball is called **conjunctivitis** (kon-junk-te-vi'tis). It may be acute or chronic, and may be caused by a variety of irritants and pathogens. "Pink-eye" is an acute conjunctivitis that is highly contagious and is caused by cocci or bacilli in most cases. Sometimes irritants such as wind and excessive glare, for example from snow, may cause an inflammation that then may cause a susceptibility to bacterial infection. In the case of the contagious epidemic form, children should be kept at home until the infection has been cured.

Trachoma (trah-ko'mah), sometimes referred to as **granular conjunctivitis,** is caused by a virus and is highly contagious, particularly in the early stages. This disease was formerly quite common in the mountains of the southern United States, and among the American Indians. It still is prevalent in the Far East, in Egypt, and in Southern Europe. This disease is characterized by the formation of granules on the lids, which may cause such serious irritation of the cornea that blindness can result. Better hygiene and the use of the sulfa drugs have reduced the prevalence and seriousness of this infection.

An eye infection of the newborn infant, called **ophthalmia neonatorum** (of-thal'me-ah ne-o-na-to'rum), is caused by the entrance of gonococci into the conjunctival sac. Neglect of this infection may cause blindness. Prevention by the instillation of an appropriate antiseptic such as a silver nitrate solution or penicillin is routine in hospitals at the time of delivery of the infant.

The iris, the choroid coat, the ciliary body and other parts of the eyeball may become infected by a number of different organisms. Such disorders are likely to be very serious; fortunately they are not very common. Syphilis spirochetes, tubercle bacilli, and a variety of cocci may cause these painful infections. They may follow sinus infections, tonsillitis, conjunctivitis, and numerous other disorders. The care of these conditions usually should be in the hands of an **ophthalmologist** (of-thal-mol'o-jist), a physician who specializes in disorders of the eye.

EYE DEFECTS AND EYESTRAIN

One defect that is often responsible for eyestrain in children is farsightedness, or **hyperopia** (hi-per-o'pe-ah). In this condition the light rays are not bent sharply enough to focus on the retina, with the result that the eye cannot focus properly on nearby objects. The eyeball may be too short, so that the actual focal point is behind the retina. This is normal in the infant, but usually corrects itself by the time the child uses his eyes much for near vision. To a certain extent it is possible to use the ciliary muscle in the process of thickening the lens to focus objects on the too-near retina. However, this causes constant strain. Visual tests may not show that the condition exists unless drops which paralyze the ciliary muscles are used. Hence any suggestion of eyestrain should lead to consulting a specialist who has a license to practice medicine and who will use the drops as necessary.

Myopia (mi-o'pe-ah) or nearsightedness is another defect of development. In this case the eyeball is too long, or the bending of the light rays is too sharp, so that the focal point is in front of the retina. Objects that are a distance away appear blurred, and may appear clear only if brought very near the eye. Only by the use of lenses that will throw the point of focus back can this disorder be corrected. In some young people this nearsightedness becomes worse each year until the person reaches his twenties. It was thought by some that much use of the eyes for school work may have played a part, but it has been found that people who do not do any reading or other close work suffer from this problem in as great a degree. Careful attention to good hygiene and changing of glasses as indicated by the ophthalmologist are desirable.

Another rather common visual defect is known as **astigmatism** (ah-stig′mah-tizm). This condition is due to irregularity in the curvature of the cornea or the lens. The surfaces do not bend the light rays the same amount, resulting in blurred vision with severe eyestrain. Astigmatism often is found in combination with hyperopia or myopia, so a careful eye examination and properly fitted glasses will reduce or prevent eyestrain.

The scientific name for cross-eyedness is internal **strabismus** (strah-biz′mus). Strabismus means that the muscles of the eyeballs do not coordinate, so that the 2 eyes do not work together. There are several different kinds of strabismus (in another sense it means **squint**), but the cross-eye type in which the eyeball is pulled inward (medially) is fairly common and is found early in life. Care by a skilled ophthalmologist as soon as possible may result in restoration of muscle balance. Each patient is treated as his needs indicate. In some, glasses and exercises may correct the defect, while in others surgery may be required. If correction is not accomplished early, the affected eye may bcome blinded, since the brain has a way of cutting out the confusing double image, and the eye suffers from disuse.

Some of the symptoms of eyestrain include:

1. Inflammation and infection of structures in the eyelids, as, for example, sty formation, in which oil glands on the lid edges become infected.

2. Excessive tear formation (lacrimation) and pain in the eyes.

3. Headaches and other nervous disturbances.

4. Digestive disturbances and loss of appetite with malnutrition.

Eyestrain is so important that more attention to hygiene of the eyes is to be highly recommended. Some points to remember are:

1. Smaller children should begin reading books in which the type is larger and the letters are spaced relatively far apart to make them easier to differentiate.

2. Be certain that there is enough light without glare.

3. The table or desk on which the work is being done should be neither too low nor too high.

4. Proper examination of the eyes and the use of adequate lenses are very important. The notion that glasses will weaken the eyes has absolutely no basis in fact.

Blindness and its Causes

The most common causes of blindness are those which affect the elderly in the largest numbers. Number one on the list is **cataract** formation. A cataract involves the lens or its capsule so that it loses its transparency. Sometimes the areas of opacity can be seen through a pupil which becomes greatly enlarged because of the reduction in the amount of light that can reach the retina. In other cases there is very gradual loss of vision, and frequent changes in glasses may aid in maintaining useful vision for some time. Removal of the lens by operation may restore vision. Remember that the cornea is the chief refracting medium, so that removal of the lens interferes essentially only with focusing for close work; and older persons usually require the use of glasses anyway.

A second very important cause of blindness, particularly in older persons, is **glaucoma,** a condition characterized by excess pressure of the eye fluid. Aqueous humor is being produced constantly from the blood; and after circulation it is reabsorbed into the bloodstream. Interference with the normal reentry of this fluid to the bloodstream leads to an increase in pressure inside the eyeball. As in the case of cataract, glaucoma usually progresses rather slowly, with vague visual disturbances and gradual impairment of vision. Halos around lights, headaches, and the need for frequent changes of glasses (particularly by people over 40) are symptoms that should be investigated by an ophthalmologist. There are different forms of glaucoma, some occurring in the very young; and each type requires a different management. Since continued high pressure of the aqueous humor may cause destruction of the optic nerve fibers, it is important to obtain continuous treatment beginning early in the disease to avoid blindness.

There are many other causes of blindness, and frequently these could have been prevented. Injuries by pieces of glass and other sharp objects are an important cause of eye damage. Industrial accidents involving the eye have been greatly reduced by the use of protective goggles. If an injury should occur, it is then very important to prevent infection. Even a tiny scratch can become so seriously infected that blindness will result.

The retina may become detached from the choroid and float into the vitreous body. If neglected, blindness may result. Treatment includes a sort of "spot welding" with an electric current or a weak laser beam (see Chap. 4). A series of pinpoint scars reattach the retina.

THE EAR

The ear is a combination sensory organ, related to both hearing and equilibrium. It may be divided into 3 main sections, namely:

1. The **external ear,** which includes the outer projection and a canal.
2. The **middle ear,** which is an air space containing 3 small bones.

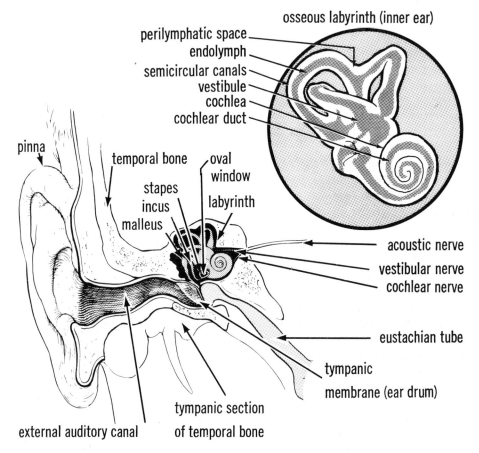

FIG. 49. The ear.

3. The **internal ear,** which is the most important part, since it contains the sensory end organs or receptors for hearing and equilibrium.

THE EXTERNAL EAR

The projecting part of the ear is known as the **pinna** (pin'nah), or the **auricle** (aw're-kl). From a functional point of view it is probably of little importance in the human. Then follows the opening itself, the **external auditory canal,** which extends medially for about 1 inch or more, depending upon which wall of the canal is measured. The skin lining this tube is very thin, and in the first part of the canal contains many wax, or **ceruminous** (se-roo'me-nus), glands. The **cerumen** (se-roo'men), or wax, may become dried and impacted in the canal so that removal by a physician is required. The same kinds of disorders that involve the skin elsewhere also may affect the skin of the external auditory canal: eczema, boils and other infections.

At the end of the auditory canal is the **tympanic** (tim-pan'ik) **membrane,** or eardrum. It serves as a boundary between the external auditory canal, or **meatus** (me-a'tus), and the middle ear cavity. It may be injured by inserted objects such as bobby pins or toothpicks. Normally the air pressure on the 2 sides of the drum is equalized by means of the **eustachian** (u-sta'ke-an) **tube** connecting the middle ear cavity and the throat (pharynx), allowing the eardrum to vibrate freely with the incoming sound waves. Sudden great changes in the pressure on either side of the eardrum may cause excessive stretching and inflammation of the membrane. There may even be perforation of the drum. In some cases pressure from pus or exudate in the middle ear cavity can be relieved only by cutting the eardrum, a procedure called a **myringotomy** (mir-in-got'o-me).

THE MIDDLE EAR

The middle ear cavity is a small flattened space that contains air and 3 small bones, or **ossicles** (os'e-kls). Air is brought into the cavity through the eustachian tube (also called the **auditory tube;** it should not be confused with the external auditory canal). The eustachian tube connects the lower part of the middle ear cavity with the pharynx. The mucous membrane of the pharynx is continuous through the eustachian tube into the middle ear cavity, and infection travels along the membrane, causing middle ear disease. This happens more often in children, partly because the tube is more horizontal in the child, while in the adult the tube tends to slant toward the pharynx. At the back of the middle ear cavity is an opening into the **mastoid air cells,** which are spaces inside a part of the temporal bone, one of the major bones of the skull.

The 3 ossicles are joined in such a way that they amplify the sound waves received by the tympanic membrane and then transmit the sounds to the fluid in the internal ear. The handlelike part of the first bone, or **malleus** (mal'e-us), is attached to the tympanic membrane, while the headlike portion connects with the second bone, which is called the **incus** (ing'kus). The innermost of the ossicles is shaped somewhat like a stirrup and is called the **stapes** (sta'pez). It is connected with the membrane of the **oval window** which in turn vibrates and conducts these waves to the fluid of the internal ear.

THE INTERNAL EAR

The most complicated and important part of the ear is the internal portion. It includes 3 separate spaces hollowed out inside the temporal bone. Because they are rather complex, they constitute what has been called the **bony labyrinth** (lab'i-rinth). Next to the oval window is the **vestibule.** This entrance area then communicates with the bony tube shaped like a snail shell, called the **cochlea** (kok'le-ah), toward the front, and with the **semicircular canals** toward the back. These spaces all contain a fluid called **perilymph.** In the fluid of the bony semicircular canals are the **membranous** (mem'brah-nus) **canals,** which contain another fluid called **endolymph.** In a similar fashion a **membranous cochlea** is situated in the perilymph of the bony cochlea, and it also is filled with endolymph. The organ of hearing, made of receptors connected with nerve fibers in the **cochlear nerve** (a part of the acoustic nerve), is located inside the membranous cochlea, or **cochlear duct.** The sound waves enter the external auditory canal and cause the eardrum to vibrate. These vibrations are amplified by the ossicles and transmitted by them to the perilymph. They then are conducted by the perilymph through the membrane to the endolymph. The waves of the endolymph are transmitted to the tiny hairlike receptors, which are stimulated and conduct nerve impulses through the nerve fibers to the brain for interpretation.

The semicircular canals contain the sensory organs related to equilibrium. The membranous canals are connected with 2 small sacs in the vestibule, and one of these sacs contains sensory end organs for obtaining information with relation to the position of the head. Nerve fibers from these sacs and from the canals form the **vestibular** (ves-tib'u-lar) **nerve** which joins the cochlear nerve to form the acoustic nerve, which latter, as we learned, is one of the 12 cranial nerves.

DISORDERS OF THE EAR

Infection of the middle ear cavity is rather common and is called **otitis media** (o-ti'tis me'de-ah). A variety of bacteria as well as viruses may cause otitis media. It also is frequently a complication of measles, influenza, scarlet fever, and other infections. Antibiotic drugs have reduced complications and have caused a marked reduction of the amount of surgery done. However, some cases cannot be cured without surgery of some kind. A complication formerly quite common was mastoid infection. It is less common now, but it still does occur, and it requires the care of a specialist in most cases.

Deafness, either partial or complete, may be caused by a variety of conditions. Obstruction of the external auditory canal by wax or foreign bodies may interfere with the conduction of sound waves to the tympanic membrane. Inflammation and scarring of the tympanic membrane or of the joints between the ossicles may prevent normal vibration and amplification of sound waves. In children, the most common problem is related to an excess of lymphoid tissue near the opening of the eustachian tube into the pharynx. This prevents the equalization of air pressure on both sides of the eardrum.

Otosclerosis (o-to-skle-ro'sis) is a type of deafness found in adults usually between 18 and 40, more frequently in women. Bone changes prevent normal vibration of the third ossicle (stapes). There seems to be a hereditary predisposition to the disease. Surgery has met with considerable success and includes an operation to release the stapes so that it will move again. If this fails, a new window can be made between the middle and inner ears. Hearing aids help most of these victims. Learning of lipreading should be encouraged.

There are many other causes of deafness, and many other kinds of deafness. Injuries of the internal ear, the acoustic nerve, or of the parts of the brain that conduct or interpret auditory messages may cause deafness. Such injuries may be due to infections such as measles, mumps, syphilis, or meningitis. In some cases alcohol, quinine, arsenic, or mercury compounds are damaging to these organs.

OTHER ORGANS OF SPECIAL SENSE

TASTE SENSE

The sense of taste involves receptors in the tongue and 2 different nerves that carry taste impulses to the brain. The taste receptors are known as **taste buds** and are located along the edges of small depressed areas called **fissures.** These taste buds are stimulated only if the substance to be tasted is in solution. Tastes have been described as essentially of 4 kinds, namely:

1. Sweet tastes, which are most acutely experienced at the tip of the tongue.
2. Sour tastes, most effectively detected by the taste buds located at the sides of the tongue.
3. Salty tastes, which, as in the case of sweet tastes, are most acute at the tip of the tongue.
4. Bitter tastes, which are detected at the back (dorsal) part of the tongue.

The nerves of taste include the facial and the glossopharyngeal nerves. The interpretation of taste impulses probably is accomplished by the lower front portion of the brain, although there may not be a sharply separate taste or **gustatory** (gus'tah-to-re) center.

SENSE OF SMELL

The sensory end organs, or receptors, for smell are located in the **olfactory** (ol-fak'to-re) **epithelium** of the upper part of the nasal cavity. Because they are high in the nasal cavity, an animal or a person "sniffs" in order to bring the gases responsible for an odor upward in the nose. The pathway of the impulses from the receptors for smell is the olfactory nerve. This leads to the olfactory center in the brain. The interpretation of smell is closely related to the sense of taste. The smell of foods is just as important in stimulating appetite and the flow of digestive juices as is the sense of taste.

HUNGER AND APPETITE

Hunger includes intermittent sensation coming from the region of the stomach. It is due, in part, to contractions of the stomach muscle, and is not continuous; that is, if a person is starving, the hunger pangs diminish instead of becoming more acute. Appetite differs from hunger in that although it is basically a desire for food, it often has no relationship to the need for food. Hunger may have been relieved by an adequate meal, but the person still may have an appetite for additional food. A loss of appetite is known as **anorexia** (an-o-rek'se-ah), and may be due to a great variety of physical and mental disorders. The location of the nerve receptors which transmit hunger impulses is still uncertain. They are probably in the stomach muscles.

SENSE OF THIRST

Although thirst may be due to a generalized lack of water in the tissues, the sense of thirst seems to be largely localized in the mouth, the tongue, and the pharynx. It is a very unpleasant sensation and is continuous up to relief or death. If there is an excessive excretion of water, as in diabetes, there may be excessive thirst, which is called **polydipsia** (pol-e-dip'se-ah).

GENERAL SENSES

As opposed to the **special** senses, in which the receptors are limited to a relatively small area in the body, the **general** senses are scattered throughout the body. These may be said to include pressure, heat, cold, pain, touch, position, and balance senses, all of which are rather widely distributed.

PRESSURE SENSE

It has been found that even though the skin is anesthetized, there still is consciousness of pressure. These end organs for deep sensibility are located in the subcutaneous and deeper tissues. They are sometimes referred to as receptors for deep touch.

TEMPERATURE SENSE

Heat and cold receptors have separate nerve fiber connections. Each has its type of end organ structure peculiar to it, and the distribution of each varies considerably. A warm object will stimulate only the heat receptors, while a cool object affects only the cold terminals. More heat receptors are found in the lips than in the hands, so that they are more sensitive to heat than are the hands. As in the case of other sensory receptors, continued stimulation results in **adaptation;** that is, the receptors adjust themselves in such a way that one does not feel a sensation so acutely if the original stimulus is continued. For example, the initial immersion of a hand in hot water may give rise to an uncomfortable sensation; however, if the immersion is prolonged, the water very soon will not feel as hot as it did at first (even if it has not cooled appreciably).

Sense of Touch

The touch receptors are small rounded bodies called **tactile** (tak'til) **corpuscles.** They are found mostly in the dermis and are especially close together in the tips of the fingers and the toes. The tip of the tongue also contains many of these receptors and so is very sensitive to touch, whereas the back of the neck is relatively insensitive.

Pain Sense

Pain is the most important protective sense. The receptors for pain are the most widely distributed sensory end organs. They are found in the skin, the muscles and the joints, and to a lesser extent in most internal organs (including the blood vessels and viscera). Pain receptors are not oval bodies as are many of the other sensory end organs, but apparently are merely branchings of the nerve fiber, called **free nerve endings. Referred pain** is a term used in cases in which pain that seems to be in an outer part of the body, particularly the skin, actually originates in an internal organ located near that particular area of skin. These areas of referred pain have been mapped out on the basis of much experience and many experiments. It has been found, for example, that liver and gallbladder disease often cause referred pain in the skin over the right shoulder. Spasm of the coronary arteries that supply the heart may cause pain in the left shoulder and the left arm. One reason for this is that some neurons have the twofold duty of conducting impulses both from visceral pain receptors and from pain receptors in neighboring areas of the skin. The brain cannot differentiate between these 2 possible sources; but since most pain sensations originate in the skin, the brain automatically assigns the pain to this more likely place of origin.

Pain sense differs from other senses in that continued stimulation does not result in adaptation. This is nature's way of being certain that the warnings of the pain sense are heeded. Sometimes the cause cannot be remedied quickly, and occasionally not at all. Then it is necessary to relieve pain. Some methods that have been found to be effective include:

1. Application of cold, especially crushed ice in ice caps, for headaches; or in bags for localized areas of injury or inflammation; or cold compresses made by wringing a towel (or gauze for small compresses) out in cold water.

2. Compression of the painful area so that the nerve does not carry the pain impulses to the brain. This may help relieve pain for a short time only.

3. **Analgesic** (an-al-je′zik) drugs, which are mild pain-relievers.
Examples are acetanilid (as-e-tan′e-lid) and aspirin.

4. **Narcotic** (nar-kot′ik) drugs, which produce stupor and sleep. These are often very effective pain-relievers. An example of a narcotic drug is morphine.

5. **Anesthetics** (an-es-thet′iks), which may be either local (i.e., that render only a certain area insensitive) or general, producing total unconsciousness. These are used largely to prevent pain during surgery.

SENSE OF POSITION

Receptors located in muscles, tendons, and joints relay impulses that aid in judging the position and changes in the locations of parts with respect to each other, as well as informing the brain of the amount of muscle contraction and tendon tension. These rather widely spread end organs, which are known as **proprioceptors** (pro-pre-o-sep′tors), are aided in this function by the semicircular canals and related internal ear structures. Information received by these receptors is needed for coordination of muscles and is important in such activities as walking, running, and many more complicated skills such as playing a musical instrument. These muscle sense end organs also play an important part in maintaining muscle tone and good posture, as well as allowing for the adjustment of the muscles for the particular kind of work to be done. The nerve fibers that carrry impulses from these receptors enter the spinal cord and ascend to the brain in the back (posterior) part of the cord.

Syphilis and certain other diseases may involve the posterior part of the spinal cord, causing degeneration of it and loss of the position sense, giving rise to a condition known as **tabes dorsalis** (ta′bez dor-sa′lis). The lower part of the body usually is affected first, with the result that the victim gradually loses not only position sense but muscular coordination. Certain activities such as walking, which because of these 2 faculties hitherto could be accomplished without the aid of sight, and by hardly thinking of them at all, now become difficult—particularly in the dark, when the victim cannot see how he plants his feet. As the disease progresses, the patient may lose the ability to walk. Early treatment of possible causes as a means of prevention is important, since once the nerve tissue is damaged, no cure is possible.

SUMMARY

1. **Senses:** sight, hearing, taste, smell, pressure, heat, cold, pain, touch, position, balance, hunger, thirst.
2. **Eye.**
   A. Parts and purposes.
      (1) Protection: orbits, lids, eyelashes, tears, epithelial sac.
      (2) Coats: sclera, choroid, retina.
      (3) Light path: cornea, aqueous humor, lens, vitreous body.
      (4) Muscles: intrinsic (iris, ciliary body); 6 extrinsic.
      (5) Nerves: optic (visual impulses from rods and cones of retina); ophthalmic (pain, touch, temperature impulses from eye and surrounding parts); 3 motor nerves.
      (6) Lacrimal apparatus: lacrimal gland produces tears which moisten conjunctiva.
   B. Disorders: infections (conjunctivitis, trachoma, ophthalmia neonatorum); defects (hyperopia, myopia, astigmatism, strabismus). Causes of blindness: cataracts (lens loses transparency); glaucoma (excess pressure of eye fluid); injuries.
3. **Ear.**
   A. Parts and purposes.
      (1) Divisions: external, middle, internal.
      (2) External: pinna, auditory canal, tympanic membrane.
      (3) Middle: ossicles (malleus, incus, stapes) amplify sounds from tympanic membrane, transmit them to oval window. Eustachian tube connects to pharynx, equalizes pressure, pathway for infection.
      (4) Internal: bony labyrinth. Oval window, vestibule, cochlea, semicircular canals, all contain perilymph. Membranous canals (in semicircular canals), membranous cochlea (in cochlea) both filled with endolymph. Receptors in cochlear duct make up the organ of hearing.
      (5) Path for sound: eardrum vibrates, vibrations amplified by ossicles, transmitted to perilymph, to endolymph, to nerve receptors, to nerves, to brain.
      (6) Equilibrium: membranous canals connected with 2 sacs, 1 sac containing sensory nerves indicating position of head.
   B. Disorders: otitis media; deafness (causes: obstruction of auditory canal, blockage of eustachian tube, otosclerosis, infections, poisons).
4. **Other special sense organs.**
   A. Taste: receptors (taste buds on tongue). Four tastes (sweet, sour, salty, bitter).
   B. Smell: receptors (olfactory epithelium of nasal cavity).
   C. Hunger and appetite: hunger due to stomach muscle contractions; not continuous; appetite (desire for food). Hunger receptors probably in stomach muscles.

D. Thirst: receptors in mouth, tongue, throat; continuous.
5. **General senses.**
   A. Pressure: end organs in deep tissues.
   B. Temperature: heat and cold receptors separate. Adaptation (common to most other senses also).
   C. Touch: receptors (tactile corpuscles). Close together in fingers, toes, tongue.
   D. Pain: protective, no adaptation. Referred pain (from deeper organs but seemingly originating in nearby skin area. Areas mapped out for diagnostic purposes). Pain relief: application of cold, compression, analgesics, narcotics, anesthetics (local, general).
   E. Position: receptors (proprioceptors in muscles, tendons, joints aided by semicircular canals). Nerve fibers enter spinal cord; can be attacked by disease (syphilis can cause tabes dorsalis).

QUESTIONS AND PROBLEMS

1. Give a general definition of a sense and name 7 of the senses.
2. Name the main parts of the eye and trace the path of a light ray from the outside of the eye to the brain. Show the action of muscles.
3. Describe 3 eye infections and 4 eye defects. What are the main causes of blindness?
4. Outline the main parts of the ear and describe the process that ensues from the time that a sound wave activates the eardrum to the registration of the sound in the brain.
5. Name and describe 2 ear disorders and list some of the causes of deafness.
6. Name the 4 kinds of taste. Where are the taste receptors?
7. Describe the olfactory apparatus.
8. What is the difference between hunger and appetite?
9. What is the difference between a general and a special sense?
10. What does "adaptation" mean, with respect to the senses? Does this occur in the case of every sense?
11. Explain referred pain and give an example of its occurrence.
12. Name 3 categories of pain-relieving drugs.
13. Where are the receptors for the senses of position and balance (equilibrium) located?

CHAPTER 12

THE HEART AND
HEART DISEASE

The heart as a pump ▪ Layers of the heart wall ▪ Two hearts and a partition ▪ Four chambers ▪ Heart valves and their location ▪ How does the heart work? ▪ The heart beat and its control ▪ Heart sounds and murmurs ▪ Kinds of heart disease ▪ Prevention of heart ailments ▪ Instruments and medications for heart cases ▪ Surgery.

CIRCULATION AND THE HEART

In the next 2 chapters we shall investigate the manner in which the blood acquires its food and oxygen to be delivered to the cells, and disposes of the waste products of cell metabolism. This continuous one-way movement of the blood is known as its **circulation.** The fact that blood circulates throughout the body implies that there must be some sort of propelling mechanism. The prime mover in this case is the **heart;** and we shall have a look at the heart before going into the circulatory vessels in any detail.

The heart is a muscular pump which drives the blood through the blood vessels. This organ is slightly bigger than a fist, and is located between the lungs in the center and a bit to the left of the midline of the body. The strokes (contractions) of this pump average about 72 per minute and are carried on unceasingly for the whole of a lifetime.

The importance of the heart has been recognized for centuries. The fact that its rate of beating is affected by the emotions may be responsible for the very frequent references to the heart in song and poetry. However, the vital functions of the heart and the tragic increase in heart disease are of more practical importance to us at this time.

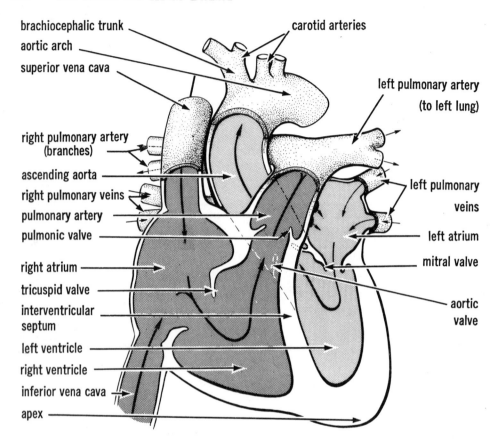

brachiocephalic trunk

aortic arch

superior vena cava

carotid arteries

left pulmonary artery
(to left lung)

right pulmonary artery
(branches)

ascending aorta

right pulmonary veins

pulmonary artery

pulmonic valve

left pulmonary
veins

left atrium

right atrium

tricuspid valve

interventricular
septum

left ventricle

right ventricle

inferior vena cava

apex

mitral valve

aortic
valve

▨ blood high in oxygen (arterial)
■ blood low in oxygen (venous)

FIG. 50. The heart and great vessels.

STRUCTURE OF THE HEART

LAYERS OF THE HEART WALL

The heart is a hollow organ the walls of which are made of 3 different layers. Just as a warm coat might have a smooth lining, a thick and bulky interlining, and an outer layer of a third fabric, so the heart wall has 3 tissue layers, named as follows:

1. **Endocardium** (en-do-kar′de-um), a very smooth layer of cells that resembles squamous epithelium. This membrane lines the interior of the heart, and also is the material of which the valves of the heart are formed.

2. **Myocardium** (mi-o-kar'de-um), which is the muscle of the heart and is much the thickest layer.

3. **Pericardium,** which forms the outermost layer of the heart wall as well as serving as the lining of the pericardial sac (see Chap. 5).

Two Hearts and a Partition

Physicians often refer to the right heart and the left heart. This is because the human heart is really a double pump. The 2 sides are completely separated from each other by a partition called the **septum.** The upper part of this partition is called the **interatrial** (in-ter-a'tre-al) **septum,** while the larger lower portion is called the **interventricular** (in-ter-ven-trik'u-lar) **septum.** This septum, as in the case of the heart wall, is largely myocardium.

Four Chambers

On either side of the heart there are 2 chambers, one of which is a receiving space and the other a pumping chamber. These 4 chambers are called:

1. **The right atrium,** which is a thin-walled space that receives the venous blood returning from the body tissues. This blood is carried in the **veins,** which are the blood vessels leading *to* the heart from the body tissues.

2. **The right ventricle,** which pumps the venous blood dropped into it from the right atrium, and sends it to the lungs.

3. **The left atrium,** which receives blood high in oxygen content as it returns from the lungs.

4. **The left ventricle,** which has the thickest walls of all in order to pump oxygenated blood to all parts of the body. This blood goes through the **arteries,** which is the name for the vessels that take blood *from* the heart to the tissues.

Four Valves

Since the ventricles are the pumping chambers, the valves, which are all of the one-way type, are located at the entrance and the exit of each ventricle. The valves at the entrances are the **atrioventricular** (a-tre-o-ven-trik'u-lar) **valves,** while the exit valves are **semilunar** (sem-e-lu'nar) **valves.** "Semilunar," means "resembling a half-moon." Each valve has a specific name, as follows:

1. **The tricuspid** (tri-kus'pid) **valve.** ("Tricuspid" means "three-pointed." Cusps are the flaps of the valves, which open and close). It closes at the time the right ventricle begins pumping in order to prevent any blood from going back into the right atrium. This is the right atrioventricular valve.

2. **The pulmonary** (pul'mo-nar-e) **semilunar valve,** located between the right

ventricle and the pulmonary artery, which leads to the lungs. As soon as the right ventricle has finished emptying itself, the value closes in order to prevent blood on its way to the lungs from returning to the ventricle.

3. **The mitral** (mi'tral) **valve,** or left atrioventricular valve, which is made of 2 rather heavy flaps or cusps. This valve closes at the time the powerful left ventricle begins its contraction. It prevents the blood from returning to the left atrium.

4. **The aortic** (a-or'tik) **valve** located between the left ventricle and the largest artery, the **aorta** (a-or'tah), prevents the return of aortic blood to the left ventricle.

PHYSIOLOGY OF THE HEART

THE WORK OF THE HEART

Although the right and the left sides of the heart are completely separated from each other, they work together. The blood is squeezed through the chambers by a contraction of heart muscle beginning in the thin-walled upper chambers, the atria, and followed by a contraction of the thick muscle of the lower chambers, the ventricles. This active phase is called **systole** (sis'to-le), and in each case it is followed by a short resting period known as **diastole** (di-as'to-le). The contraction of the walls of the atria is completed at the time the contraction of the ventricles begins. Thus the resting phase (diastole) begins in the atria at the same time as the contraction (systole) begins in the ventricles. As soon as the ventricles have emptied, the atria (which meanwhile have been filling with blood) contract while the ventricles relax and again fill with blood. Then the ventricular systole begins.

CONTROL OF THE HEART BEAT

If the nerves which supply the voluntary muscles are cut, these muscles cease to function; that is, they are completely paralyzed. If the nerves which supply the heart are severed, however, the heart will continue to beat. The reason for this is that although the heart is under the control of the nervous system, heart muscle itself is capable of contracting rhythmically independently of outside control. Despite this property of **automaticity** (au-to-mah-tis'e-te), the impulses from the nervous system are required to cause a rapid enough beat to maintain circulation effectively. Without nerve connection the heart rate might be less than 40 beats per minute instead of the usual 70 to 90 per minute.

THE CONDUCTION SYSTEM OF THE HEART

Specialized masses of tissue in the heart wall form the conduction system of the heart, regulating the order of events. Two of these are called **nodes,** while the third is a branching structure called the **atrioventricular bundle.** The **sinoatrial node** is

left atrium

superior vena cava

sinoatrial node

right atrium

atrioventricular node

atrioventricular
bundle
(bundle of His)

right ventricle

left ventricle

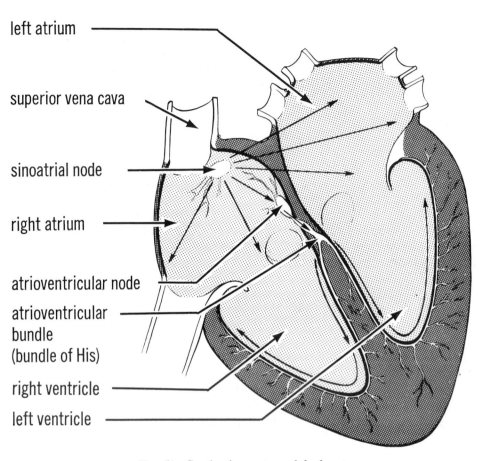

FIG. 51. Conduction system of the heart.

located in the upper wall of the right atrium and acts as a pacemaker. The second
node is called the **atrioventricular node** and is located in the septum at the junction
between the interatrial portion and the interventricular part (see Fig. 51). The
atrioventricular bundle, which is also known as the **bundle of His,** is located in the
interventricular septum with branches extending to all parts of the ventricle walls.
The order in which the impulses travel is as follows:

1. The beginning of the heartbeat is in the sinoatrial node, the pacemaker.

2. The excitation (contraction) wave travels throughout the muscle of the atria,
causing them to contract.

3. The atrioventricular node next is stimulated, and transmits the wave to the
bundle of His, with a rapid spread to all parts of the ventricle walls.

4. The entire ventricular musculature contracts practically all at once.

HEART SOUNDS AND MURMURS

The normal heart sounds are usually described by the 2 syllables "lubb" and "dupp." The first is a longer and lower-pitched sound which occurs during the ventricular systole. It is probably caused by a combination of sounds made by the muscle of the ventricles and the closure of the atrioventricular valves. The second, or "dupp," sound is shorter and sharper. It occurs during the beginning of ventricular relaxation, and is due in large part to the sudden closure of the semilunar valves. Abnormal sounds are called **murmurs** and are due to faulty action of the valves. If, for example, the valves fail to close tightly and blood leaks back, a murmur is heard. Another condition giving rise to an abnormal sound is the narrowing (stenosis) of a valve orifice. The many conditions which can cause an abnormal heart sound may be due to congenital defects, to disease, or to physiologic variations. A murmur may be called a **functional murmur;** that is, not necessarily involving an abnormality. On the other hand, an abnormal sound caused by any structural change in the heart or the vessels connected with the heart is called an **organic murmur.**

HEART DISEASE

CLASSIFICATION OF HEART DISEASE

There are many ways of classifying heart disease. The 3 layers of the heart wall form the basis for one grouping of heart pathology, as follows:

1. **Endocarditis** (en-do-kar-di'tis), which means "inflammation of the lining of the heart cavities," but which most commonly refers to valvular disease.

2. **Myocarditis** (mi-o-kar-di'tis), or inflammation of heart muscle.

3. **Pericarditis** (per-e-kar-di'tis), referring to disease of the serous membrane on the heart surface, as well as that lining the pericardial sac.

Another more generally used classification of heart disease is based on causative and age factors. On this basis the more common kinds of heart disease are:

1. **Congenital** heart disease; that is, present at birth.

2. **Rheumatic** heart disease, which begins with an attack of rheumatic fever in childhood or in youth.

3. **Coronary** (kor'o-na-re) heart disease, which involves the walls of the blood vessels that supply the muscle of the heart.

4. **Degenerative** heart disease, which is most common after the age of 45 and is due to deterioration of tissues such as muscles because of the prolonged effects of various disease conditions.

CONGENITAL HEART DISEASE

This category of heart disease includes certain abnormalities which have been present since birth, and which usually represent a failure of normal development.

In recent years many of these congenital defects have been remedied by heart surgery, one of the more spectacular advances in modern medicine.

The circulation of the fetus differs in several respects from that of the child after birth, one difference being that the lungs are not used until the child is born. Prior to birth the unused lungs are bypassed by a blood vessel which normally closes of its own accord once the lungs are in use. Sometimes, however, the vessel fails to close, with the result that much of the blood is detoured around the lungs instead of through them; and therefore the blood does not receive enough oxygen. This condition can be corrected by surgery.

Another congenital heart defect is an obstruction or narrowing of the pulmonary artery which prevents the blood from passing in sufficient quantity from the right ventricle to the lungs. This condition also can be remedied surgically.

RHEUMATIC FEVER AND THE HEART

Infection plays an important part in initiating heart disorders in the young. Bacteria may first involve the tonsils, then the joints, and finally the heart. The "strep" throat may be followed by an attack of so-called inflammatory rheumatism or rheumatic fever. The joints swell to a very large size, in some cases; but as a rule the inflammation of the joints subsides with no permanent damage. The heart is damaged in about 60 per cent of rheumatic fever patients. The injury may include all 3 layers of the heart; but most commonly there results a condition known as **rheumatic endocarditis.** The infection causes the heart valves, particularly the mitral valve, to become inflamed. Small deposits of material from the blood produce **vegetations,** which form along the edges of the valves. The cusps thicken and tend to stick together; that is, to form **adhesions.** The valvular opening may become permanently narrowed as a consequence; and if, as is usually the case, the mitral valve is so affected, the resulting condition is called **mitral stenosis.** This condition prevents an adequate flow of blood from the left atrium to the left ventricle, so that there is congestion in the pulmonary circulation. In addition to this, the right ventricle is forced to work much harder than usual in compensation, and eventually may fail. Recently operations to break adhesions have greatly lengthened the life expectancy of rheumatic heart patients.

When the infection subsides, and the once-inflamed valves begin to heal, the formation of new tissue on the valve cusps may cause them to retract, so that they are unable to meet when the valve attempts to close itself. This causes a leakage of blood through the valve and is known as **incompetence** of the valve.

Since rheumatic fever is most common between the ages of 4 and 20 years of age, rheumatic heart disease is really a disease of youth. It is the most important cause of death between the ages of 10 and 14 years of age. In addition to this many are crippled for life, with the need of greatly limiting their physical activities. Prevention of serious respiratory illnesses and the removal of diseased tonsils will help prevent many cases of rheumatic heart disease.

CORONARY HEART DISEASE

The heart muscle receives its own blood supply through 2 vessels known as the **coronary** ("crownlike") arteries. A common cause of sudden death, or at least disability, from heart disease is **occlusion** (ok-klu′zhun); that is, closure, of the coronary arteries. Here it should be clearly understood that the coronary arteries are by no means the only arteries that can become occluded; later on we shall see some effects of the occlusion of certain other arteries upon the organs with which they are associated.

Our concern here is with the heart muscle. Any interference with its blood supply will result in damage to the muscle. The degree of injury sustained depends upon a number of factors, including whether the cutting off of the artery was gradual or sudden.

It may happen that the space (lumen) inside the vessel narrows gradually owing to progressive thickening and hardening of the arteries. As a consequence of this the volume of blood supplied to the heart muscle is reduced, resulting in scarring of that muscle. The action of the heart is thereby greatly weakened. In spite of the heart damage, it may be possible for a victim of this disease to lead a fairly normal life so long as he curtails sharply all activities requiring exertion, takes time out for periodic rest periods and avoids obesity (fatness) and emotional disturbances.

When an artery wall undergoes degenerative changes, the inside surface often becomes roughened as well. This roughening of the passage is highly conducive to the formation of a blood clot, or **thrombus.** Such a thrombus may cause sudden closure of the vessel with complete obstruction of the blood flow. This condition is known as **coronary thrombosis;** and if it occurs, the victim's life is in immediate danger, the outcome depending upon whether or not the other branches of the artery can supply enough blood to maintain the heart's action. If a smaller branch is blocked, the heart may continue to function; but the blockage of the arterial branch results in the formation of an area of dead tissue in the heart wall. Such an area of dead tissue formed as a result of the lack of blood supply anywhere in the body is called an **infarct** (in′farkt). The infarct eventually may give way and cause death.

When the blood is cut off from the heart muscle, there results a characteristic agonizing pain, felt in the region of the heart and in the left arm and the shoulder, called **angina pectoris** (an-ji′nah pek′to-ris). Angina pectoris may be accompanied by a feeling of suffocation and a general sensation of forthcoming doom. Heart disease is a common cause of angina pectoris, although there are other causes as well.

The victim of an acute coronary occlusion must be put on complete bed rest for a considerable period of time, depending upon the severity of the attack and upon the time required for the damaged heart muscle to be replaced by scar tissue. During this period the most meticulous medical and nursing care are required.

DEGENERATIVE HEART DISEASE

During a person's lifetime many toxins, infections and other kinds of injuries may cause weakening of the heart muscle. High blood pressure, known as **hypertension,** over a period of years may cause an enlargement of the heart, and finally heart failure. Malnutrition, chronic infections (including syphilis) and severe anemias may cause degeneration of heart muscle. Hyperthyroidism (Chap. 18) with its tendency to cause overactivity of all parts of the body, including the heart, is another cause of heart failure. Although heredity may be responsible for an undue susceptibility to degenerative heart disease, correct health habits beginning in childhood and continuing throughout vigorous youth and early middle age can do much to prevent early submission to degenerative heart disease.

PREVENTION OF HEART AILMENTS

Although there may not be complete agreement on any set of rules for preventing or at least delaying the onset of heart disease, most authorities might concur on the following:

1. Proper nutrition, including all the basic food elements, will aid in maintaining all tissues, including those of the heart, in their optimum condition. The avoidance of eating more than is necessary, in order to prevent obesity, will be better for the heart.

2. Infections should be avoided as much as possible. Mild infections should be cared for to prevent serious complications from developing. Dental care should include the treatment of abscesses and the cleaning and filling of decayed teeth.

3. Temperate habits and adequate rest are desirable. People who wish to avoid heart disease need to avoid excesses in the use of tobacco, of alcohol, and of food. Emotional bouts and psychological upheavals are not conducive to maintaining a healthy heart. Playing too hard is just as damaging as working too hard.

4. Regular physical examinations should be instituted. All those over 40, as well as others who have had any symptoms that suggest possible disease, should have regular health inspections given by a well-qualified practitioner.

SOME PRACTICAL ASPECTS OF TREATMENT

INSTRUMENTS USED IN HEART STUDIES

The **stethoscope** (steth'o-skope) is a relatively simple instrument used for conveying sounds from within the patient's body to the ear of the examiner. Experienced listeners can gain much information using this device. The **electrocardiograph,** which was mentioned in Chapter 3, is used for making records of the changes in the minute electric currents produced by the contracting heart muscle. It is valuable in detecting certain myocardial injuries.

The **fluoroscope** (floo-o'ro-skope), which is an instrument used in examining deep structures with x-rays, may be used for noting heart action as well as for observing the size and relationships of some of the thoracic organs. It may be used in conjunction with **catheterization** (kath-e-ter-i-za'shun) of the heart. In this procedure a tiny tube (a catheter) is passed through the veins of the right arm and then into the right side of the heart. During the passage of this tube the fluoroscope is used for observing the route taken by the catheter, and samples of blood are removed through the tube. Finally, the tube is passed all the way through the pulmonary valve and into the large lung arteries. Further samples of blood, removed for testing, are obtained along the way, pressure readings being taken meanwhile.

SOME MEDICINES USED FOR HEART DISEASE

The most important, one of the oldest, and still a very valuable drug for many heart patients is **digitalis** (dij'e-tal-is or dij-e-ta'lis). Digitalis acts as a tonic and a regulator for certain types of heart ailments. It is obtained from the leaf of the foxglove, a plant originally found growing wild in many parts of Europe. Foxglove is now being grown artificially as a means of maintaining a constant supply of digitalis for medical purposes. The leaves are processed, and active ingredients are removed in such a way that a definite dosage is obtained. Digitalis and other drugs are tested on small animals such as mice and guinea pigs in order that the accuracy and quality of dosages may be closely controlled.

Anticoagulants (an-te-ko-ag'u-lants) also are valuable drugs for heart patients. They are used in cases in which there may be blood vessel damage, in order to prevent blood clots from forming and hence thrombosis. The antibiotic drugs are valuable in preventing and eliminating infection. All such medications should be used only under the supervision of a physician, since insufficient amounts are as undesirable as excessive dosages.

PACEMAKERS

Electric-battery-operated pacemakers which supply impulses to regulate the heart beat have been implanted under the skin of many thousands of patients. The site of implantation is usually in the left abdominal area below the beltline. Electrode catheters attached to the pacemaker are then passed beneath the skin to the heart muscle where they are sutured through a previously made incision on the thoracic wall. The batteries usually last from 3 to 5 years, and it is important that they be replaced at intervals to prevent mechanical failure. Many people whose hearts cannot beat effectively alone have been saved by this rather simple device. In an emergency, a similar stimulus can be supplied to the heart muscle through electrodes placed externally on the chest wall.

SURGERY INVOLVING THE HEART

The heart-lung machine (pump-oxygenator) is a valuable addition to the modern operating room. This machine has made it possible to perform many operations on the heart and other thoracic organs which could not otherwise be done. There are several types of machines in use, all of which serve as a temporary substitute for the patient's heart and lungs.

The machine siphons off the blood from the large vessels entering the heart on the right side so that no blood passes through the heart and lungs. The blood is returned to the general circulation for body distribution through one of the large arteries. While passing through the machine, the blood is oxygenated by means of an oxygen inlet, and carbon dioxide is removed by various chemical means. These are the processes that normally take place between the blood and the air in the lung tissue. While in the machine, the blood is also "defoamed" to be sure that all air bubbles are removed, since such bubbles could be fatal to the patient by obstructing blood vessels. An electric motor in the machine serves as a pump during the surgical procedure to distribute the processed blood throughout the body by means of the artery mentioned above.

Diseased valves may become deformed and scarred from endocarditis so that they are ineffective and often obstructive. In some cases a special small knife can be inserted into the heart chamber and the valve can be cut so that it no longer obstructs the blood flow. The valve may even become partially functional. In other cases there may be so much damage that replacement is the only resort. Substitute valves made of plastic materials have proved to be a lifesaving measure for many patients. Very thin butterfly valves made of Dacron or other synthetic material have also been successfully used.

Artificial hearts or parts of hearts designed to assist the ventricles in their pumping function have not proved as successful as the artificial valves. However, research continues and it is quite possible that an effective device may soon be ready for use. More spectacular is the transplantation of a human heart from the body of a person who has recently died. Tissues of the donor and the recipient should be as closely matched as possible to avoid rejection by the recipient's antibody mechanism. This rejection syndrome is the most serious problem related to heart transplants and is discussed further at the end of Chapter 20.

SUMMARY

1. **Structure of the heart.**
    A. Three layers: endocardium, myocardium and pericardium.
    B. Two separate pumps, with an intervening septum.
    C. Four chambers: left and right atria and the left and right ventricles.
    D. Four valves: tricuspid, pulmonary, mitral and aortic.

2. **Physiology of the heart.**
   A. Cardiac cycle includes contraction (systole) and resting phase (diastole).
   B. Heart contractions self-sustaining, though nervous control essential for adequate circulation.
   C. Events in heart action regulated by a conduction system of tissue: sinoatrial node, atrioventricular node and bundle of His.
   D. Heart sounds and murmurs.
      (1) First and second sounds: lubb, dupp.
      (2) Murmurs caused by faulty valve action; are functional or organic.

3. **Heart disorders.**
   A. One grouping according to layer of heart wall: endocarditis, myocarditis, and pericarditis.
   B. Another grouping based on age and causation: congenital, rheumatic, coronary and degenerative.
   C. Congenital heart disease: some forms can be corrected by surgery.
   D. Rheumatic fever: usually causes endocarditis, leaving scars and adhesions.
   E. Coronary heart disease: damaged arteries to heart wall can cause sudden death.
   F. Degenerative heart disease: weakening of heart muscle because of prolonged effects of other diseases.

4. **Prevention of heart ailments.**
   A. Proper nutrition.
   B. Prevention and care of infections.
   C. Temperate habits and adequate rest.
   D. Regular evaluation of physical condition.

5. **Some practical aspects of treatment.**
   A. Instruments used in heart studies.
      (1) Stethoscope detects abnormal sounds.
      (2) Electrocardiograph records electric current changes in heart muscle.
      (3) Fluoroscope and catheterization of the heart are used together in visualization and evaluation of heart action and blood circulation.
   B. Medications for heart patients.
      (1) Digitalis derived from foxglove. A tonic and regulator in some heart ailments.
      (2) Anticoagulants prevent thrombosis.
      (3) Antibiotics prevent and eliminate infection.
      (4) Medications must be taken only under doctor's supervision.
   C. Pacemakers to regulate the heart beat.
   D. Heart surgery.
      (1) Artificial valves as replacements.
      (2) Transplants and rejection problems.

QUESTIONS AND PROBLEMS

1. What are the 3 layers of the heart wall?
2. What are the 2 parts of the partition of the heart called? How do they differ from one another?
3. Name each of the chambers of the heart and tell what each does.
4. Name the valves of the heart. Explain the purpose of each valve.
5. Explain systole and diastole and tell how these phases are related to each other in the 4 chambers of the heart.
6. How does the heart's ability to contract differ from that of other muscle? What is required to maintain an effective rate of heart beat?
7. What are the parts of the heart's conduction system called and where are these structures located? Outline the order in which the excitation waves travel.
8. What 2 syllables are used to indicate normal heart sounds, and at what time in the heart cycle can they be heard?
9. What are the 2 kinds of murmurs and how do they differ from each other? Name 2 conditions which give rise to murmurs.
10. Inflammation of the heart tissues is the basis for a classification of heart pathology. Give the 3 terms in this classification and explain each.
11. What is meant by congenital heart disease? Give 2 examples, and tell what can be done to remedy them.
12. What part does infection play in heart disease? Give specific examples.
13. What type of heart disease is the most frequent cause of sudden death?
14. What is the effect of a thrombus in an artery supplying the heart wall? What are some of the precautions that need to be taken if such a thrombus is formed?
15. What are some of the factors that aid in causing degenerative heart disease?
16. What are some rules that may at least delay the onset of heart ailments?
17. What is a fluoroscope, and what is its purpose in heart studies?
18. Of what value is heart catheterization and how is this procedure carried out?
19. What is an electrocardiograph and what is its purpose?
20. How does digitalis help the person who has heart muscle damage?
21. Of what value are anticoagulants and antibiotics to heart patients?
22. What are artificial heart valves made of and how valuable are they?
23. What is the most serious problem related to heart transplants?

CHAPTER 13

BLOOD VESSELS AND
BLOOD CIRCULATION

A closed system ▪ Kinds of blood vessels ▪ Of what are blood vessels made? ▪ Names of arteries ▪ Names of larger veins ▪ Pulse and its meaning ▪ Blood pressure, normal and abnormal ▪ Arterial disease ▪ Hemorrhage and shock ▪ Disorders of veins.

Blood vessels, together with the 4 chambers of the heart, form a closed system for the flow of blood; only if there is an injury to some part of the wall of this system does any blood escape. The circulatory system will be easy to understand now that we know what the blood does and where it is supposed to go. If you keep one eye on the diagrams and the other on the text as the vessels are described, a picture of the system as a whole will gradually emerge.

KINDS OF BLOOD VESSELS

FUNCTIONAL CLASSIFICATION

On the basis of function, blood vessels may be divided into 3 groups, as follows:

1. **Arteries,** which carry blood from the pumping chambers of the heart (ventricles) out to the organs and other parts of the body.

2. **Veins,** which drain the tissues and the organs, and return the blood to the heart.

3. **Capillaries,** which allow for exchanges between the blood and the body cells, or between the blood and the air in the lung tissues. The capillaries connect the smaller arteries and veins.

Arteries and veins both may be subdivided into 2 groups or circuits:

1. **Pulmonary** vessels, which are related to the lungs. They include the pulmonary artery and its branches to the lungs, and the veins that drain the lung capillaries. The pulmonary arteries carry blood low in oxygen from the right

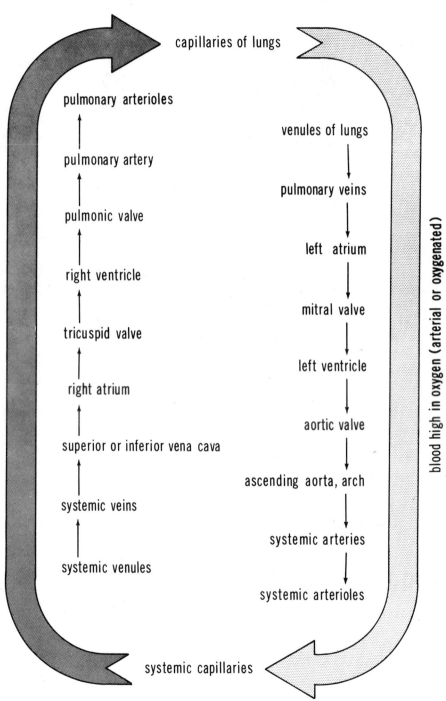

blood low in oxygen (venous or deoxygenated)

blood high in oxygen (arterial or oxygenated)

capillaries of lungs

pulmonary arterioles

↑

pulmonary artery

↑

pulmonic valve

↑

right ventricle

↑

tricuspid valve

↑

right atrium

↑

superior or inferior vena cava

↑

systemic veins

↑

systemic venules

venules of lungs

↓

pulmonary veins

↓

left atrium

↓

mitral valve

↓

left ventricle

↓

aortic valve

↓

ascending aorta, arch

↓

systemic arteries

↓

systemic arterioles

systemic capillaries

FIG. 52. Diagram to show circuit of blood flow. Note that changes in oxygen content occur as the blood flows through capillaries.

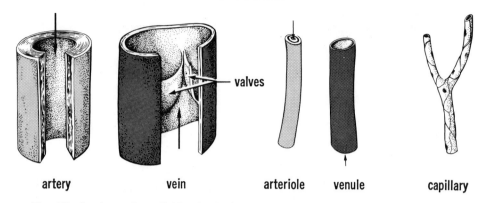

artery   vein   arteriole   venule   capillary

FIG. 53. Sections of small blood vessels to show the thicker arterial walls and the thin walls of veins and of capillaries. Valves in veins are also shown. The arrows indicate the direction of the blood flow.

ventricle, while the pulmonary veins carry blood high in oxygen from the lungs into the left atrium. This circuit concerns itself with eliminating carbon dioxide from the blood and replenishing its supply of oxygen.

2. **Systemic** (sis-tem′ik) arteries and veins, which are related to the rest of the body. This circuit is concerned with supplying food and oxygen to all the tissues of the body and carrying away waste materials from the tissues for disposal.

STRUCTURE OF BLOOD VESSELS

ARTERY WALLS

The arteries have much the thickest walls because they receive the pumping drive from the ventricles of the heart. There are 3 coats (tunics) which resemble the 3 tissue layers of the heart. These are:

1. The innermost membrane of **endothelium,** which forms a smooth surface over which the blood may easily move.

2. The second, more bulky layer, which is made of **involuntary muscle** combined with elastic connective tissue.

3. An outer tunic, which is made of a supporting **connective tissue.**

The largest artery, the **aorta,** is about 1 inch in diameter and has the thickest wall. The smallest subdivisions of arteries, the **arterioles** (ar-te′re-oles), have thinner walls in which there is very little connective tissue but relatively more muscle.

CAPILLARY WALLS

The microscopic branches of these tiny connecting vessels have the thinnest walls of any vessels: 1 cell layer. The capillary walls are transparent and are made of smooth platelike cells that continue from the lining of the arteries. Because of the thinness of these walls, exchanges between the blood and the body cells are possible. The capillary boundaries are the most important center of activity for the entire circulatory system. Their function will be explained later on in the chapter.

WALLS OF VEINS

The smallest veins, called **venules** (ven'ules), are formed by the union of capillaries. Their walls are only slightly thicker than those of the capillaries. As the veins become larger, the walls become thicker. However, veins have much thinner walls than those of comparable arteries. Although there are 3 layers of material in the walls of the larger veins, as in the artery walls, the middle tunic is relatively thin in vein walls. Therefore, veins are easily collapsed, and slight pressure by a tumor or some other mass may interfere with the return blood flow. Most veins are equipped with one-way valves which permit the blood to flow in only one direction. They are most numerous in the veins of the extremities (see Fig. 53).

NAMES OF SYSTEMIC ARTERIES

THE AORTA AND ITS PARTS

The aorta is by far the largest artery of the body. It extends upward and to the right from the left ventricle. Then it curves backward and to the left. It continues down behind the heart just in front of the vertebral column, through the diaphragm and into the lower dorsal part of the abdomen. The sections of the aorta are named in much the same manner in which a street is divided into north and south portions. The aorta is one continuous tube divided into the following regions:

1. The **ascending aorta,** which is near the heart and inside the pericardial sac.
2. The **aortic** (a-or'tik) **arch,** which curves from the right to the left, and also extends backward.
3. The **thoracic** (tho-ras'ik) **aorta,** which lies just in front of the vertebral column behind the heart and in the space behind the pleura.
4. The **abdominal aorta,** which is the longest section of the aorta, spanning the abdominal cavity.

BRANCHES OF THE ASCENDING AORTA

The first, or ascending, part of the aorta has 2 branches called the left and right **coronary arteries,** which supply the heart muscle. These form a crown around the base of the heart and give off branches to all parts of the myocardium.

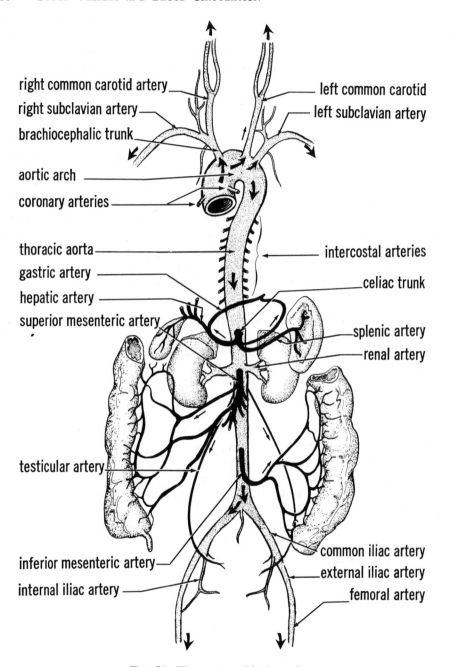

right common carotid artery

left common carotid

right subclavian artery

left subclavian artery

brachiocephalic trunk

aortic arch

coronary arteries

thoracic aorta

intercostal arteries

gastric artery

celiac trunk

hepatic artery

superior mesenteric artery

splenic artery

renal artery

testicular artery

inferior mesenteric artery

common iliac artery

external iliac artery

internal iliac artery

femoral artery

FIG. 54. The aorta and its branches.

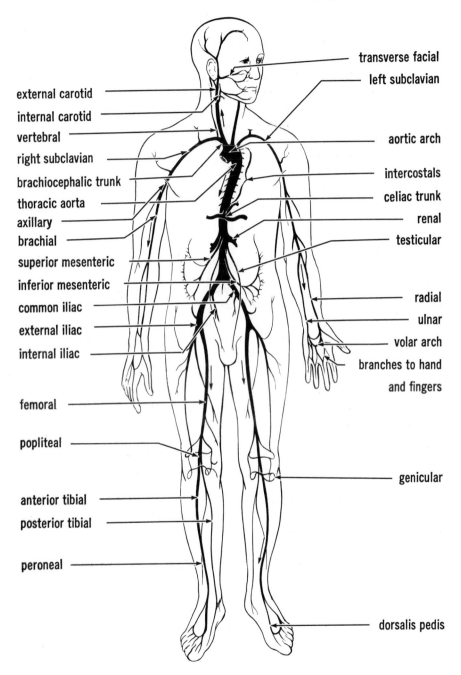

transverse facial

left subclavian

external carotid

internal carotid

vertebral

right subclavian

brachiocephalic trunk

thoracic aorta

axillary

brachial

superior mesenteric

inferior mesenteric

common iliac

external iliac

internal iliac

femoral

popliteal

anterior tibial

posterior tibial

peroneal

aortic arch

intercostals

celiac trunk

renal

testicular

radial

ulnar

volar arch

branches to hand
and fingers

genicular

dorsalis pedis

FIG. 55. Principal arteries.

BRANCHES OF THE AORTIC ARCH

The arch of the aorta, located immediately beyond the ascending aorta, sends off 3 large branches:

1. The **brachiocephalic** (brak-e-o-se-fal'ik) **trunk,** which is a short artery formerly called the innominate. After extending upward somewhat less than 2 inches, it divides into the **right subclavian** (sub-kla've-an) **artery,** which supplies the right upper extremity (arm), and the **right common carotid** (kah-rot'id) **artery,** which supplies the right side of the head and the neck.

2. The **left common carotid artery,** which extends upward from the highest part of the aortic arch. It supplies the left side of the neck and the head.

3. The **left subclavian artery,** which extends under the left collar bone (clavicle) and supplies the left upper extremity. This is the last branch of the aortic arch.

BRANCHES OF THE THORACIC AORTA

The third part of the aorta supplies branches to the chest wall, to the esophagus (swallowing tube), and to the bronchi (the treelike subdivisions of the windpipe) and their subdivisions in the lungs. There are usually 9 or 10 pairs of **intercostal** (in-ter-kos'tal) **arteries** that extend between the ribs, sending branches to the muscles and other structures of the chest wall.

BRANCHES OF THE ABDOMINAL AORTA

As in the case of the thoracic aorta, there are unpaired branches extending forward and paired arteries extending toward the side. The unpaired vessels are large arteries that supply the abdominal viscera. The most important of these visceral branches are:

1. The **celiac** (se'le-ak) **trunk,** which is a short artery about a half inch long that subdivides into 3 branches, namely, the **left gastric** to the stomach, the **splenic** (splen'ik) to the spleen, and the very important **hepatic** (he-pat'ik) **artery** which carries oxygenated blood to the liver.

2. The **superior mesenteric** (mes-en-ter'ik) **artery,** which is the largest of these branches, and which carries blood to most of the small intestine as well as to the first half of the large intestine.

3. The much smaller **inferior mesenteric artery,** which is located lower near the end of the abdominal aorta and supplies the last half of the large intestine.

The lateral (paired) branches of the abdominal aorta include the following right and left divisions:

1. The **phrenic** (fren'ik) **arteries,** which supply the diaphragm. The diaphragm is the muscular partition between the abdominal and the thoracic cavities.

2. The **suprarenal** (su-prah-re′nal) **arteries,** which provide blood for the vascular adrenal (suprarenal) glands.

3. The **renal** (re′nal) **arteries,** largest in this group, which carry blood to the kidneys.

4. Arteries that supply the sex glands, called **ovarian arteries** in the female and **testicular** (tes-tik′u-lar) **arteries** in the male (formerly called the spermatic arteries).

5. Four pairs of **lumbar** (lum′bar) **arteries,** which extend into the heavy musculature of the abdominal wall.

Iliac Arteries and their Subdivisions

The abdominal aorta finally divides into 2 common **iliac arteries.** Each of these vessels is about 2 inches long and extends into the pelvis, where each one subdivides into **internal** and **external** iliac arteries. The internal iliac vessels then send branches to the pelvic organs, including the urinary bladder, the rectum, and some of the reproductive organs. The external iliac arteries continue into the thigh, where the name of these tubes is changed to **femoral** (fem′or-al). These vessels give off branches in the thigh and then become the **popliteal** (pop-li-te′al) **arteries** which subdivide below the knee. The subdivisions include the **tibial arteries,** which extend into the ankle and foot.

Other Parts and Subdivisions of Systemic Arteries

Just as the larger branches of a tree give off limbs of varying sizes, so the arterial tree has a multitude of subdivisions. Hundreds of additional names might be included, but we shall mention only a few here. The hand receives blood that courses through the subclavian artery, which becomes the **axillary** (ak′si-lar-e) in the armpit. The longest part of this vessel is that in the arm proper. This portion is called the **brachial** (bra′ke-al) **artery.** It subdivides into 2 branches near the elbow. These are the **radial artery,** which continues down the thumb side of the forearm and wrist, and the **ulnar artery,** which extends along the medial or little finger side into the hand. The common carotid artery sends branches to the thyroid gland and other neck structures, and near the jaw it divides into an **external** and an **internal carotid.**

Anastomoses

A communication between 2 arteries is called an **anastomosis** (ah-nas-to-mo′sis). By this means blood reaches vital organs via more than one route. Some examples of such unions of end arteries are:

1. The **circle of Willis,** which receives blood from the 2 internal carotid arteries as well as from the **basilar** (bas′i-lar) **artery,** which is formed by the union of 2

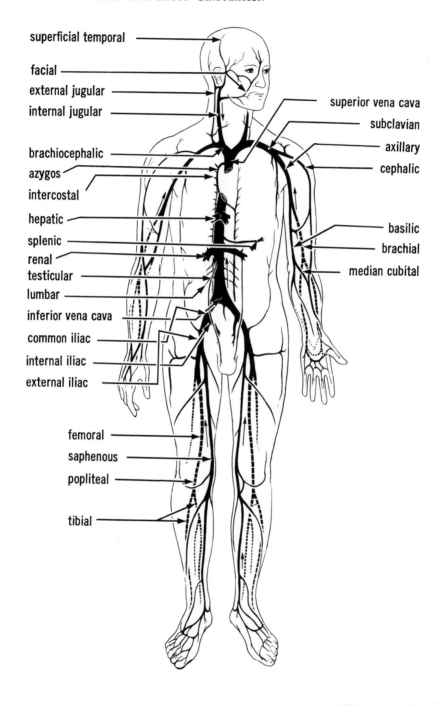

superficial temporal

facial

external jugular

internal jugular

brachiocephalic

azygos

intercostal

hepatic

splenic

renal

testicular

lumbar

inferior vena cava

common iliac

internal iliac

external iliac

femoral

saphenous

popliteal

tibial

superior vena cava

subclavian

axillary

cephalic

basilic

brachial

median cubital

FIG. 56. Principal veins.

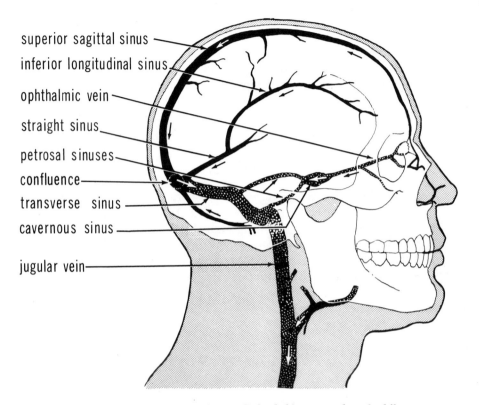

superior sagittal sinus
inferior longitudinal sinus
ophthalmic vein
straight sinus
petrosal sinuses
confluence
transverse sinus
cavernous sinus
jugular vein

FIG. 57. Cranial venous sinuses. Paired sinuses are dotted while unpaired ones are in solid black.

vertebral arteries. This arterial circle lies just under the center of the brain and sends branches to the **cerebrum,** the largest division of the brain, and to other parts of the brain.

2. The **volar** (vo′lar) **arch,** which is formed by the union of the radial and ulnar arteries in the hand. It sends branches to the hand and the fingers.

3. The **mesenteric arches,** which are made of communications between branches of the vessels that supply blood to the intestinal tract.

4. Arches which are formed by the union of the tibial arteries in the foot, and similar anastomoses which are found in various parts of the body.

NAMES OF SYSTEMIC VEINS

SUPERFICIAL VEINS

Whereas most arteries are located in protected and rather deep areas, many veins are found near the surface. The most important of these superficial veins are to be found in the 2 pairs of extremities. These include:

1. The veins on the back of the hand and at the front of the elbow. Those at the elbow, incidentally, are used often for removing the blood for testing purposes, as well as for intravenous injections. The largest of this group of veins are the **cephalic** (se-fal'ik), **basilic** (bah-sil'ik), and the **median cubital** (ku'be-tal) **veins.**

2. The **saphenous** (sah-fe'nus) **veins** of the lower extremities, which are the longest veins of the body. The great saphenous vein begins in the foot and extends up the medial side of the leg, the knee and the thigh. It finally empties into the femoral vein near the groin.

Deep Veins

The deep veins tend to parallel arteries and usually have the same names as the corresponding arteries. Examples of these include the **femoral** and the **iliac** vessels of the lower part of the body and the **brachial,** the **axillary** and the **subclavian** vessels of the upper extremities. However, exceptions are found in the veins of the head and the neck. The **jugular** (jug'u-lar) **veins** drain the areas supplied by the carotid arteries. Two **brachiocephalic** (innominate) **veins** are formed, one on each side, by the union of the subclavian and the jugular veins. (Remember, there is but one brachiocephalic artery.)

Superior Vena Cava

The veins of the head, the neck, the upper extremities and the chest all drain into the **superior vena cava** (ve'nah ka'vah), which goes to the heart. It is formed by the union of the right and the left brachiocephalic veins which drain the head, the neck and the upper extremities, while a special vein carries blood from the chest wall. The **azygos** (az'i-gos) **vein** drains the veins of the chest wall and empties into the superior vena cava just before the latter empties into the heart.

Venous Sinuses

The word "sinus" means "a space" or "a hollow." The sinusoids (the word means "like a sinus") found in the liver, the spleen, the thyroid gland and other structures are channels within the tissues of the organ. Larger channels which do not have the usual tubular structure of the veins also may drain deoxygenated blood. They are known as **venous sinuses** (see Fig. 57). An important example of a venous sinus is the **coronary sinus,** which receives most of the blood from the veins of the heart wall. It lies between the left atrium and left ventricle on the under (inferior) surface of the heart. It empties directly into the right atrium along with the 2 venae cavae.

Other important venous sinuses are located inside the skull. They are the

cranial venous sinuses which drain the veins that come from all over the brain. The largest of the cranial venous sinuses include:

1. The **cavernous** (kav'er-nus) **sinuses,** situated behind the eyeball, which serve to drain the **ophthalmic** (of-thal'mik) **veins** of the eye.

2. The **superior sagittal** (saj'i-tal) **sinus,** which is a single long space located in the midline above the brain and in the fissure between the 2 large hemispheres of the cerebrum. It ends in an enlargement called the **confluence** (kon'floo-ens) of sinuses.

3. The 2 **transverse sinuses** which also are called the **lateral sinuses.** These sinuses are large spaces between the layers of the dura mater (a brain membrane) and extend toward each side after beginning at the center back in the region of the confluence of sinuses. As each sinus extends around the inside of the skull, it receives blood draining those parts not already drained by the superior sagittal and the other sinuses that join the back portions of the transverse sinuses. This means that nearly all the blood that comes from the veins of the brain eventually empties into one or the other of the lateral sinuses. On either side the sinus extends far enough forward to empty into an internal jugular vein, which then passes through a hole in the skull to continue downward in the neck.

INFERIOR VENA CAVA

The **inferior vena cava** is much longer than the superior vena cava. The inferior vena cava returns the blood from the parts of the body below the diaphragm. It begins in the lower abdomen with the union of the 2 common iliac veins. It then ascends along the back wall of the abdomen, through a groove in the posterior part of the liver, through the diaphragm, and finally through the lower thorax to empty into the right atrium of the heart.

The drainage into the inferior vena cava is more complicated than that of the superior vena cava. We may divide the large veins below the diaphragm into 2 groups:

1. Those right and left veins that drain paired parts and organs. They include the **iliac veins** from near the groin; 4 pairs of **lumbar veins** from the dorsal part of the trunk and from the spinal cord; the veins from the testes of the male and the ovaries of the female called either the **testicular** (spermatic) **veins** or the **ovarian veins;** the **renal** and **suprarenal veins** from the kidneys and some glands near the kidneys; and finally the large **hepatic veins** from the liver. For the most part, these vessels empty directly into the inferior vena cava. The left testicular (spermatic) in the male and the left ovarian in the female empty into the left renal vein, which then takes this blood to the inferior vena cava, and thus constitute exceptions to the rule that the paired veins empty directly into the vena cava.

2. Unpaired veins which come for the most part from parts of the digestive tract (i.e., the bowel and the stomach) and empty into a special vein called the

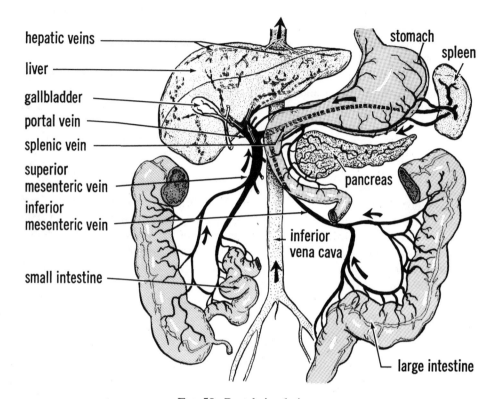

FIG. 58. Portal circulation.

portal tube. This portal vein subdivides in the liver in order to permit blood from the spleen and the intestine to come into closer contact with the liver cells. Thus the complex functions of the liver may be performed (see Chap. 15).

THE PORTAL CIRCULATION

The unusual and exceptional feature of the portal vein is that after receiving the tributaries from the unpaired organs it enters the liver and subdivides into small vessels. All other veins continue to unite until they enter one of the 3 tubes that carry the blood to the right atrium, or one of the 4 pulmonary veins that enter the left atrium. The largest tributary of the portal tube is the **superior mesenteric vein.** It is joined by the **splenic vein** just under the liver. Other tributaries of the portal circulation are the **gastric,** the **pancreatic** and the **inferior mesenteric veins.** The final subdivisions of the portal tube in the liver are spaces called **sinusoids** (si'nus-oids) which take the place of capillaries in the liver. The blood from the hepatic

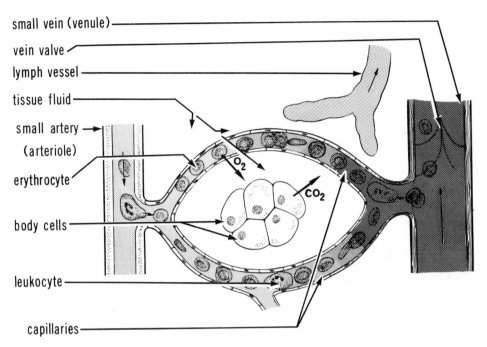

small vein (venule)

vein valve

lymph vessel

tissue fluid

small artery (arteriole)

erythrocyte

body cells

leukocyte

capillaries

O_2

CO_2

FIG. 59. Diagram to show the connection between the small blood vessels through capillaries. Note the lymph capillary, a part of tissue drainage.

arterioles also enters these sinusoids. The blood in these spaces therefore is a combination of arterial and venous blood. It is collected finally by the hepatic veins, which empty into the inferior vena cava.

The portal circulation is interesting from another standpoint, because it is in this system that food products enter the blood circulation, to be carried eventually to the tissues. Food products are absorbed from the small intestine into the bloodstream, and then travel to the liver through the portal vein. In the liver the food is altered, stored, and released as needed into the main circulatory system.

HOW CAPILLARIES WORK

We have spoken hitherto of the circulatory system as "bringing blood to the tissues." Actually, this is not entirely accurate, because blood does not touch the tissues directly (with the exception of the spleen).

If we think back to the discussion of the cells, it will be recalled that the cells are surrounded by a salty liquid called tissue fluid. We might think of the cells as a multitude of individual islands implanted in the middle of a lake. At the edge of this lake of tissue fluid runs a capillary, connected at one end to an artery and at the other to a vein (like the crossbar on the letter H). As the blood from the artery, charged with oxygen and food, passes through the capillary, those materials necessary for the life of the cells pass through the capillary walls into the lake of tissue fluid. From there they make their way to the cell islands. From the islands, in the opposite direction, come the waste products of cell metabolism. These pass into the capillary through its walls and proceed to the veins, whence they reach their organs of excretion.

It must be remembered, of course, that the capillaries are tiny, hairlike vessels; that the letter H of which we spoke has not one crossbar but millions of them. But the principle remains the same.

PULSE AND BLOOD PRESSURE

MEANING OF THE PULSE

The ventricles pump blood into the arteries regularly about 70 to 80 times a minute. The force of ventricular contraction starts a wave of increased pressure which begins at the heart and travels along the arteries. This wave is called the **pulse.** It can be felt in the arteries that are relatively close to the surface, particularly if the vessel can be pressed down against a bone. At the wrist the radial artery passes over the bone on the thumb side of the forearm, and the pulse is most commonly obtained here. Other vessels sometimes used for obtaining the pulse include the carotid artery in the neck and the **dorsalis pedis** (dor-sa'lis pe'dis) of the top of the foot.

Normally the pulse rate is the same as the heart rate. Only if a heartbeat is abnormally weak may it be lost and thus not detected as a pulse motion. In checking the pulse of another person it is important to use the second or third fingers. If you use your thumb, you may find that you are getting your own pulse. A trained person can tell a great deal about the condition of the circulatory system and can gauge the strength as well as the regularity and the rate of the pulse.

Various factors may influence the pulse rate. We will enumerate just a few:

1. The pulse is somewhat faster in smaller people, and usually is slightly faster in women than in men.

2. In a newborn infant the rate may be from 120 to 140 beats per minute. As the child grows, the rate tends to become slower.

3. Muscular activity influences the pulse rate. During sleep the pulse may slow down to 60 a minute, while during strenuous exercise the rate may go up to well over 100 a minute. If a person is in good condition, the pulse does not remain rapid despite a continuation of exercise.

4. Emotional disturbances may increase the pulse rate.

5. In many infections the pulse rate increases with the increase in temperature.

6. An excessive amount of secretion from the thyroid gland may cause a rapid

pulse. The pulse rate may serve as a partial guide for the person who must take thyroid extract.

BLOOD PRESSURE AND ITS DETERMINATION

Since the pressure inside the blood vessels varies with the condition of the heart and the arteries as well as with other factors, the measurement of blood pressure together with careful interpretation may prove a valuable guide in the care and evaluation of a person's health. The pressure decreases as the blood flows from arteries into capillaries and finally into veins. Ordinarily, measurements are made of arterial pressure only. The instrument used is called a **sphygmomanometer** (sfig-mo-mah-nom'e-ter). The 2 measurements made are of:

1. The **systolic** (sis-tol'ik) **pressure,** which occurs during heart muscle contraction and averages around 120, expressed in millimeters of mercury.

2. The **diastolic** (di-ah-stol'ik) **pressure,** which occurs during relaxation of the heart muscle and averages around 80 millimeters of mercury.

The sphygmomanometer is essentially a graduated column of mercury connected to an inflatable cuff. The cuff is wrapped around the patient's upper arm and is inflated with air until the brachial artery is compressed and the blood flow cut off. Then, listening with a stethoscope, the doctor or nurse slowly lets air out of the cuff until the first pulsations are heard. At this point the pressure in the cuff is equal to the systolic pressure; and this pressure is read off the mercury column. Then, more air is let out until another characteristic sound indicates the point at which the diastolic pressure is to be read off. Considerable practice is required to insure an accurate reading.

ABNORMAL BLOOD PRESSURE

Lower than normal blood pressure is called **hypotension** (hi-po-ten'shun). Many apparently healthy persons have systolic blood pressures below 110. The sudden lowering of blood pressure is an important symptom of shock. It may occur also in certain chronic diseases as well as in heart block.

Hypertension (hi-per-ten'shun), which is high blood pressure, has received a great deal of attention. Often it occurs temporarily as a result of excitement or exertion. It may be persistent in a number of conditions including:

1. Kidney disease and uremia or other toxic conditions.
2. Endocrine disorders such as hyperthyroidism and acromegaly.
3. Artery disease including the so-called hardening of the artery walls.
4. Tumors of the adrenal (suprarenal) medulla.

Although stress has been placed on the systolic blood pressure, in many cases the diastolic pressure is even more important. The condition of small arteries may have more effect on the diastolic pressure. At any rate, the determination of what really constitutes hypertension should be left to the physician. A blood pressure that is normal for one individual may be low for another and too high for a third.

DISORDERS INVOLVING THE BLOOD VESSELS

ANEURYSM OF THE AORTA

An **aneurysm** (an'u-rizm) is a sac or bulged-out section of the wall of an artery or a vein, owing to a localized weakness in that part of the vessel. The aorta is the vessel most commonly involved. The damage to the wall may have originally been caused by syphilis or by degenerative changes referred to as hardening of the arteries. Whatever the cause, the aneurysm continues to grow in size. Sometimes, as it swells, it may cause some derangement of other structures, in which case definite symptoms are manifested. Eventually, however, the walls of the weakened area yield to the pressure, and the aneurysm bursts like a balloon, usually causing immediate death.

ARTERIAL DEGENERATION

Changes in the walls of arteries frequently lead to loss of elasticity. This loss of elasticity is accompanied by irregular thickening of the artery wall at the expense of the lumen (space inside the vessel). Areas of yellow fatlike material may replace the muscle and elastic connective tissue, leading to a disorder called **atherosclerosis** (ath-er-o-skle-ro'sis). Sometimes the lining of the artery is damaged, and a blood clot **(thrombus)** may form at this point. Such a thrombus may more or less completely obstruct the vessel, as it sometimes does in coronary thrombosis. In other cases calcium salts and scar tissue (fibrous connective tissue) may cause hardening of the arteries, known as **arteriosclerosis** (ar-te-re-o-skle-ro'sis).

Artery damage may be present for years without causing any noticeable symptoms. As the thickening of the wall continues and the diameter of the passage for blood flow is decreased, a variety of symptoms will appear. The nature of these disturbances will vary with the parts of the body affected and with the extent of the changes in the artery walls. Here are some examples:

1. Muscle cramps and sudden lameness while walking may be due to insufficient blood supply to the lower extremities as a result of artery wall damage.

2. Headaches, dizziness, and mental disorders may be the result of cerebral artery sclerosis.

3. Hypertension may be due to the decrease in size of many arteries all over the body. Although hypertension may be present in many younger persons with no

apparent artery damage, and arteriosclerosis may be present without causing hypertension, the two are more often found together in older people.

4. Palpitation, dyspnea, paleness, weakness, and other symptoms may be the result of arteriosclerosis of the coronary arteries. The severe pain of angina pectoris may follow the myocardial damage associated with sclerosis of the vessels that supply the heart.

5. An increase in the amount of urine with the appearance of **albumin** (al-bu'min). Albumin is a normal body protein usually found in the urine only if there is kidney damage. Other symptoms referable to the kidneys may be due to damage to the arteries that supply these organs.

The gradual narrowing of the interior of the arteries, with a consequent reduction of the volume of blood which passes through them, gives rise to a general condition known as **ischemia** (is-ke'me-ah), which means literally "a suppression of blood." Those parts which are supplied by the damaged artery therefore will suffer from an inadequate blood supply, and the result is that certain vital cells of these organs will gradually die. The death of cells, for whatever cause, is called **necrosis** (ne-kro'sis).

Once these vital cells die, the organ loses its effectiveness. One example of necrosis due to ischemia is the death of certain cells of the brain, with mental disorders as a possible result (as was noted above). Another example of this is the chain of complications resulting from the gradual closure of the arteries of the leg or (rarely) of the arm. The circulation of blood in the toes or the fingers, never too brisk even at the best of times, may cease altogether. Necrosis occurs; the dead tissue is invaded by bacteria, and putrefaction sets in. This condition is called **gangrene** (gang'grene). Gangrene can result from a number of disorders involving the arteries, among them diabetes. Diabetic gangrene is a fairly common occurrence in elderly diabetic patients.

Hemorrhage and First Aid

A profuse escape of blood from the vessels is known as **hemorrhage,** a word which means "a bursting forth of blood." Such bleeding may be external or internal, from vessels of any size, and may involve any part of the body. Capillary oozing usually is stopped by the normal process of clot formation. Flow from larger vessels can be stopped by appropriate first-aid measures by anyone who happens to be at the scene. In most cases pressure with a clean bandage directly on the wound will stop the bleeding effectively.

The loss of blood from a cut artery may be rapid and unpleasantly spectacular. It often is rapidly fatal, and yet immediate appropriate action can be lifesaving. The Red Cross and other organizations that give instructions in first aid agree that excessive loss of blood can and should be prevented. Since hemorrhage is the number one problem in case of an accident, everyone should know that certain arteries can be pressed against a bone to stop hemorrhage. The most important of these "pressure points" are:

1. The facial artery, which may be pressed against the lower jaw as the vessel extends along the side of the face, for hemorrhage around the nose, the mouth, and the cheek.

2. The temporal artery, which may be pressed against the side of the skull just in front of the ear, to stop hemorrhage on the side of the face and around the ear.

3. The carotid artery in the neck, which may be pressed back against the spinal column, for bleeding in the neck and the head. Avoid prolonged compression which can cause brain anemia.

4. The subclavian artery, which may be pressed against the first rib by a downward push with the thumb, to stop bleeding from the shoulder or arm.

5. The brachial artery, which may be pressed against the arm bone, if one pushes inward along the natural groove between the 2 large muscles of the arm. This stops hand, wrist and forearm hemorrhage.

6. The femoral artery (in the groin) which may be pressed in order to avoid serious hemorrhage of the lower extremity.

Shock

The word "shock" has many meanings; but where the blood circulation is concerned, it refers to a highly dangerous condition owing to sudden failure of the circulation. The state of shock can be precipitated by a number of factors: severe hemorrhage, a sudden nervous disturbance, burns, prolonged surgery, certain drugs, anything causing a lack of oxygen in the blood, and such accessory factors as cold and exhaustion.

What happens in shock is essentially this: one or a number of these precipitating factors may by a complicated process cause the small vessels to expand (dilate), with the result that the blood drains from the large vessels into the small vessels of the tissues. Here the blood lies and stagnates instead of circulating. The victim of shock will die very quickly unless something is done to restore circulation immediately. The usual treatment is to administer blood plasma or whole blood intravenously; this increases the blood volume and helps to restore the circulation to normal.

The symptoms of shock are a cold, clammy skin, a pale and drawn face, lowered temperature, very low blood pressure, and shallow breathing. Immediate first-aid measures for a person in shock include placing him in a horizontal position, keeping him warm with blankets and hot-water bottles, and making sure that his head is kept to one side so that he will not inhale his own vomitus (an important cause of death in shock).

VARICOSE VEINS

Varicose (var′e-kose) **veins** is a condition in which the superficial veins have become swollen, tortuous and ineffective. It frequently is a problem in the esophagus, the rectum, the spermatic cord in the male, and in the broad ligament of the uterus in the female. The veins which are most commonly found to be abnormally enlarged are those that involve the saphenous veins of the lower extremities, and this condition is found frequently in people who spend a great deal of time standing—salespeople, for instance. Also pregnancy, with the accompanying pressure on the veins in the pelvis, may be a predisposing cause. Varicose veins in the rectum are commonly referred to as **piles,** or more properly, **hemorrhoids** (hem′o-roids). The general term for these enlarged veins is **varices** (var′i-sez), the singular form being **varix** (var′iks).

PHLEBITIS

Inflammation of a vein is called **phlebitis** (fle-bi′tis). There is marked pain, often considerable swelling, and involvement of the entire vein wall. A blood clot may form, causing the dangerous condition called **thrombophlebitis** (throm-bo-fle-bi′tis), with the possibility of a piece of the clot becoming loosened and floating in the blood as an **embolus** (em′bo-lus). If this embolus reaches the lungs, as it does too often, sudden death from **pulmonary embolism** (em′bo-lizm) may be the result. Prevention of infection, early activity to insure circulation following an injury or an operation, and the use of anticoagulant drugs have greatly reduced the number of sufferers from this complication.

SYNTHETIC ARTERIES

Replacement of damaged parts of arteries by synthetic tubes is proving very satisfactory. Such tubes have replaced parts of the aorta, the iliac and other arteries. Various materials (polymers), such as nylon, Dacron, and Plexiglas or medical silicones, have been used to make replacements for parts of the body, including sections of arteries.

SUMMARY

1. **Functional classification of blood vessels.**
   A. Arteries carry blood from the heart to other parts of the body. Smallest subdivisions are arterioles.
   B. Veins drain tissues and return blood to the heart. Smallest subdivisions are venules.
   C. Capillaries allow exchanges between blood and body cells. These take place through the tissue fluid.

2. **Two circuits.**
   A. Pulmonary vessels: connected with the lungs.
   B. Systemic vessels: form a network in all other parts of the body.
3. **Structure of blood vessels.**
   A. Arteries have thick walls in 3 layers: endothelium, involuntary muscle and connective tissue.
   B. Capillaries are a single cell layer thick, a continuation of the endothelial lining of larger vessels.
   C. Veins have 3-layer walls but are more easily collapsed than arteries because of their thinner walls, having less muscle and elastic connective tissue. Most have one-way valves.
4. **Names of systemic arteries.**
   A. Parts of the aorta are the ascending aorta, aortic arch, thoracic aorta and abdominal aorta.
   B. Branches of the ascending aorta are the 2 coronary arteries that supply the heart muscle.
   C. Three branches of the aortic arch.
      (1) Brachiocephalic trunk (formerly the innominate artery).
      (2) Left common carotid artery.
      (3) Left subclavian artery.
   D. Branches of the thoracic aorta.
      (1) Esophageal artery.
      (2) Bronchial arteries.
      (3) Intercostal arteries: 9 or 10 pairs.
   E. Branches of the abdominal aorta.
      (1) Unpaired branches to the viscera.
         (a) Celiac artery to stomach, spleen and liver.
         (b) Superior mesenteric to small intestine and first half of large intestine.
         (c) Inferior mesenteric artery to last half of large intestine.
      (2) Paired branches.
         (a) Phrenic arteries to the diaphragm.
         (b) Suprarenal arteries to the adrenal (suprarenal) glands.
         (c) Renal arteries to the kidneys.
         (d) Ovarian arteries or testicular (spermatic) arteries to the sex glands.
         (e) Lumbar arteries (4 pairs) to muscles of abdominal wall.
      (3) Iliac arteries.
         (a) Internal (hypogastric) arteries to pelvic organs.
         (b) External (femoral) arteries to thigh, which continues as the popliteal arteries. These subdivide below knee; latter group includes tibial arteries.
   F. Other arteries and structures.
      (1) Parts of subclavian artery include axillary and brachial arteries.
      (2) Anastomoses are unions of end arteries.

      (a) Circle of Willis to the brain.

      (b) Volar arch in the hand to supply fingers.

      (c) Mesenteric arches to the bowel.

      (d) Arches formed by the tibial arteries.

5. **Names of systemic veins.**

    A. Superficial veins near the surface in extremities.

      (1) Basilic, cephalic, and the median cubital veins, all in the upper extremities.

      (2) Saphenous veins in lower extremities.

    B. Deep veins accompany or parallel arteries and have the same names as the arteries.

      (1) Examples: femoral, iliac, brachial, axillary, subclavian.

      (2) Jugular veins from head and neck are important exceptions to the naming rule.

      (3) Superior vena cava receives all tributaries from above the diaphragm.

      (4) Inferior vena cava receives paired vessels from below diaphragm.

    C. Portal circulation.

      (1) Portal tube receives unpaired vessels from spleen, bowel and stomach.

      (2) Portal tube subdivides in the liver until sinusoids are formed.

      (3) Blood of sinusoids collected by the hepatic veins which empty into the inferior vena cava.

6. **Venous sinuses.**

    A. Coronary sinus.

    B. Cranial sinuses. Largest are 2 cavernous, a single superior sagittal and 2 transverse (lateral) sinuses.

7. **Pulse and blood pressure.**

    A. Pulse is a wave in the arteries due to contraction of the heart muscle.

    B. Pulse varies with the size, sex, age, and activity of the healthy person.

    C. Pulse rate may be increased by emotional disturbances, fever, or excessive thyroid secretion.

    D. Blood pressure systolic during heart contraction, diastolic during relaxation of ventricles.

    E. Stethoscope and sphygmomanometer used for obtaining readings.

    F. Hypotension is an important symptom of shock.

    G. Hypertension may be temporary in cases of excitement and exertion.

    H. Hypertension is likely to be persistent in kidney, endocrine and artery diseases.

8. **Disorders involving the blood vessels.**

    A. Aneurysm is saclike enlargement of a vessel, commonly the aorta.

    B. Arterial degeneration embraces many changes.

      (1) Atherosclerosis.

      (2) Arteriosclerosis.

      (3) Ischemia, necrosis and gangrene can be complications of above.

C. Hemorrhage from arteries most serious emergency.
   (1) Direct pressure on wound often effective.
   (2) Use pressure points in certain cases.
D. Shock, another serious emergency. Treated with whole blood or blood plasma.
E. Varicose veins: swollen and ineffective. Common in legs and rectum (hemorrhoids).
F. Phlebitis: inflammation of a vein. Thrombophlebitis, a dangerous complication, may cause fatal pulmonary embolism.

9. **Synthetic parts for damaged arteries.**

QUESTIONS AND PROBLEMS

1. Name the 3 main groups of blood vessels and describe their functions. How has function affected structure?
2. Trace a drop of blood through the shortest possible route from the capillaries of the foot to the capillaries of the head.
3. What are the names and functions of some cranial venous sinuses? Where is the coronary venous sinus and what does it do?
4. What large vessels drain the blood low in oxygen from most of the body into the right atrium? What vessels carry blood high in oxygen into the left atrium?
5. How does the portal vein differ from other veins? Why?
6. What is meant by pulse? Where is it most often obtained? If a large part of the body were burned, leaving only the lower extremities accessible for obtaining the pulse, what vessel would you try to use?
7. What are some factors that cause an increase in the pulse rate?
8. What is the usual effect of emotional disturbances or physical activity on the pulse? How long should these effects disturb the healthy person as he continues to exercise, for example?
9. What instrument is used for obtaining the blood pressure? What are the two values usually obtained called and what is the significance of each?
10. What are some examples of disorders that cause hypertension of a persistent kind? Of what importance is diastolic blood pressure?
11. What are some symptoms of arteriosclerosis and how are these produced?
12. What is the meaning of hemorrhage? What vessels cause the most serious bleeding if they should be cut? What are some of the most effective ways of stopping hemorrhage?
13. What is shock, and why is it so dangerous? Name some symptoms of shock.
14. In what organs are varicose veins found most commonly? In what situations are they given special names? Give examples.
15. What is the most serious complication of phlebitis of lower extremity veins?

CHAPTER 14

THE LYMPHATIC SYSTEM
AND LYMPHOID TISSUE

What lymph is ▪ The lymphatic system and lymph circulation ▪ Lymphoid tissue ▪ Lymph nodes ▪ The tonsils, the thymus and the spleen ▪ Disorders of the lymphatic system and lymphoid tissue.

THE LYMPHATIC SYSTEM

It may be recalled, from the section called "How Capillaries Work" in the preceding chapter, that exchanges are carried on between the islandlike groups of cells and the capillaries across the lake of tissue fluid. The food and oxygen that pass through the capillary walls into the tissue fluid are dissolved in water and leave the blood plasma as a solution; consequently, the volume of tissue fluid is constantly being added to, and some provision must be made for draining off this excess fluid in order to keep the level constant.

One drainage pathway for the tissue fluid is the **lymphatic system.** Besides the capillary carrying blood, there is another pipeline at the shore of the lake of tissue fluid which we had not hitherto noticed. It is called a **lymphatic capillary,** and is nothing more than a drainpipe (see Fig. 59). As the cells send waste products across the lake to be taken away and disposed of, some of the waste products pass through the walls of the blood (vascular) capillary and go directly to the veins. However, certain other waste products pass into the lymphatic capillary along with the excess tissue fluid. This fluid, as it passes into the lymphatic capillary, now is called **lymph.** The lymphatic capillaries join to form the larger **lymphatic vessels,** and these vessels (which we shall have a closer look at in a moment) eventually empty into the veins. However, before the lymph reaches the veins, it is passed through a series of filters called **lymph nodes,** where certain solid particles are taken out. Thus the lymph nodes may be compared in one way with the oil filter in an automobile.

Let us now have a closer look at the lymphatic capillaries, vessels and nodes.

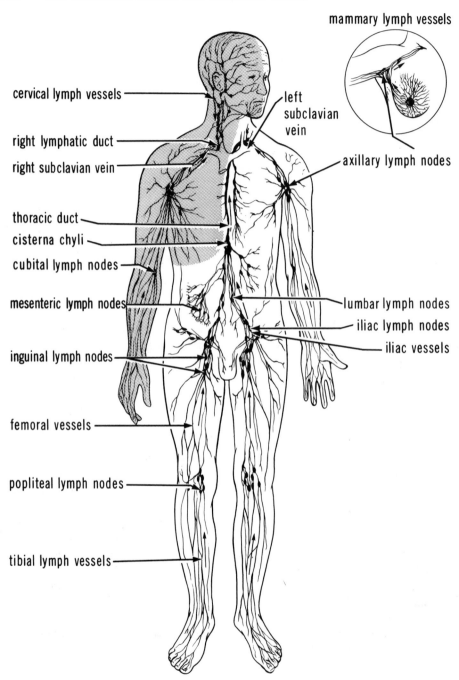

mammary lymph vessels

cervical lymph vessels

left subclavian vein

right lymphatic duct

right subclavian vein

axillary lymph nodes

thoracic duct

cisterna chyli

cubital lymph nodes

mesenteric lymph nodes

lumbar lymph nodes

iliac lymph nodes

iliac vessels

inguinal lymph nodes

femoral vessels

popliteal lymph nodes

tibial lymph vessels

FIG. 60. The lymphatic system. The vessels in the shaded area drain into the right lymphatic duct; the rest drain into the thoracic duct.

LYMPHATIC CAPILLARIES

The lymphatic capillaries resemble the blood capillaries in that they are made of one layer of flattened cells to allow for easy passage of soluble materials and water through them. Unlike the capillaries of the bloodstream, the lymphatic capillaries begin blindly; that is, they do not serve to bridge 2 larger vessels. Instead, one end simply lies within the lake of tissue fluid, while the other communicates with the larger lymphatic vessel.

In the intestine are some specialized lymphatic capillaries called **lacteals** (lak′te-als) which act as one pathway for the transfer of fats from digested food to the bloodstream. This process is covered in the chapter dealing with the digestive system. A lacteal is pictured in Figure 63.

LYMPHATIC VESSELS AND RIGHT LYMPHATIC DUCT

The lymphatic vessels are thin-walled and delicate, and have a beaded appearance because of indentations at the regions at which valves are located. These valves prevent backflow just as do those which are found in some veins. Exercise and changes in the position of parts of the body help in maintaining the flow of lymph; there is no "lymph heart."

Lymphatic vessels include **superficial** and **deep** sets. The surface lymphatics are immediately below the skin, often continuing near the superficial veins. The deep vessels usually are larger, and accompany the deep veins. All the lymphatic vessels form networks, and at certain points they carry lymph into the regional lymph nodes (i.e., the nodes which "service" a particular area). Lymphatic vessels are named according to their location. For example, those on the lateral or thumb side of the forearm are called **radial lymphatic vessels,** while those in the medial part of the forearm are called the **ulnar lymphatic vessels.** Nearly all of the lymph from the upper extremity and from the breast is carried into the **axillary lymph nodes** (i.e., in the axilla, or armpit). From the axillary lymph nodes, lymphatic vessels extend to one of the 2 large drainage ducts which finally empty into the bloodstream.

The **right lymphatic duct** is a short tube about ½ inch long which receives the lymph that comes from the right side only of the head, of the neck, of the thorax, and also from the right upper extremity. It empties into the right subclavian vein. Its opening into this vein is guarded by 2 pocketlike semilunar valves to prevent blood from entering the duct. The rest of the body is drained by the **thoracic duct.**

THE THORACIC DUCT

All parts of the body except those above the diaphragm on the right side are drained by the thoracic duct, which is the larger of the 2 main lymph channels. This tube is about 16 inches long. It begins at the back of the abdomen and below the attachment of the diaphragm. The first part of this tube is enlarged to form a cistern or temporary storage pouch called the **cisterna chyli** (sis-ter'nah ki'li). **Chyle** (kile) is the milky-appearing fluid formed by the combination of fat globules and lymph, which comes from the intestinal lacteals. Chyle passes through the intestinal lymphatic vessels and the lymph nodes of the mesentery, finally entering the cisterna chyli. In addition to chyle, all the lymph from below the diaphragm empties into the cisterna chyli by way of the various clusters of lymph nodes and then is carried by the thoracic duct into the bloodstream.

The thoracic duct extends upward through the diaphragm and along the back wall of the thorax up into the root of the neck on the left side. Here it receives the left jugular lymphatic vessels from the head and the neck, the left subclavian vessels from the left upper extremity, and other lymphatic vessels from the thorax and its parts. In addition to the valves along the duct, there are 2 at its entrance into the left subclavian vein. Thus lymph and fat enter the bloodstream to be distributed to all parts of the body (see Fig. 60).

STRUCTURES OF LYMPHOID TISSUE

The foregoing section is a brief survey of the system of lymph vessels and lymph conduction. The lymph nodes, or filters, have been mentioned repeatedly; but detailed discussion of them has been withheld until now. There has been a reason for this. The lymph nodes are made of a specialized tissue called **lymphoid** (lim'foid) **tissue.** A number of other organs also are made of lymphoid tissue, but some of them have nothing directly to do with the system of lymph conduction itself. Therefore, it seems advisable to look at these lymphoid tissue structures as a group, taking the lymph nodes first so that the lymph conduction system will have received some consideration before the other "filter masses" are studied.

Before looking at some typical organs of lymphoid tissue, let us first consider some properties of this kind of tissue and see what characteristics these organs have in common.

FUNCTIONS OF LYMPHOID TISSUE

Some of the general functions of lymphoid tissue include:

1. Removal of impurities such as carbon particles, cancer cells, pathogenic organisms and dead blood cells.

2. Manufacture of lymphocytes, which make up 20 to 25 per cent of the white blood cells.

3. Production of **antibodies,** which are chemical substances that aid in combating infection. These will be discussed in a later chapter.

LYMPH NODES

The lymph nodes, as we have seen, are designed to filter the lymph once it is drained from the tissues. The lymph nodes are small rounded masses varying from pinhead size to as much as an inch in length (1 to 25 mm.). Each node has a fibrous connective tissue capsule from which partitions extend into the substance of the organ. Inside the node are masses of lymphatic tissue, with spaces set aside for the production of lymphocytes. At various points in the surface of the node lymphatic vessels pierce the capsule in order to carry lymph into the spaces inside the pulplike nodal tissue. An indented area called the **hilum** (hi'lum) serves as the exit for lymph vessels carrying lymph out of the node. At this region other structures, including blood vessels and nerves, connect with the organ.

Lymph nodes seldom are isolated. As a rule they are massed together in groups, the number in each group varying from 2 or 3 up to well over 100. Some of these groups are placed deeply, while others are superficial. Those of the most practical importance include:

1. **Cervical** (ser've-kal) **nodes,** located in the neck. They are divided into deep and superficial groups, which drain various parts of the head and the neck. They often become enlarged during upper respiratory infections as well as in certain chronic disorders.

2. **Axillary** (ak'si-lar-e) **nodes,** located in the armpits. They become enlarged from infections of the upper extremities and the breasts. Cancer cells from the breasts (mammary glands) often invade these lymph nodes, and so must be removed at the time the breast is removed in order to prevent the further spread of cancer.

3. **Tracheobronchial** (tra-ke-o-brong'ke-al) **nodes,** found near the trachea and around the larger bronchial tubes. In city dwellers these nodes become so filled with carbon particles that they are solid black masses resembling pieces of coal.

4. **Mesenteric** (mes-en-ter'ik) **nodes,** found between the 2 layers of peritoneum that form the mesentery. There are some 100 to 150 of these nodes.

5. **Inguinal** (ing'gwi-nal) **nodes,** located in the groin region. They receive lymph drainage from the lower extremities and from the external genital organs. When they become enlarged, they often are referred to as **buboes** (bu'boes). The name for **bubonic** (bu-bon'ik) **plague,** which killed so many people during the Middle Ages, arose from the fact that the bacteria caused enlargement of various lymph nodes, especially the inguinal ones.

This discussion of the lymph nodes completes our short outline of lymph circulation. The following organs of lymphoid tissue perform somewhat different functions, particularly with respect to the substances which they filter.

THE TONSILS

There are other masses of lymphoid tissue which are designed to filter not lymph, but tissue fluid. These masses are found beneath certain areas of moist epithelium which are exposed to the outside, and hence to contamination. Such areas include parts of the digestive, the urinary, and the respiratory tracts. With this last-named system are associated those well-known masses of lymphoid tissue known as the **tonsils.**

The different tonsils include:

1. The **palatine** (pal'ah-tin) **tonsils,** which are oval bodies located at each side of the soft palate. These are most commonly known as the tonsils.

2. The **pharyngeal** (fah-rin'je-al) **tonsil,** which, when enlarged, is commonly referred to as **adenoids.** It is located behind the nose on the back wall of the upper pharynx.

3. The **lingual** (ling'gwal) **tonsils,** which are little mounds of lymphoid tissue at the back of the tongue.

Any or all of these tonsils may become so loaded with bacteria that the pathogens come to have the upper hand; removal then is certainly advisable. A slight enlargement of any of these will not call for surgery. All lymphoid tissue masses tend to be larger in childhood, so that consideration must be made of the patient's age in determining whether or not these masses are enlarged abnormally.

THE THYMUS

Because of its appearance under the microscope, the **thymus** (thi'mus) has been considered a part of the lymphoid system. Recent studies point to its having a much more basic function than was originally thought. It now seems apparent that the thymus plays a key role in the formation of antibodies in the first few weeks of life and in the development of immunity. It manufactures lymphocytes and is essential to fetal growth. It seems that the factors which stimulate the formation of lymphocytes come from the thymus itself. Removal causes a decrease in the production of these cells, and a decrease in the size of the spleen and of lymph nodes throughout the body. The thymus is most active during early life. After puberty, the tissue undergoes changes and is replaced by adipose tissue.

THE SPLEEN

The spleen is an organ in which there is found lymphoid tissue designed to filter blood. It is located in the upper left quadrant of the abdomen and is normally protected by the lower part of the rib cage because it is high up under the dome of the diaphragm. The spleen is rather soft and of a purplish color. It is a somewhat flattened organ about 5 or 6 inches long and 2 or 3 inches wide. The capsule of the spleen, as well as its framework, is more elastic than that of the lymph nodes. It contains involuntary muscle which makes it possible for the splenic capsule to contract, and also makes it able to withstand some swelling.

The spleen has an unusually large blood supply, considering its size. The organ is filled with a soft pulp, one of the functions of which is to filter out the worn-out red blood cells. There are also generated in the spleen numbers of white blood cells of the type that are capable of **phagocytosis,** which, as mentioned in Chapter 7, is the process of engulfing bacteria and other foreign cells. Prominent structures inside the spleen are round masses of lymphoid tissue, and it is because of these that the spleen often is classified with the other organs made of lymphoid tissue (although some other category might be better because of the other specialized functions of the spleen).

Some of the functions of the spleen are:

1. To destroy used-up red blood cells and to return some of the products of this decomposition to the liver via the portal tube, so that the liver can use them in the manufacture of bile (an important secretion in the process of fat digestion).

2. To serve as a reservoir for blood which can be supplied to the bloodstream by contraction of the capsule in case of a hemorrhage or some other emergency.

3. To produce lymphocytes and another type of white cell (monocytes).

4. To produce red cells before birth (this function is abandoned afterward).

5. To aid in removing all sorts of foreign and undesirable matter from the tissues, as also do parts of the lymph nodes, the bone marrow, and the liver. All of these organs possess cells called **macrophages** (mak'ro-fajes), which absorb and destroy this foreign matter.

6. To produce antibodies which lend immunity to certain diseases.

7. To remove iron from hemoglobin and to direct it for reuse by the bone marrow in manufacturing new red blood cells.

A final comment on the characteristics of lymphoid tissue: nature has furnished the human organism with thousands of these masses, many more than are required to combat infection; and so there is a large reserve. Tonsils may become infected and removal of them for that reason is common. The spleen may need to be removed in certain disorders. Lymph nodes may be invaded by cancer and should be completely extirpated (removed). No one group or mass of these tissues is necessary for life.

SOME DISORDERS OF THE LYMPHATIC SYSTEM AND LYMPHOID TISSUE

LYMPHANGITIS

Inflammation of the lymphatic vessels is called **lymphangitis** (lim-fan-ji'tis). Red streaks can be seen to extend along an extremity, usually beginning in the region of an infected and neglected injury. Such inflamed vessels are a danger signal, since the lymph nodes may not be able to stop such a serious infection. The next step would be entrance of the pathogens into the bloodstream, causing **septicemia** (sep-ti-se'me-ah), or blood poisoning. Streptococci often are the invading organisms in such cases.

ELEPHANTIASIS

As was mentioned in chapter 2, **elephantiasis** (el-e-fan-ti'ah-sis) is a great enlargement of the lower extremities resulting from stoppage of lymphatic vessels by small worms, called **filariae** (fi-la're-e). These tiny parasites, carried by insects such as flies and mosquitoes, invade the tissues as embryo or immature forms. They grow in the lymph channels and thus obstruct the flow of lymph. The swelling of the legs or, as sometimes happens in men, the scrotum, may be so great that the victim becomes incapacitated. This disease is especially common in certain parts of Asia and in some of the Pacific islands. No cure is known.

ADENITIS

The word **adenitis** (ad-eh-ni'tis) really means "inflammation of a gland," but is used most frequently to mean "enlarged, tender, and inflamed lymph nodes [which are not truly glands at all] owing to the presence of a disease." Cervical adenitis occurs during measles, scarlet fever, septic sore throat, diphtheria, and frequently during the common cold. Chronic adenitis may be due to the organisms of tuberculosis. The so-called cold abscess may begin as a tuberculous adenitis. Glands in the thorax, especially the tracheobronchial nodes, frequently are involved in tuberculosis.

HODGKIN'S DISEASE

Hodgkin's disease is a chronic disorder characterized by enlargement of the lymph nodes. The nodes in the neck particularly, and often those in the armpit, thorax, and groin enlarge. The spleen also may enlarge. The condition is more common in young men. The cause of Hodgkin's disease is not well understood, but reseach indicates that it may be due to some infection like tuberculosis. It is ultimately fatal, though radiation has been used as a temporary check of its progress.

LYMPHOSARCOMA

Lymphosarcoma (lim-fo-sar-ko'mah) is a malignant tumor of lymphoid tissue. It is likely to be a rapidly fatal disorder. Fortunately it is not a common disease. Early surgery together with appropriate radiotherapy offers the only possible cure at this time. (Note: a **lymphoma** is any tumor, benign or malignant, that occurs in lymphoid tissue.)

SPLENOMEGALY

Enlargement of the spleen is known as **splenomegaly** (sple-no-meg′ah-le). Certain acute infectious diseases are accompanied by splenic enlargement. Among these are scarlet fever, typhus fever, typhoid fever, and syphilis. Many tropical parasitic diseases cause splenomegaly. A certain blood fluke (flatworm) which is fairly common among workers in Japan and other parts of Asia causes a marked splenic enlargement.

Splenic anemia is a disease in which enlargement of the spleen is one of a number of symptoms, others being hemorrhages from the stomach and accumulation of fluid in the abdomen. In this disease and others of the same nature, **splenectomy** (sple-nek′to-me), total surgical removal of the spleen, appears to constitute a cure.

SUMMARY

1. **Lymph.**
    A. Drainage from tissues.
    B. Composed of tissue fluid.
    C. Takes away some cellular waste products.
    D. Goes through capillaries and vessels, is filtered in nodes, returns to blood.
2. **Lymphatic conduction.**
    A. Lymphatic capillaries drain lymph directly from tissues (some capillaries in intestine are lacteals).
    B. Lymphatic vessels receive lymph from capillaries. Have valves; lymph flow caused by muscular action.
    C. Lymphatic vessels lead through lymph nodes (filters) and then to 2 main ducts: right lymphatic, thoracic.
    D. Right lymphatic duct drains right side of the body above diaphragm. Empties into right subclavian vein.
    E. Thoracic duct drains rest of body. Has cisterna chyli, an enlargement at its beginning. Empties into left subclavian vein.
3. **Lymphoid tissue.**
    A. Found in other structures than those in lymph conduction system.
    B. Functions: removes bacteria and other foreign particles, manufactures lymphocytes, produces antibodies.
    C. Individual masses of tissue expendable.
4. **Lymph nodes.**
    A. Act as lymph filters.
    B. Main groups: cervical, axillary, tracheobronchial, mesenteric, inguinal.

5. **Tonsils.**
   A. Are but 1 example of a group of lymphoid masses located beneath moist exposed epithelium.
   B. Forms: palatine, pharyngeal, lingual.
6. **Thymus.**
   A. Most active during early life.
   B. Plays role in development of immunity.
   C. Manufactures lymphocytes.
7. **Spleen.**
   A. Soft flattened organ.
   B. Functions: filters blood, is reservoir for blood, produces erythrocytes in embryo, produces lymphocytes and monocytes, destroys bacteria and other foreign matter, produces antibodies, removes iron from hemoglobin and directs it for reuse in erythrocyte formation.
8. **Disorders of lymphatic system and lymphoid tissue.**
   A. Lymphangitis: infection of lymphatic vessels.
   B. Elephantiasis: enlargement of lower extremities caused by parasitic blockage of lymph vessels.
   C. Adenitis: usually refers to lymph node inflammation, enlargement, tenderness owing to disease.
   D. Hodgkin's disease: a chronic disease occurring mostly in young men, characterized by enlargement of lymph nodes.
   E. Lymphosarcoma: a malignant growth of lymphoid tissue.
   F. Splenomegaly: enlargement of spleen. Splenectomy: removal of spleen.

QUESTIONS AND PROBLEMS
 1. What is lymph? Name some of its purposes.
 2. Briefly describe the system of lymph circulation.
 3. Describe the lymphatic vessels with respect to design, appearance, and depth of location.
 4. Name the 2 main lymphatic ducts. What part of the body does each drain, and into what blood vessel does each empty?
 5. What is the cisterna chyli and what are its purposes?
 6. Name 3 characteristics of lymphoid tissue.
 7. Describe the structure of a typical lymph node.
 8. What are the neck nodes called and what are some of the causes of enlargement of these lymph nodes?
 9. What parts of the body are drained by vessels entering the axillary nodes and what conditions cause enlargement of these nodes?
10. What parts of the body are drained by lymphatics that pass through the inguinal lymph nodes? What is the relationship of bubonic plague to these nodes?
11. What are the different tonsils called and where are they located? What is the purpose of these and related structures?

12. What is the function of the thymus?
13. Give the location of the spleen and name several of its functions.
14. What is lymphangitis?
15. Describe elephantiasis and its cause.
16. Describe: Hodgkin's disease; lymphosarcoma.
17. What is splenomegaly and what can cause it?

CHAPTER 15

DIGESTION AND INDIGESTION

Digestion and absorption ▪ Organs of digestion ▪ The mouth ▪ Baby and permanent teeth ▪ Diseases of the mouth and teeth ▪ Salivary glands ▪ Swallowing tubes and the stomach ▪ Small intestine ▪ Juices and what they do ▪ Large intestine ▪ Disorders of the stomach and intestine ▪ The liver and its diseases ▪ The gallbladder, infections and stones ▪ The pancreas and its juices ▪ Diets and other food facts.

WHAT THE DIGESTIVE SYSTEM DOES

In this chapter we shall study the mechanism by which the food that we eat manages to reach the cells of every part of the body. This process is not so simple as it might seem. A solitary cell would be baffled if a fragment of food, in the state that is familiar to us, appeared across the lake of tissue fluid and sought admission. Food must be converted to a state in which it is capable of being taken into the cells by way of the blood plasma. This conversion process is known as **digestion.** Once the food is digested, however, it must be transferred to the bloodstream; and the process by which this transfer occurs is called **absorption.** Digestion and absorption are the 2 chief functions of the digestive system.

For purposes of study, the digestive system may be divided into 2 groups of organs:

1. The **alimentary canal,** which is a continuous passageway beginning at the mouth, where food is taken in, and terminating at the anus, where the solid waste products of digestion are expelled from the body.

2. The **accessory organs** which, while vitally necessary for the digestive process, do not happen to be part of the alimentary canal.

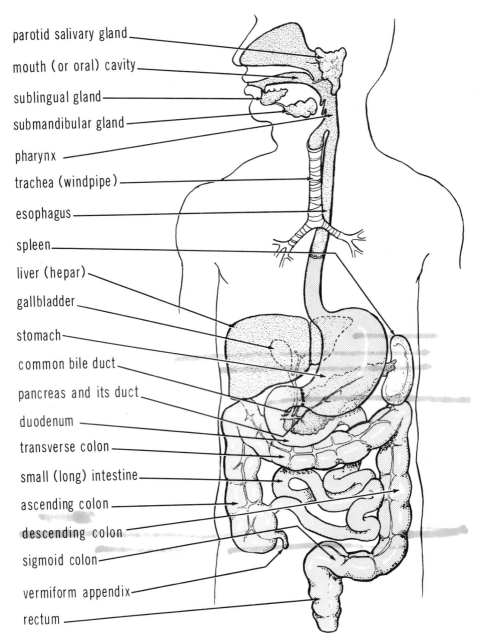

parotid salivary gland

mouth (or oral) cavity

sublingual gland

submandibular gland

pharynx

trachea (windpipe)

esophagus

spleen

liver (hepar)

gallbladder

stomach

common bile duct

pancreas and its duct

duodenum

transverse colon

small (long) intestine

ascending colon

descending colon

sigmoid colon

vermiform appendix

rectum

Fig. 61. The digestive system.

THE ALIMENTARY CANAL

The **alimentary** (al-e-men'tar-e) **canal** is a muscular digestive tube extending through the body. It is composed of several members: the **mouth,** the **pharynx,** the **esophagus,** the **stomach,** the **small intestine** and the **large intestine,** all of which will be defined and described as we encounter them. In this chapter there will be a separate section devoted to the accessory organs, though we shall be familiar with at least the main functions of all of them by the time we have finished our survey of the alimentary canal.

The word "aliment" comes from a Latin word which means "food" or "nutrients." Those foods which undergo changes and are absorbed into the blood leave the tube from the region of the small intestine. Indigestible substances such as coins, safety pins, and the cellulose in food pass the whole distance through the alimentary canal and are expelled from the body.

THE MOUTH, OR ORAL CAVITY

The mouth also is called the oral cavity. A digestible lump of sugar as well as an indigestible coin would begin the tour of the alimentary canal in this cavern. The oral cavity has 3 purposes:
1. To receive food.
2. To prepare food initially for the digestive process.
3. To aid in the accomplishment of speech.

Into this space there projects a muscular organ called the **tongue.** The tongue is an aid to chewing and swallowing, and in addition is one of the principal organs of speech (the Latin word "lingua," meaning "tongue," gave rise to our word "language"). The tongue has on its surface a number of special organs called **taste buds,** by means of which we can differentiate taste sensations (bitter, sweet, sour, or salty).

Within this cavity are also a number of stonelike structures, the teeth. There are 20 of these stony structures in a child between 2 and 6 years of age. The adult who has the good fortune to have a complete set would have 32 teeth. The cutting teeth, or **incisors** (in-si'zers), occupy the front part of the buccal cavity, while the larger grinding teeth, called the **molars,** are in the back portion of the oral cavity (see Fig. 62).

Deciduous, or Baby, Teeth. The first 8 of the **deciduous** (de-sid'u-us) **teeth** to make their appearance through the gums are the incisors. Later the **canines** (eyeteeth) and molars appear. Usually the 20 baby teeth have all made their appearance by the time the baby has passed his second birthday. During this time the permanent teeth continue development within the jawbones. The first permanent tooth to make its appearance is the very important 6-year molar. This permanent tooth comes in before the baby incisors are lost, and many people do not realize that a key permanent tooth has appeared. Decay and infection of the

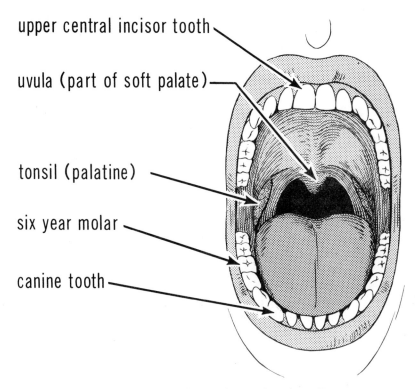

upper central incisor tooth

uvula (part of soft palate)

tonsil (palatine)

six year molar

canine tooth

Fig. 62. The mouth, showing teeth and tonsils.

adjacent deciduous molars may spread to and involve the new permanent molar tooth. Deciduous teeth need proper care in order to help preserve the 6-year molars and other permanent teeth.

Permanent Teeth. Although the buds for the second set of teeth are present at birth, the first permanent tooth does not usually make its appearance in the mouth until the child is about 6 years old. At that time the first molar, the keystone for the future grinding surfaces, appears in the space now present behind the baby molars. As the child grows, the jawbones grow also; therefore there is space for more teeth than are in the first set. After the first permanent molar has made its appearance, the baby incisors loosen and are replaced by **permanent incisors.** Then the baby canines are replaced by **permanent canines,** and finally the baby molars are replaced by the **cuspids** (premolars) of the permanent set. Now the larger jawbones are ready for the appearance of the 12-year or second permanent molar teeth. Somewhat later, the third molars, or so-called **wisdom teeth,** appear. In some cases the jaw is not large enough, or there are other abnormalities, so that these teeth may have to be removed early in life.

Diseases of the Mouth and the Teeth. Infection of the gum is called **gingivitis** (jin-je-vi'tis), while infection of the rest of the mucous lining of the mouth is called **stomatitis** (sto-mah-ti'tis). Stomatitis has recently become a problem for people who use antibiotic types of lozenges. These medicated wafers may encourage fungous infections of the mouth and the tongue. **Vincent's angina** is a kind of gingivitis, causing redness and ulceration of the mucous membrane of the mouth and gums. It is contagious and is caused by a spirochete. **Pyorrhea** is an inflammation involving the tooth socket or **alveolus** (al-ve'o-lus). It is accompanied by discharge of pus, so the name is really **pyorrhea alveolaris** (pi-o-re'ah al-ve-o-la'ris). "Pyo" means "pus," "rrhea" means "flow" or "discharge," while "alveolaris" refers to a canal or socket.

Tooth decay or dental **caries** (ka're-ez), which means "rottenness," has a number of causes. For Americans, it is a particularly expensive disease. Primitive peoples and others who do not indulge in the elegant foods so characteristic of the American diet have much less tooth decay. In addition to diet, such factors as heredity, mechanical problems, and endocrine disorders are believed to play a part. Since a baby's teeth begin development before birth, the diet of the mother during pregnancy also is most important in forestalling tooth decay.

The Salivary Glands. Another contribution to the digestive mechanism furnished by the oral cavity is the production of **saliva.** The purpose of saliva is to dissolve the food and to facilitate the processes of chewing **(mastication)** and swallowing **(deglutition).** Saliva also coats the food with mucus, allowing it to "go down" more easily. The chemical function of saliva will be discussed later in this chapter.

Saliva is manufactured by 3 pairs of glands, the first of the accessory organs:

1. The **parotid** (pah-rot'id) glands, the largest of the group.
2. The **submandibular** (sub-man-dib'u-lar), or **submaxillary** (sub-mak'si-ler-e), glands, located near the body of the lower jaw.
3. The **sublingual** glands, under the tongue.

The parotid salivary glands, located near the ear, are infected in the contagious disease commonly called **mumps.** The infecting agent is a virus. The patient should remain quiet in the hope of preventing the spread of the infection to the sex glands, the pancreas, and the other salivary glands. Research leading toward the development of a suitable vaccine has been successful.

THE WALLS OF THE ALIMENTARY CANAL

Beyond the oral cavity, the walls of the parts of the alimentary canal from the swallowing tubes to the anus are all of more or less uniform design. First of all, the canal is lined with mucous membrane. Beneath the mucosa is a layer of "packing" tissue (connective) containing blood vessels and nerves. Next come layers of involuntary muscle tissue with a most interesting function. When food reaches the swallowing tubes, this muscle tissue is stimulated to produce a rhythmic wavelike motion known as **peristalsis** (per-e-stal′sis), as a result of which the food is transported the entire length of the alimentary canal and mixed with digestive juices en route.

The final layer of the alimentary canal is of fibrous connective tissue—except for those parts that extend into the abdominal cavity, which have an additional layer called peritoneum—to be discussed later in this chapter.

THE SWALLOWING TUBES AND THEIR ACCESSORIES

The **pharynx** (far′inks) is often referred to as the **throat.** The digestible food and the indigestible coin are both pushed by the tongue into the pharynx. The tongue and the walls of the pharynx are made of voluntary muscle with a lining of mucosa. The tonsils may be seen at either side of the pharynx. The **soft palate** forms the back of the roof of the oral cavity. From it hangs a soft, fleshy, V-shaped mass called the **uvula** (u′vu-lah) (see Fig. 62). This muscular tissue guards the opening from the nasal cavity and the upper pharynx, preventing foods and liquids from entering the nasal cavities. During the process of swallowing, the muscles of the pharynx contract and so constrict the space. At this time the openings into the air spaces both above and below the mouth are closed off, by the soft palate above and by the **epiglottis,** like a small lid, below.

The **esophagus** (e-sof′ah-gus), or **gullet,** receives the contents of the contracting pharynx and forces them on by peristalsis. The esophagus is about 9 inches long and extends through the neck and the chest (thorax). Finally the esophagus reaches the abdominal cavity after extending through the diaphragm. There it empties into a saclike structure called the **stomach.**

THE STOMACH

The stomach is actually an enlarged (dilated) section of the alimentary tube. It is shaped somewhat like a gourd, and both ends of it are guarded by valves which normally permit the passage of substances in only one direction. The first of these is the **cardiac valve,** located between the esophagus and the stomach. We frequently are aware of the existence of this valve; sometimes it does not relax as it should, and then there is a feeling of having a place one can't swallow past. At the bottom end of the stomach, connecting it with the small intestine, is the other valve called the **pyloric sphincter** (pi-lor′ik sfingk′ter). This valve is especially important in that it determines the length of time in which the food remains in the stomach.

The stomach, so often abused and misunderstood, is a combination storage pouch and churn. If the stomach is empty, there will be many folds in the lining. These folds are called **rugae** (ru′ge), and they disappear as the stomach fills (it may be stretched so that it holds a half gallon of food and liquid). When the stomach is filled, the pyloric sphincter closes and retains the contents until the food has been mixed with certain digestive juices collectively called **gastric juice.** These juices are secretions given out by tiny glands in the stomach wall. The mixture of gastric juice and food is known as **chyme** (kime).

The gastric juice itself has 2 main components: **hydrochloric acid** and **enzymes.**
Stomach Acid. The hydrochloric acid in the stomach juice has 3 important functions:

1. It softens the connective tissues in meat.
2. It kills bacteria and thus destroys many potential disease-producing agents.
3. It activates at least one of the stomach enzymes, which are chemicals that convert food into soluble and absorbable substances (see Chap. 4).

An abnormally low production of stomach acid may cause digestive disturbances which are greatly aggravated by taking soda or other alkaline substances contained in many of the patent medicines purporting to aid in curing indigestion. Such substances neutralize the valuable normal functions of the stomach acid, and in many cases grave harm is done by such self-medication. Occasionally, hydrochloric acid is produced in excess, but this condition is rather uncommon and can be diagnosed easily by an analysis of the stomach contents. What the layman thinks is excess acidity (**hyperacidity**) really may be underacidity (**hypoacidity**) and may indicate serious disease, possibly even cancer.

Heartburn, Vomiting and Related Disorders. A burning sensation in the region of the esophagus and stomach is popularly known as **heartburn.** It may be caused by the sudden intake of a large amount of fluid with excessive stretching of the lower part of the esophagus. It is also a common complaint in stomach irritation due to excessive food intake or food poisoning. It is not due to overacidity of the stomach contents, since it is often found in cases of abnormally low acidity. **Nausea** is a feeling of illness that may follow distention or irritation of the lower esophagus or of the stomach from various nervous and mechanical factors. It may be a symptom of interference with the normal forward peristaltic motion of the stomach and intestine and thus may be followed by vomiting. **Vomiting** refers to the expulsion of stomach (and sometimes bowel) contents through the mouth by reverse peristalsis. The contraction of the abdominal wall muscles forcibly empties the stomach. Vomiting is frequently caused by overeating, by irritants that may be found in food or drink, and by a variety of generalized diseases.

Flatus (fla'tus) usually refers to excessive amounts of air (gas) in the stomach or intestine. The resulting condition is referred to as **flatulence** (flat'u-lens). In some cases it may be necessary to insert tubes into the stomach or rectum to aid the patient in expelling flatus.

Stomach Cancer. About a fourth of all the cancers involve the stomach, and to this type of cancer males are somewhat more susceptible than females. The growth nearly always develops from the epithelial or mucosal lining of the stomach and is often of the type called **adenocarcinoma** (ad-e-no-kar-si-no'mah). Sometimes the

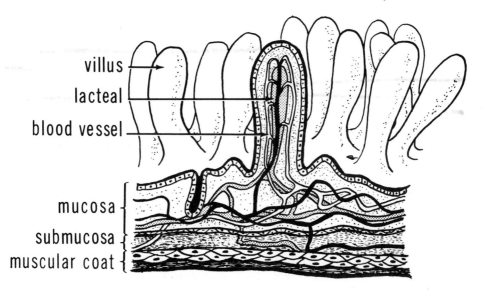

villus
lacteal
blood vessel

mucosa
submucosa
muscular coat

FIG. 63. Structure of a villus.

victim has suffered from long-standing indigestion but has failed to consult a physician until the growth has spread to other organs such as the liver, in which there may be secondary (metastatic) growths by the dozen. Persistent indigestion is one of the important warning signs of cancer of the stomach.

Peptic Ulcer. An ulcer as such is defined as an area of the skin or of a mucous membrane within which the substance is being lost and the tissues of which are gradually disintegrating. A **peptic ulcer** is that which is found on the mucous membrane of the esophagus, the stomach, or the **duodenum** (du-o-de′num), the first, or proximal, part of the small intestine. It may be the result of the acid action of the gastric juice. Peptic ulcers are found most frequently in people between the ages of 30 and 45. The intestinal (or duodenal) type is much more common in males. Emphasis is now being placed on mental and emotional factors as playing a part in the cause of ulcers. The person suffering from peptic ulcer needs the best medical and nursing care, and most certainly should not depend on patent medicines.

More About the Pyloric Valve. The pyloric valve (or sphincter) is a ringlike muscle surrounding the end of the stomach. Normally the stomach contents escape through this valve in about 2 to 6 hours. This action may be delayed by a spasm of the muscle **(pylorospasm),** or there may be present an actual constriction of the opening. Some infants, most often males, are born with an abnormally small opening. This condition is called **pyloric stenosis** (ste-no′sis), and usually surgery is required to prevent starvation of the infant. The exit valve from the stomach opens into the **small intestine.**

THE SMALL INTESTINE

The small intestine is by far the longest part of the alimentary canal. More appropriately, it might be called the long intestine, because it is about 4 or 5 times as long as the large intestine. However, it is called the small intestine because of its smaller diameter. The small intestine averages about 20 feet in length as compared with some 4 or 5 feet for the large intestine. In addition to this, the mucosa which lines the small intestine is greatly increased in area by tiny, fingerlike projections called **villi** (vil′li) (see Fig. 63). The first 10 or 12 inches of the small intestine is called the **duodenum.** In the duodenum is an opening into which lead 2 conduits, or **ducts,** carrying digestive juices from 2 accessory organs of digestion. One of these juices is **pancreatic juice,** which arrives via the **pancreatic duct** from the **pancreas** (pan′kre-as). The other juice is **bile,** carried by the **common bile duct** from the **liver.** (Bile is not primarily a digestive juice in that it contains no enzymes, but it is important in the digestion of fats.) The small intestine secretes its own **intestinal juice.** Thus, as the food and the coin pass into the duodenum, they are deluged by a cloudburst of digestive juices.

Beyond the duodenum there are 2 more divisions of the small intestine: the **jejunum** (je-joo′num), which forms the next two-fifths; and finally the **ileum** (il′e-um), constituting the remainder. The ileum joins the large intestine through another muscular valve called the **ileocecal** (il-e-o-se′kal) sphincter.

The food in the stomach is partially digested by the gastric juices, but the small intestine is the organ in which the greater part of the digestive process takes place, and where absorption occurs. We shall have a closer look at these 2 functions.

Absorption in the Small Intestine. Before the process of digestion is discussed in any detail, let us assume for the moment that the food in the small intestine has already been digested—that is, reduced by the concerted action of the digestive juices to the state in which it is ready to go to the bloodstream and ultimately to the body cells. The means by which the digested food reaches the bloodstream is known as **absorption.**

The small intestine is the chief organ of absorption, this process taking place through the mucosa by means of the countless minute projections of it known as villi. The villi are so small and so numerous that they give a velvety appearance to the lining of the small intestine. Each villus is of epithelium underlaid with connective tissue. Within each is a system of miniature arteries and veins, bridged with capillaries. All the basic food materials, including water and salts, but with the exception of some fats, are absorbed into the bloodstream through the capillary walls in the villi. From here they pass by way of the portal system to the liver, to be stored or released and used as needed.

Fats have an alternate method of reaching the bloodstream. As was noted, some fat is absorbed via the blood capillaries of the villi. However, some fats also are absorbed by way of the lymphatic capillaries of the villi, which are called lacteals (these were mentioned in the chapter covering the lymphatic system). According to some authorities about 40 per cent of fat is absorbed via the lacteals. The word "lacteal" means "like milk," an apt description of the appearance of the mixture of lymph and fat globules that is drained from the small intestine after a quantity of fat has been digested. This mixture of fat and lymph, which as we learned is called chyle, collects in the cisterna chyli and eventually reaches the bloodstream.

The Process of Digestion. In the chapter on blood, it was pointed out that the blood plasma contains the water, the food substances, and the mineral salts which together are necessary for the life and growth of the cells. We now know the means by which these materials reach the blood plasma in the first place; but it yet remains for us to find out how these simple chemical substances are derived from the complex foods that we eat. This conversion process is, of course, known as digestion.

Let us review once more these basic materials which the cells need, and which are found in foods:

1. **Carbohydrates** (kar-bo-hi′drates), which include starches and sugars, and contain the elements carbon, hydrogen, and oxygen.

2. **Fats,** which are more concentrated in fuel value than carbohydrates, and may, in some cases, carry important vitamins.

3. **Proteins,** which form the stuff of which, besides water, protoplasm is made.

4. **Mineral salts,** which include a large variety of somewhat simpler compounds than those mentioned above. Salts maintain the proper conditions for osmosis in the cells, form a part of the body structure (as in bone), and play an important part in such life processes as muscle contraction and nerve responses.

5. **Vitamins,** which among other things help to regulate cell metabolism. They are food substances which are essential for good health.

6. **Water,** which constitutes about 66 per cent of man's entire body composition. Eighty per cent or more of many fruits and vegetables, and from 50 per cent to 75 per cent of meats and fish is water.

The digestive juices, by their chemical action, extract these various materials so that they can be absorbed. Most of the digestive juices contain the chemicals known as **enzymes,** and it is the enzymes that actually do the work of breaking down foods chemically. It should be pointed out that although the enzymes cause the chemical reaction to take place, they themselves do not enter into the reaction. For example, an enzyme may cause the basic protein to separate itself from the rest of the food, but the enzyme itself does not become a part of the protein. There are several different enzymes, and each acts on a specific food compound and no other. For example, some enzymes act only on fats; others act only on starches, and so forth. But let us see for ourselves what happens to a mass of food from the time it is taken into the mouth to the moment that it is ready to be absorbed.

The food is now being chewed; and saliva, the first of the digestive juices, is acting on it, softening it so that it can be swallowed easily. The saliva contains the enzyme **ptyalin** (ti'ah-lin), which initiates the process of digestion by changing some of the starches into sugars. Recall at this point that carbohydrates are found in the blood plasma in the form of simple sugar—glucose—and so now we should begin to understand where this blood sugar comes from.

When the food reaches the stomach, it is acted upon by the gastric juice, which contains hydrochloric acid and certain enzymes. The most important functions of the gastric juice are those related to the actions of the hydrochloric acid (as previously outlined) and the liquefying of the food. In addition, there is some action, particularly on proteins, by the enzymes listed below:

1. **Pepsin.** This begins the breakdown of protein into simpler forms, so that the juices in the small intestine can work on them more effectively.

2. **Rennin.** This enzyme is the one that causes the curdling of milk, and is probably secreted in larger amounts in babies; possibly not at all in adults.

3. **Lipase** (lip'ace). This enzyme acts on fat but is of very minor importance in the stomach, partly because most of the fat particles found in the stomach are too large.

At this point the food is a liquid (chyme) and proceeds to the small intestine for more chemical treatment.

Here the chyme is mixed with the greenish-yellow bile from the liver via the gallbladder. The bile does not contain enzymes; its action is purely mechanical. It works on fat, acting as a sort of liquid crowbar that splits the bits of fat into ever smaller particles so that the next digestive juice, the powerful secretion from the pancreas, can act more efficiently. The pancreatic juice contains a number of enzymes including the following:

1. **Lipase.** This enzyme was mentioned in connection with the gastric juice where it is present in small quantities. Following the physical division of fats into tiny particles by the action of bile, the powerful pancreatic lipase actually does almost all of the digesting of fats. In this process fats are usually broken down into 2 simpler compounds, glycerol and fatty acids, which are more readily absorbable. If pancreatic lipase is absent, fats are expelled with the feces in undigested form.

2. **Amylopsin** (am-i-lop'sin). This changes starch to sugar.

3. **Trypsin** (trip'sin). This splits proteins into amino (am'e-no) acids, which are the form in which proteins enter the bloodstream.

The intestinal juice contains a number of enzymes including 3 that act on the sugars to transform them into the simpler form in which they are absorbed. These are **maltase, sucrase,** and **lactase.** It must be emphasized that most of the chemical changes in foods occur in the intestinal tract because of the pancreatic juice, which could probably adequately digest all foods even if no other digestive juice were produced. If pancreatic juice is absent, serious digestive disturbances always occur.

TABLE OF DIGESTIVE JUICES AND ENZYMES

Juices & Glands	Place of Action	Enzymes	Changes in Foods
Saliva from 3 pairs of salivary glands	Oral cavity	Ptyalin	Begins starch digestion
Gastric juice from the stomach wall	Stomach	Pepsin	Begins protein digestion
		Lipase	Digestion of fats
		Rennin	Curdling of milk protein
Pancreatic juice from the pancreas	Small intestine	Amylopsin	Acts on starches
		Trypsin	Acts on proteins
		Lipase	Acts on fats
Intestinal juice from the small intestine (tubular glands)	Small intestine	Lactase Maltase Sucrase	Break down complex sugars into simpler forms
Bile from the liver	Small intestine	None	Breaks down fats physically so that lipase can digest them

This, in a nutshell, is the process of digestion. It should be noted that the food materials which the enzymes separate and reduce to absorbable forms are carbohydrates (i.e., sugars and starches), fats and proteins. The mineral salts are dissolved in the water, and this solution is absorbed as it is. The vitamins behave a bit differently according to their type. Some are incorporated in fats and are absorbed along with the fats (unless mineral oil is taken; and in that case the fat-soluble vitamins may be carried out in the feces). Other vitamins are dissolved in water and are absorbed in much the same way that mineral salts are. Still other vitamins (such as vitamin K) are produced by the action of bacteria in the colon and are absorbed from the large intestine.

THE LARGE INTESTINE

Once the processes of digestion and absorption have taken place, all that remains of the food is of no further use to the body, and so can be expelled. Also, anything else that may be indigestible (such as the coin that was swallowed) will pass out of the body through the large intestine.

The materials to be eliminated will continue through the exit or ileocecal valve from the small intestine and enter the small pouch at the beginning (proximal) part of the large intestine. This pouch is called the **cecum** (se′kum) and is located in the lower right quadrant of the abdomen. To the cecum is attached a small blind tube called the **vermiform** (ver′me-form) **appendix.** "Vermiform" means wormlike. The appendix contains relatively large amounts of lymphoid tissue such as is found in the tonsils; and as is frequent in the case of the tonsils, this tissue may become infected, a condition called **appendicitis.**

No enzymes are secreted by the large intestine. Its walls are lined with mucous membrane and contain layers of involuntary muscle which move the solid waste products, called **fecal matter,** on toward the rectum. Absorption of water takes place through the walls of the large intestine, though there are no villi. The action of bacteria within the large intestine is a further aid to the absorption of nutrients.

The Colon and the Rectum. The colon, which is the name for the longer part of the large intestine, extends up from the cecum along the right side and then bends to extend across the abdomen to the left side. It then descends on the left side of the abdomen into the pelvis. The lower part of the colon bends in an S shape to form the **sigmoid flexure** (sig'moid flek'sher). Hence the names for the 4 divisions: **ascending colon, transverse colon, descending colon,** and **sigmoid colon** (see Fig 61). The sigmoid colon empties into the **rectum,** which is about 6 to 8 inches long. The rectum serves as a temporary storage area for the indigestibles and unabsorbables. A narrow portion of the distal part of the large intestine is called the **anal canal,** which leads to the outside through an opening called the **anus** (a'nus). The whole journey from mouth to anus usually requires some 36 hours or more.

INTESTINAL DISORDERS

Gastritis and Enteritis. Indigestion may be due to a **gastritis,** which means inflammation of the stomach lining, or to an **enteritis,** which means intestinal infection. More commonly the stomach and the small intestine are both involved, so that the illness is known as **gastroenteritis** (gas-tro-en-ter-i'tis). The symptoms include nausea, vomiting, and diarrhea as well as acute abdominal pain or colic. Gastroenteritis may be caused by a variety of pathogenic organisms including staphylococci, dysentery bacilli, the cholera bacterium, and the protozoa of amebic dysentery. Chemical irritants such as alcohol, spray residues on fruits and vegetables, and other toxins have been known to cause gastritis and enteritis.

Diarrhea and Dysentery. Diarrhea means "to flow through," and is a symptom in which there is an abnormally frequent watery bowel movement. **Dysentery** means "difficulty in the intestine," and usually refers to an inflammation of the mucosal lining, although deeper tissues also may be affected. The 2 main types of dysentery are:

1. **Bacillary** (bas'e-la-re) dysentery, which is caused by rod-shaped bacteria that are transferred to food and water primarily by human carriers.

2. **Amebic** dysentery, which is due to an infestation by a one-celled animal called *Entamoeba histolytica.*

Bacillary dysentery may be prevented by a combination of water chlorination, milk pasteurization, and observation of all sanitary measures in the handling of food. Restaurant workers should receive periodic examinations and should observe ordinary precautions such as frequent hand washing, particularly after every trip to the toilet. Amebic dysentery is especially prevalent in areas in which food is grown in fields where human waste is used for fertilizer. When traveling in countries in which this is the custom, one should avoid the use of raw food and unboiled or unsterilized water. The traveler should carry chemical tablets to kill contaminants in water if he is unable to boil it.

Diarrhea is a symptom found in many conditions in addition to the dysenteries. Some of these disorders include:

1. Epidemic diarrhea, or diarrhea of the newborn, which is somewhat more common in the premature infant.

2. Bacterial food poisoning, which is usually due to the growth of staphylococci with the formation of poisons, especially in custards and cooked potatoes that are not kept refrigerated.

3. Ptomaine poisoning which is sometimes confused with the bacterial food poisoning caused by staphylococci but is actually due to putrid meat. It is now rather rare.

4. Deficiency diseases such as pellagra (pel-lag′rah or pel-la′grah) or sprue.

5. Acute emotional disturbances, such as those sometimes experienced by students just before and during an important test (so-called State Board diarrhea).

6. Asiatic cholera, typhoid fever, paratyphoid infections, and related diseases.

7. Cancer, in which constipation may alternate with diarrhea.

8. Tuberculosis and other infections of the bowel, including **diverticulitis** (di-ver-tik-u-li′tis), which is an inflammation of saclike bulges in the wall.

In order to determine the cause of the diarrhea, an examination of the intestinal excretions may be required. Various terms are used to refer to this bowel waste including feces (fe′sez), fecal material, excrement (eks′kre-ment), and most commonly the word "stool." A stool examination may reveal the presence of amebae, bacteria, or the ova of worms.

Constipation. About 50 million dollars are spent each year in an effort to remedy a condition called constipation. What is constipation? Many people erroneously think of themselves as constipated if there are any days in which there are no bowel movements. Actually, normal people vary greatly, so that one person may be perfectly well although he has a bowel movement only once in 2 or 3 days, while another may be equally well with more than 1 elimination daily.

On the basis of its onset, constipation may be classified as acute or chronic. Acute constipation occurs suddenly and may be due to appendicitis or to an intestinal obstruction. Laxatives and enemas should be avoided and a physician should be consulted at once. Chronic constipation, on the other hand, has a more gradual onset and may be divided into 2 groups:

1. **Spastic** constipation in which the intestinal musculature is overstimulated, so that the canal becomes narrowed and the space (lumen) inside the intestine is not large enough to permit the passage of fecal material.

2. **Flaccid** (flak′sid) constipation which is characterized by a lazy or atonic (ah-ton′ik) intestinal muscle.

The overactive spastic type of constipation is probably much more common than the atonic lazy kind. Nervous tensions, excessive amounts of bulky foods, and the use of laxatives increase the muscle tone of the intestine. The person who has sluggish intestinal muscles may be helped by moderate exercise, an increase in vegetables and other bulky foods in the diet, and an increase in fluid intake.

The use of enemas and so-called colonic flushings is unnecessary and should be discouraged for most persons. The lining of the intestine may be injured by streams of water that remove the normal protective mucus. In addition to this, those who have piles (hemorrhoids) will aggravate this condition by enemas. Enemas should be done on the order of a physician, and sparingly.

THE ACCESSORY STRUCTURES

THE LIVER

The liver, or **hepar** (he'par), is the largest of the glandular organs of the body. It is located under the dome of the diaphragm so that, if of normal size, it cannot be felt through the abdominal wall. The human liver is the same brownish-red color as the animal livers that you see in the market. It has a large right lobe and a somewhat smaller left lobe, as well as 2 other lesser lobes. It is a most remarkable organ, with so many functions that only a partial list can be mentioned here. Some of these include:

1. The production of bile from the pigment of broken-down red blood cells.
2. The removal of poisons (toxins) that have been absorbed from the intestine.
3. The storage of simple sugar in a form called **glycogen,** which is released as needed in the form of glucose.
4. The final treatment of fats so that they can be more efficiently utilized by the cells.
5. The storage of certain vitamins, including A, D, and some of the B group.
6. The manufacture of **heparin** (hep'ah-rin), an acid which prevents clotting of the blood.
7. The formation of antibodies, which act against disease organisms.
8. The production of certain blood plasma proteins such as fibrinogen and albumin.
9. The removal of a waste product called **urea** (u-re'ah) from amino acids.

Diseases of the Liver. Inflammation of the liver is called **hepatitis** (hep-ah-ti'tis). Epidemic hepatitis is caused by a virus. Outbreaks of this disease occur in military establishments and in other populous institutions as epidemics, which are more common in the fall and in winter. It varies in severity from cases that are so mild as to be scarcely recognizable to such a serious infection that the liver may become permanently damaged. Because of the fact that the blood from the intestinal tract passes through the liver, any toxins or microorganisms which may get into the intestinal (mesenteric) veins enter the liver. The most important of these organisms is the *Entamoeba histolytica* which causes amebic colitis (i.e., in the colon) at first. If it is carried into the liver, it causes the same destruction of tissue that it does in the colon. However, since the liver is not open to the outside as the colon is, the softened and liquid area becomes an abscess. This condition is very hard to treat.

Cirrhosis (si-ro'sis) of the liver is a chronic disease in which the active liver cells are replaced by inactive scar tissue (connective tissue). The most usual type is the **portal cirrhosis,** which is fairly common in alcoholics. Many believe that the cause is related to poor nutrition. Destruction of the liver cells curtails the portal circulation, causing blood to accumulate in the spleen and the gastro-intestinal tract, and fluid in the peritoneal cavity. This fluid may have to be removed periodically by puncture, or **paracentesis** (par-ah-sen-te'sis).

Cancer of the liver also is common in cases which begins as a cancer in one of the organs of the abdominal cavity. The tumor cells are carried from the intestine or other organ through the veins that go to the liver. Secondary growths or metas-tases in the liver therefore are fairly common.

THE GALLBLADDER

The gallbladder is a muscular sac that serves as a storage pouch for bile. While the liver may manufacture bile continuously, the need for it is likely to arise only a few times a day. Consequently, bile from the liver flows into the liver ducts and then up through the duct connected with the gallbladder. On the occasion when the semiliquid food mass (chyme) enters the duodenum, the gallbladder squeezes bile into the small bowel.

The gallbladder may become infected, a condition called **cholecystitis** (ko-le-sis-ti'tis), while the presence of stones in the gallbladder is called **cholelithiasis** (ko-le-le-thi'ah-sis). Sometimes a chronic gallbladder infection may lead to stone formation. If a stone finds its way into the tube from the gallbladder, the person may suffer from **biliary** (bil'e-a-re) **colic** (i.e., acute pain) because of the muscle spasm in the wall of the duct.

THE PANCREAS

The pancreas not only produces the pancreatic juice which we recently have noted, it also manufactures a substance called **insulin** which is released directly into the blood and has the function of regulating the amount of sugar which is "burned" in the tissues. We shall have a closer look at this latter function in Chapter 18.

Pancreatic juice, as was noted, is extremely powerful; but of course is harmless as long as it is confined to its proper channels. However, it may happen that the pancreatic duct becomes blocked, with the result that these enzymes become backed up in tissues which are not supposed to receive them. Also, in some cases of gallbladder disease, the infection of that organ may extend into the duct connected with the pancreas and cause an abnormal activation of the pancreatic enzymes. In either circumstance the pancreas will suffer destruction by its own juice, and the outcome can be fatal. This condition is known as **acute pancreatitis.** Additional disorders that may involve the pancreas include cancer and other tumors.

THE PERITONEUM

The **peritoneum** is a serous membrane which covers the surface of most of the abdominal organs to form the visceral serosa and lines the abdominal wall to form the parietal layer. In addition to these parts of the peritoneum, there are more complex double layers of membrane which separate the abdomen into areas and spaces, and in some cases aid in supporting the organs and holding them in place.

The **mesentery** (mes'en-ter-e) is a double-layered peritoneal structure shaped somewhat like a fan, with the handle portion attached to the back wall. The expanded long edge is attached to the small intestine. Between the 2 layers of membrane that form the mesentery are the blood vessels, nerves and other structures which supply the intestine.

Another double-layered peritoneal structure, called the **greater omentum** (o-men'tum), hangs downward from the lower border (greater curvature) of the stomach. This double layer of peritoneum extends into the pelvic part of the abdomen and then loops back and up to the transverse colon. It has been aptly described as an apron inside the abdomen. It may, in some cases, serve to prevent the spread of infection inside the abdominal cavity. There is also a peritoneal structure called the **lesser omentum,** which extends between the stomach and the liver.

DISORDERS INVOLVING THE PERITONEUM

Peritonitis. This is inflammation of the peritoneum and its most important disease. It has in the past been a dreaded complication following infection of one of the organs which the peritoneum covers—generally the appendix. The frequency of peritonitis has been greatly reduced by the use of antibiotic drugs. However, it still occurs and can be very dangerous. If the infection is kept in one area, it is said to be a **localized** peritonitis. A **generalized** peritonitis may cause so much absorption of disease organisms and their toxins that the outcome will be fatal. A ruptured appendix or ulcer may pour such masses of bacteria into the abdominal cavity that the resulting peritonitis could overwhelm the victim. Immediate surgery to repair the rupture, together with meticulous nursing care, will be needed to save the person's life.

Since many of the infections of such epithelial membranes have their origins in relatively mild disorders such as tonsillitis, appendicitis, sinusitis, and related infections, careful attention to the general health, as well as nursing care directed toward the prevention of the extension of lesser infections, is the best way to forestall these serious complications.

Ascites. An accumulation of fluid in the abdominal (peritoneal) cavity is called ascites (ah-si'tez). The abdomen becomes greatly enlarged and the pressure on the organs may require removal of liquid by paracentesis. Obstruction of the portal flow, as sometimes occurs in cirrhosis of the liver, is one important cause of ascites.

SOME PRACTICAL ASPECTS OF NUTRITION

Good nutrition is absolutely essential for the maintenance of health. This means basically that all the fundamental food materials necessary for the life and growth of the body cells must be continuously provided, in adequate quantity, in the food that we eat. If one or more of these vital materials are not supplied, the body will suffer in a number of ways, the effect being **malnutrition,** meaning bad nutrition. We commonly think of a malnourished person as one who does not have enough to eat; but malnutrition can occur just as easily from eating too much of the wrong foods. The normal manner by which malnutrition is avoided is to adhere to a balanced diet; that is, to insure that most of what is eaten includes adequate quantities of the basic nutrients.

In order that homemakers and others who plan meals may understand more easily how to provide a balanced diet, food groupings called the "Basic Seven" or the "Basic Four" have been publicized. Another division arranges foods in 3 groups as follows:

1. **Protective** foods, which are those especially high in vitamins and mineral salts. These include citrus and other fruits plus a variety of vegetables, particularly leafy green and yellow ones. Protective foods are especially valuable in staving off disease.

2. **Protein** foods, which are required for growth and repair of tissues. Since they cannot be stored, they should be included daily.

3. **Energy** foods, which contain fats and carbohydrates. They are needed in larger amounts by those who are especially active physically.

Many assertions about food combinations, such as the common one that cherries and ice cream (or fish and milk) are poisonous mixtures, are not based on the laws of nature; nor can any scientific basis be found for such ideas. For the normal, healthy person a balanced diet including a variety of fruits, vegetables, and cereals, together with adequate amounts of such protein foods as milk and milk products, eggs and meats, will maintain health.

A few people develop severe allergic (hypersensitive) manifestations if they eat certain foods. Some find that strawberries cause such a response. In others, shellfish cause a reaction resembling poisoning. However, the great majority of people can eat any food without such a reaction. The most common causes of temporary digestive disturbances are overeating, bacterial contamination and virus infections.

SUMMARY

1. **Digestive system as a whole.**
   A. Functions: digestion and absorption.
   B. Components: alimentary canal, accessory organs.
2. **Alimentary canal.**
   A. Mouth, or oral cavity.
      (1) Structures.
          (a) Tongue.
          (b) Teeth: deciduous and permanent.
          (c) Salivary glands: parotid, submandibular (submaxillary), sublingual.
      (2) Diseases: gingivitis, stomatitis, pyorrhea, caries, mumps.
   B. Swallowing tubes and their accessories.
      (1) Pharynx (throat).
      (2) Uvula.
      (3) Epiglottis.
      (4) Esophagus ("gullet"). Has peristaltic action.
      (5) From swallowing tubes to anus, alimentary canal is lined with mucous membrane; has involuntary muscle for peristaltic action.
   C. Stomach.
      (1) Characteristics and accessory structures.
          (a) Cardiac valve (guards entrance to stomach).
          (b) Stomach a storage pouch and churn (for chyme).
          (c) Rugae (folds in mucosa).
          (d) Juice contains hydrochloric acid and enzymes.
          (e) Pyloric valve (sphincter)—exit from stomach.
      (2) Disorders of stomach and accessory structures.
          (a) Heartburn and vomiting.
          (b) Hyperacidity and hypoacidity.
          (c) Stomach cancer.
          (d) Peptic ulcer (emotional factors a cause).
          (e) Pyloric stenosis.
   D. Small intestine.
      (1) Divisions: duodenum, jejunum, ileum.
      (2) Digestive juices and sources.
          (a) Intestinal juice (own secretion).
          (b) Bile from liver through common bile duct (no enzymes).
          (c) Pancreatic juice from pancreas via pancreatic duct.

(3) Absorption: through villi.
    (a) Most food materials absorbed in blood capillaries.
    (b) Some fats absorbed in lacteals (lymphatic).
(4) Digestion: review table of enzymes.
  E. Large intestine.
    (1) Has no enzymes. Water absorption occurs through walls.
    (2) Ileocecal valve (sphincter).
    (3) Cecum and appendix.
    (4) Colon (ascending, transverse, descending, and sigmoid parts).
    (5) Rectum and anal canal, surrounded by anal sphincter.
  F. Intestinal disorders.
    (1) Gastritis and enteritis (inflammations of stomach and intestines).
    (2) Diarrhea (a symptom).
    (3) Dysentery (bacillary or amebic).
    (4) Spastic and flaccid constipation.

3. **Accessory structures.**
  A. Liver and its diseases
    (1) Liver has 9 major functions.
    (2) Hepatitis may be epidemic.
    (3) Cirrhosis results in excessive fluid in abdomen.
    (4) Cancer metastasizes to liver.
  B. Gallbladder and its diseases.
    (1) Gallbladder a storage pouch for bile; discharges bile when needed.
    (2) Cholecystitis means inflammation of gallbladder.
    (3) Cholelithiasis means gallstones.
    (4) Biliary colic is due to spasm of bile duct.
  C. Pancreas.
    (1) Produces insulin (regulates use of sugar in cells).
    (2) Produces pancreatic juice (3 enzymes).
    (3) Acute pancreatitis: pancreas digests itself.

4. **The peritoneum.**
  A. Serous membrane lining abdominal wall and covering abdominal organs.
  B. Peritoneal structures: mesentery, greater omentum, lesser omentum.
  C. Disorders: peritonitis, ascites.

5. **Nutrition.**
  A. Balanced diet necessary for health.
  B. Malnutrition: inadequate nutrition.
  C. Three basic foods: protective, protein, energy.
  D. Most food combinations harmless.
  E. A minority of people allergic to some foods.

QUESTIONS AND PROBLEMS
1. Trace the path of an indigestible object from the mouth through all parts of the alimentary canal to the outside, and tell what happens on the way.

2. Differentiate between deciduous and permanent teeth as to kinds and numbers of the 2 sets.
3. What is the pharynx? What spaces connect with it?
4. How would you distinguish between "stomach" and "abdomen"?
5. What is peristalsis? Name some structures in which it occurs.
6. Name and describe the purposes of the acid in the stomach juice.
7. Describe the process of absorption.
8. What are the principal enzymes, and what is their origin? What does each do?
9. Name several diseases which involve the organs of digestion.
10. Describe what happens in the formation of a peptic ulcer. Where do such occur?
11. What is an important symptom of stomach cancer?
12. What is the mesentery and where is it located? The greater and lesser omenta? What is the principal disease of the peritoneum?
13. In what ways are the tonsils and the appendix alike?
14. What constitutes a balanced diet? What are some examples of food fallacies?
15. What are the most important causes of indigestion?

CHAPTER 16

RESPIRATION

Purposes and meaning of breathing ▪ Pathway for air ▪ Normal and abnormal respiration ▪ Disorders involving the mucous membranes of air pathway ▪ How infection spreads ▪ Colds, influenza and pneumonia ▪ Tuberculosis and lung cancer ▪ Pleurisy and some allergic disorders ▪ Ventilation ▪ Special equipment.

RESPIRATION

The word "respiration" means "to breathe again," and the fundamental purpose of breathing is to supply oxygen to the individual tissue cells and to remove their gaseous waste product, carbon dioxide. Respiration has 2 aspects; the first is that which takes place only in the lungs, where oxygen from the outside air enters the blood, and carbon dioxide is taken off from the blood to be breathed into the outside air. This aspect is known as **external respiration.** The second aspect is called **internal respiration.** Internal respiration refers to the gas exchanges within the body cells. Oxygen leaves the blood and enters the cells at the same time that carbon dioxide leaves the cells and enters the blood. Internal respiration also is known as **cellular respiration** (see Fig. 65).

The respiratory system is an intricate arrangement of spaces and passageways which serve to conduct air into the lungs. These spaces include the **nasal cavities;** the **pharynx,** which is common to the digestive and respiratory systems; the voice box, or **larynx** (lar′inks); the windpipe, or **trachea** (tra′ke-ah), and the **lungs** themselves, with their tubes and air sacs. The entire system might be thought of as a pathway for air between the atmosphere and the blood.

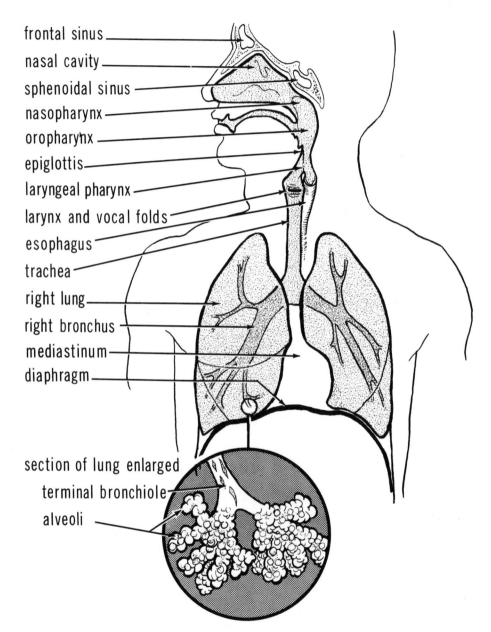

frontal sinus
nasal cavity
sphenoidal sinus
nasopharynx
oropharynx
epiglottis
laryngeal pharynx
larynx and vocal folds
esophagus
trachea
right lung
right bronchus
mediastinum
diaphragm

section of lung enlarged
terminal bronchiole
alveoli

FIG. 64. The respiratory tract.

THE RESPIRATORY SYSTEM

NASAL CAVITIES

Air makes its initial entrance into the body through the openings in the nose called the **nostrils.** Immediately within are the 2 spaces known as the **nasal cavities,** located between the roof of the mouth and the cranium (the chamber that contains the brain). These 2 spaces are separated from each other by a partition, the **nasal septum.** The septum and the walls of the nasal cavities are constructed of bone covered with mucous membrane. At the side (lateral) walls of each nasal cavity are 3 projections called the **conchae** (kong'ke). The conchae greatly increase the surface over which the air must travel on its way through the nasal cavities.

The lining of the nasal cavities contains many blood vessels; hence it is described as a **vascular membrane.** The blood brings heat and moisture to the mucosa. As much as a quart of liquid secretion is believed to be produced daily by this membrane. The advantages of breathing through the nasal cavities over breathing through the mouth are due to the various changes effected on the air as it comes in contact with the parts of the nose, particularly the lining. These changes include:

1. The removal of foreign bodies, such as dust particles and pathogens, which are either strained out by the hairs of the nostrils or are caught in the surface mucus.

2. The warming of the air by the blood in the vascular mucosa.

3. The moistening of the air by the liquid secretion.

The sum of these changes amounts to a kind of air-conditioning in a very real sense.

Also included in the discussion of the nasal cavities are the **sinuses,** which are small cavities, lined with mucous membrane, in the bones of the skull. The sinuses communicate with the nasal cavities, and they are highly susceptible to infection (see Chap. 9).

Another feature of the nasal cavities is a small duct communicating indirectly with the glands that produce tears. This is the **nasolacrimal** (na-zo-lak're-mal) **duct,** and its presence explains why the nose runs when the tears flow freely.

The nasal cavities also contain the nerves and other structures which give us the sense of smell.

THE PHARYNX

The muscular pharynx serves as a passageway for foods and liquids into the digestive system, and for air into the respiratory tract. The upper portion located immediately behind the nasal cavity is called the **nasopharynx** (na-zo-far'inks). The middle section located behind the mouth is called the **oropharynx** (o-ro-far'inks); and finally the lowest portion is the **laryngeal** (lah-rin'je-al) **pharynx.** This last section opens into 2 spaces:

1. The air passageway into the larynx, which is toward the front.
2. The food path, toward the back (dorsally), entering the esophagus.

THE LARYNX

The **larynx,** or voice box, is located between the pharynx and the windpipe. It has a framework of cartilage which protrudes in the front of the neck and sometimes is referred to as the Adam's apple. The larynx is considerably larger in the male than in the female; hence the Adam's apple is much more prominent in the male. At the upper end of the larynx are the **vocal folds.** These cordlike structures serve in the production of speech. They are set into vibration by the flow of air from the lung. It is the difference in the size of the larynx that accounts for the characteristic male and female voices. Because a man's larynx is larger than a woman's, his voice is lower in pitch. The nasal cavities, the sinuses and the pharynx all serve as resonating chambers for speech, just as does the cabinet for a radio loudspeaker.

The space between these 2 vocal cords is called the **glottis** (glot'is), and the little leaf-shaped structure that closes this opening during swallowing is called the **epiglottis** (ep-e-glot'is). By the action of the epiglottis food is kept out of the remainder of the respiratory tract.

THE WINDPIPE, OR TRACHEA

The **trachea** (tra'ke-ah) is a tube that extends from the lower edge of the voice box to the center of the chest behind the heart. It has a framework of cartilage to keep it open. These cartilages, shaped somewhat like a tiny horseshoe or the letter C, are placed near each other along the entire length of the trachea. All the open sections of these cartilages are at the back part so that the esophagus can bulge into this region during swallowing. The purpose of the trachea is to conduct air to and from the lungs.

THE BRONCHI

Near the center of the chest behind the heart the trachea divides into 2 **bronchi** (brong'ki). These are the 2 main air tubes entering the lungs, one on each side. The right bronchus is considerably larger in diameter than the left and extends downward in a more vertical direction. Therefore, if a foreign body is inhaled, it is likely to enter the right lung. Each bronchus enters the lung at a notch or depression called the **hilus** (hi'lus) or **hilum** (hi'lum). At this same region the blood vessels and the nerves also connect with the lung.

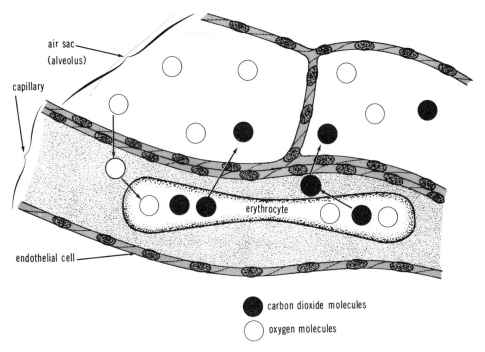

air sac
(alveolus)

capillary

erythrocyte

endothelial cell

● carbon dioxide molecules

○ oxygen molecules

Fig. 65. Diagram to represent the diffusion of molecules through the membranes of cells and throughout the air in the air sac and the blood in the capillary.

THE LUNGS

The **lungs** are the organs in which external respiration takes place; that is, where blood and air meet through the medium of the extremely thin and delicate lung tissues. There are 2 lungs, set side by side in the thoracic cavity, and each of them is constructed in the following manner:

As soon as each bronchus enters the lung at the hilum, it immediately subdivides. These branches or subdivisions of the bronchi resemble the branches of a tree, hence the common name, **bronchial tree.** Each individual bronchial tube subdivides again and again, forming progressively smaller divisions. The smallest are called **bronchioles** (brong'ke-oles). These tubes of assorted sizes contain small bits of cartilage which give firmness to the walls and serve to hold the tubes open so that air can pass in and out easily. However, as the tubes become smaller, the cartilage also decreases in amount until finally, in the most minute subdivisions there is no cartilage at all.

At the end of each of the smallest subdivisions of the bronchial tree called **terminal bronchioles,** there is a whole cluster of air sacs, resembling a bunch of grapes, known as **alveoli** (al-ve'o-li). Each air sac is made of 1 cell layer of squamous (flat) epithelium. This very thin wall provides an easy passage for the gases entering and leaving the blood which is contained in the millions of tiny capillaries of the alveoli. Some estimates indicate that there are some 700,000,000 of these alveoli in the human lung. The resulting surface in contact with gases approximates 75 square yards, about 3 times as much lung tissue as is necessary for life. Surely nature has allowed an ample margin of safety! Because of the many air spaces, the lung is light; and normally a piece of lung tissue dropped into a glass of water will float.

It will be recalled that the pulmonary circuit brings the blood to and from the lungs. The blood passes through the capillaries of the alveoli, where the gas exchange takes place.

THE LUNG CAVITIES

The lungs occupy a considerable portion of the chest (thoracic) cavity, which is separated from the abdominal cavity by the muscular partition known as the **diaphragm.** Each lung is enveloped in a sac of serous membrane called the **pleura;** hence there are 2 pleurae. The chest cavity is lined with this membrane also, this layer being known as the parietal pleura, while the lung covering is called the visceral pleura. Between the lungs is a space called the **mediastinum** (me-de-ah-sti'num), containing the heart among other things.

The entire thoracic cavity is flexible, capable of expanding and contracting along with the lungs. Its interior is well sealed off from the outside by its layer of membrane; and, as we shall see, this is a feature of the mechanism of breathing.

PHYSIOLOGY OF ~~RESPIRATION~~ *Ventilation*

Respiration may be described in another way as the mechanical process of breathing in and out, a function which involves both the respiratory system and the muscles of respiration. The 2 phases of breathing are:

1. **Inhalation,** during which air is drawn into the lungs.
2. **Exhalation,** which refers to the expulsion of air from the alveoli.

Inhalation is the active phase of breathing, since it is then that the muscles of respiration, notably the diaphragm, contract in order to enlarge the chest cavity. The dome of the diaphragm is pulled downward, a partial vacuum is formed in the sealed pleural spaces, causing a pull on the elastic lung tissue so that air rushes in to fill the air sacs.

Exhalation is the inactive phase, since the muscles of respiration then relax, allowing the elastic tissues in the thorax to recoil and the abdominal organs to press upward against the diaphragm. Air is pushed outward by the weight of the chest wall and the upward boost of the abdominal viscera.

RESPIRATORY RATES

Normal rates of breathing vary from 12 to 25 times per minute, and are normally higher in children than in adults. The term **hyperpnea** (hi-perp-ne'ah) means "over-breathing due to abnormally rapid respiratory movements." **Apnea** (ap'ne-ah) means "a temporary cessation of breathing." It may be compensatory following forced respiration. In some fevers the respiratory rate increases in direct proportion to the increase in temperature, while in other cases there is no correlation between the respiratory rates and the temperature. It is important that the nurse check respiratory rates and record them properly. Observations should be done in such a way that the patient is unaware that a check is being made.

THE CONTROL OF BREATHING

Breathing is controlled by the respiratory center of the brain, which is located in the stem portion, called the **medulla** (me-dul'ah), immediately above the spinal cord. From this center, nerve fibers extend down into the spinal cord. From the neck part of the cord these nerve fibers continue through the **phrenic** (fren'ik) **nerve** to the diaphragm. Unlike the heart, the diaphragm does not continue to work if it is cut off from its nerve supply. If one nerve is cut, the diaphragm on that one side is paralyzed. This is done in certain cases of tuberculosis in order to rest the lung on the diseased side. This operation is called a **phrenicotomy** (fren-i-kot'o-me).

The diaphragm and the other muscles of respiration are voluntary in the sense that they can be regulated by messages from the higher brain centers. It is possible for a person deliberately to breathe more rapidly or more slowly, or to hold his breath and not breathe at all for a time. Usually we breathe without thinking about it, while the respiratory center in the medulla does the controlling. This center is governed by variations in the chemistry of the blood. If there is an increase in carbon dioxide in the blood, the cells of the respiratory center are stimulated; and they in turn send impulses down the phrenic nerves to the diaphragm.

ABNORMAL RESPIRATION

The following is a list of terms designating various abnormalities of respiration. They are not specific diseases, but are symptoms of disease or some other injurious condition.

1. **Anoxia** (an-ok'se-ah), which means "lack of oxygen." Certain tissues, such as the brain, may be permanently damaged because of oxygen lack.

2. **Asphyxia** (as-fik'se-ah), a term indicating an increase in carbon dioxide in the tissues accompanied by an oxygen deficiency. Synonymous with suffocation.

3. **Dyspnea** (disp'ne-ah), which means "difficult or labored breathing."

4. **Cheyne-Stokes** (chane-stokes) respiration, which is a type of rhythmical variation in the depth of respiratory movements found in certain critically ill or unconscious patients.

5. **Suffocation,** which refers to any stoppage of respiration. It can result, for example, from strangulation, inhalation of a foreign object, sleeping with the face buried in a pillow (as infants sometimes do), drowning, or overinhalation of smoke. Suffocation can refer also to the asphyxia that it causes.

6. **Cyanosis** (si-ah-no'sis), which refers to a bluish color of the skin and visible mucous membranes caused by an insufficient amount of oxygen in the blood.

Cyanosis may result from asphyxiation or suffocation, but it also may be caused by other factors. Heart disease can cause a lack of circulation through the lungs with a resulting insufficient oxygenation.

DISORDERS OF THE RESPIRATORY SYSTEM

SINUSITIS AND NASAL POLYPS

"I have a sinus" is an expression many people use to indicate disease of the sinuses. The sinuses are located close to the nasal cavities, and in one case near the ear. Infection may easily travel into these sinuses from the mouth, the nose and the throat along the mucous membrane lining, and the resulting inflammation is called **sinusitis.** Long-standing, or chronic, sinus infection may cause changes in the epithelial cells, resulting in tumor formation. Some of these growths have a grape-like appearance and cause obstruction of the air pathway. These tumors are called **polyps** (pol'ips).

DEVIATED SEPTUM

The partition separating the 2 nasal spaces from each other is called the nasal septum. Since many of us have minor structural defects, it is not surprising that the nasal septum is rarely exactly in the midline. If it is markedly to one side, it is described as a **deviated septum.** In this condition one nasal space may be considerably smaller than the other. If such a person has an attack of hay fever or becomes the victim of a cold with the accompanying swelling of the mucosa, this smaller nasal cavity may be completely closed. Sometimes the septum is curved in such a way that both nasal cavities are occluded, forcing the victim to breathe through the mouth. Such an occlusion also may prevent proper drainage from the sinuses and aggravate a case of sinusitis.

NOSEBLEED

The most common cause of nosebleed, also called **epistaxis** (ep-e-stak′sis), is an injury or a blow to the nose. Other causes include inflammation and ulceration such as may occur following a persistent discharge from a sinusitis. Growths including polyps also can be a cause of epistaxis. Sometimes an abnormally high blood pressure will cause the vessels in the nasal lining to break resulting in varying degrees of hemorrhage. To stop the nosebleed, the victim should remain quiet with the head slightly elevated. Pressure applied to the nostril of the bleeding side, as well as cold compresses over the nose, usually are helpful. In some cases it may be necessary to insert a plug into the bleeding side in order to encourage adequate clotting. If these methods fail, a physician should be consulted.

ADENOIDS

The pharyngeal tonsil, a mass of lymphoid tissue located in the upper back part of the nasopharynx, may become enlarged and infected. It is then called **adenoids,** and often causes mouth breathing, coughing and earache, and may produce a dull facial expression. The only effective treatment is surgical removal, or **adenoidectomy** (ad-e-noid-ek′to-me).

THE SPREAD OF INFECTION

In the introductory chapter on membranes it was pointed out that very often membranes act as pathways for the spread of disease. The mucosa of the respiratory tract is an excellent example of such a pathway; it serves as one of the most important portals of entry for disease-producing organisms. This transfer of disease organisms from the respiratory system of one human being to another occurs much more rapidly in crowded areas such as schools, auditoriums, theaters, churches and prisons. Droplets from one sneeze may be loaded with many billions of disease-producing organisms. To a certain extent the mucous membranes can protect themselves by producing larger quantities of mucus. The runny nose, an unpleasant symptom of the common cold, is an attempt on the part of nature to wash away the pathogens and so protect the deeper tissues from further invasion by the infection. If the resistance of the mucous membrane is reduced, however, the infection may travel along the membrane into the nasal sinuses, into the middle ear, or down into the lung. Infections also may spread from the respiratory tract to the digestive system, or the reverse, because of the continuity of the mucosa.

Among the infections transmitted through the respiratory passageways are the common cold, diphtheria, chickenpox, measles, influenza, smallpox and tuberculosis. Any infection which is confined to the nose, the throat, the larynx, or the trachea is called an **upper respiratory infection** (often recorded simply as URI). In children's wards in hospitals the records show that the great majority of patients with these diseases had first developed symptoms of an upper respiratory infection. Very often, too, such an infection can precipitate the onset of such a serious disease as rheumatic fever.

The respiratory passageways may become infected one by one as the organisms travel along the lining membrane. The disorder is named according to the part involved, as for example:

1. **Rhinitis** (ri-ni'tis), which means inflammation of the nasal mucosa.

2. **Pharyngitis** (far-in-ji'tis), which is inflammation of the pharynx, referred to also as sore throat.

3. **Laryngitis** (lar-in-ji'tis), which is inflammation of the larynx, and is often characterized by hoarseness.

4. **Tracheitis** (tra-ke-i'tis), or inflammation of the windpipe.

5. **Bronchitis** (brong-ki'tis), which includes infection of the bronchi and their many subdivisions in the lungs.

6. **Pneumonia,** in which the lung alveoli are involved.

THE COMMON COLD

The common cold is the most widespread of all respiratory diseases—or any communicable disease, for that matter. The cause is a virus which is very easily spread about; and one characteristic of the cold virus is that it may fail to produce an immunity, so that some persons suffer one cold after another. Medical science has yet to produce a method of preventing the common cold, although there are preventive inoculations which may be helpful for one person but ineffective for another.

The symptoms of the common cold are familiar: first the swollen and inflamed mucosa of the nose and the throat, then the copious discharge of watery fluid from the nose, and finally the thick and ropy discharge which occurs when the cold is subsiding. The scientific name for the common cold is **acute coryza** (ko-ri'zah); the word "coryza" also can mean simply "a nasal discharge."

A discharge from the nasal cavities may be a symptom not only of the common cold; it also may stem from sinusitis or be an important forerunner of a more serious disease. Another word used to designate the discharge from an inflamed mucous membrane (especially the mucosa of the air passages) is **catarrh** (kah-tar'); this word, however, is practically obsolete as a scientific term.

The notion that all nasal mucus is undesirable is wrong. Normal mucous secretions are valuable and are required to keep the tissues moist as well as to help protect the cells against invasion by pathogens. The idea that excess secretion is caused by diets of eggs, milk, or any other food has no basis in fact.

INFLUENZA

Influenza, or "flu," is an acute contagious disease characterized by an inflammatory condition of the upper respiratory tract accompanied by generalized aches and pains. It is caused by a virus and may spread to the sinuses as well as downward to the lungs. Inflammation of the trachea and the bronchi causes the characteristic cough of influenza, and the general infection brings about an extremely weakened condition of the victim. The great danger of influenza is its tendency to develop into a particularly severe form of pneumonia. At intervals in history there have been tremendous epidemics of influenza in which millions of people have died. Vaccines have been effective, though the immunity is of short duration.

PNEUMONIA

Pneumonia is an inflammation of the alveoli and may be caused by a diplococcus known as the **pneumococcus,** although pneumonia also can be caused by a streptococcus, a staphylococcus or a virus. Any or all of these pathogens may be carried by a healthy person in the mucosa of the upper respiratory tract. If the person remains in good condition, these pathogens may be carried for an indefinite period with no ill effect. However, if the individual's resistance to infection is lowered, the pathogens then may invade the tissues and work their damage. Exposure to inclement weather for long periods of time, alcoholism, malnutrition, a severe injury or other debilitating (de-bil'i-ta-ting) or weakening conditions may cause a susceptibility to pneumonia.

There are 2 main kinds of pneumonia as determined by the method of lung involvement and other factors. These are:

1. **Lobar pneumonia,** in which an entire lobe of the lung is infected at one time. The organism usually is a pneumococcus, although other pathogens also may cause this disease.

2. **Bronchopneumonia,** in which the disease process is scattered here and there throughout the lung. The cause may be a staphylococcus or a virus. Bronchopneumonia most often is secondary to an infection or to some agent which has lowered the individual's resistance to disease. This is the more common form of pneumonia.

Lobar pneumonia may develop suddenly in an apparently well individual, often in a fairly young hale-appearing male. Bronchopneumonia, on the other hand, is much more common in the very young and the very old.

There is a less serious type of pneumonia known as **atypical pneumonia** (a form of virus pneumonia) that differs from the forms already discussed in that the air sacs of the lungs are probably not involved; the infection may extend only as far as the minute subdivisions of the bronchi. Virus pneumonia is rarely fatal. Some do not consider it a true pneumonia at all. X-rays do show lung involvement in some cases, however.

A characteristic of most types of pneumonia is the formation of a fluid, or **exudate,** in the infected alveoli; this fluid consists chiefly of serum and pus cells, products of infection. Some red blood cells may be present, as indicated by red streaks in the sputum. Sometimes so many air sacs become filled with fluid that the victim finds it hard to absorb enough oxygen to maintain life. The more of these alveoli that become affected, the more difficult respiration becomes; and a double pneumonia involving the lower lobes of both lungs frequently has been fatal. Antibiotic drugs have greatly improved the outlook for pneumonia victims. These drugs, combined with rest, adequate nursing care, and oxygen therapy, have returned most pneumonia patients to health.

TUBERCULOSIS

Tuberculosis is an inflammation caused by the bacillus *Mycobacterium tuberculosis.* It is still one of the most serious and costly of present-day illnesses and is the number one killer in the communicable disease group. Briefly, the action of the tuberculosis bacillus is this: when the bacilli invade a tissue, the cells of the tissue proceed to build a protective capsule about the invading organism, thus effectively isolating it from the rest of the body. This tiny mass, or capsule, of new tissue is called a **tubercle** (tu'ber-kl). If the resistance of the body is high, the imprisoned organisms may eventually die, and the tubercle then is transformed into a small harmless mass of fibrous tissue. If, on the other hand, the resistance of the body is lowered, the tissue of the tubercle may become necrotic (i.e., its cells will die), and the dead tissue will become a cheesy mass, a process called **caseation** (ka-se-a'shun). Eventually the cheesy material is changed to a liquid, and a cavity remains where there was once living tissue. As caseation occurs, the bacilli which once were walled off within the tubercles are liberated; they spread to other parts of the body by means of the blood or the lymphatic system, and the destructive process is repeated.

The lungs, with the pleura, are the organs affected most often by tuberculosis. The bacillus can be spread in a number of ways, chiefly by means of inhalation. The sputum deposited by a person who carries the organism dries out; and the bacilli, which are extremely hardy, are carried about for long periods of time in the dust of the air, whence they are inhaled by another individual. This organism withstands exposure to many disinfectants, but it is vulnerable to sunlight. Therefore, we might expect to find the greatest frequency of tuberculosis to be among the poorer inhabitants of the large cities, where disease and malnutrition are common and where there is a maximum of crowding and a minimum of fresh air and sunlight.

A reservoir of contagion among the elderly is another important means by which tuberculosis is spread. For example, a grandmother may have recovered from a mild attack in her youth. With advancing age decreased resistance may result in the breaking down of a sealed-off tubercular lesion, so that it now opens into a bronchial tube and thus to the outside. The grandmother may show little or no evidence of the disease but nevertheless may spread the organisms with every cough or sneeze. An infant cared for by this grandparent may receive repeated small doses of the disease organisms, which may eventually cause a generalized tuberculosis. The child may die of a tuberculous meningitis or of a tuberculous pneumonia, while the grandmother may live on for many years without realizing that she is the source of the contagion.

Besides the human type of tuberculosis organism, involving the lungs for the most part, there is also the **bovine** type of tubercle bacillus, which may be transferred from cattle to the human via milk. Inspection of cattle and pasteurization of milk has nearly eliminated this type of tuberculosis. When it does occur, it is more probable that it will involve the digestive tract.

In addition to the lungs and digestive tract many other organs may become infected by tubercle organisms. The lymph nodes in the thorax, especially those surrounding the trachea and the bronchi, frequently are involved. Tuberculous pleurisy (i.e., inflammation of the pleura) with fluid formation is fairly common. The fluid may collect in the pleural space, and such a collection is referred to as an **effusion** (e-fu'zhun). Over a period of time it may be absorbed if it is not removed artificially to relieve the lung compression. Chronic hoarseness may be due to tuberculosis (or cancer) of the larynx. Other organs which may be infected by tubercle organisms include the kidneys, certain tubes of the reproductive system, and in children particularly, the bones of the vertebral column. Occasionally vast numbers of the organisms may enter the bloodstream and cause a rapidly fatal tuberculosis sometimes called galloping consumption.

The most important factor in the prevention of tuberculosis is the removal of infected patients from the surroundings of any susceptible person. Tuberculosis is a reportable disease, and those who are afflicted with an active infection should be isolated. Those who must work with or care for tuberculous persons may protect themselves to a certain degree by using appropriate masks and observing other standard precautionary techniques.

Drugs are used quite successfully in many cases of tuberculosis. However, this **chemotherapy** (ke-mo-ther'ah-pe) may have the undesirable effect of producing resistant strains of bacteria. These resistant organisms can be transmitted to additional victims, who then cannot be treated effectively with these particular medications. Best results have been obtained by the use of a combination of several drugs, plus prompt, intensive and uninterrupted treatment once such a program is begun. Such therapy is usually continued for a minimum of 12 to 18 months, therefore close supervision by the doctor and the paramedical personnel is important. Adverse drug reactions are rather common, necessitating changes in the drug combinations.

A variety of other measures may be undertaken in the treatment of tuberculosis. Where the lungs are seriously involved, the first principle is to allow the affected lung to rest. One way of accomplishing this is to perform an **artificial pneumothorax** (nu-mo-tho'raks). This procedure consists of admitting air into the pleural cavity between the lung and the wall of the chest. This causes the lung to collapse and remain idle in spite of the normal breathing movements of the other lung. If for some reason this procedure fails or is impractical, a more drastic means of collapsing the lung is by performing a **thoracoplasty** (tho'rah-ko-plas-te), an operation in which several ribs are removed. Still another way of immobilizing a lung is by resorting to a **phrenicotomy,** the nerve-severing operation mentioned previously in this chapter. In addition to restriction of lung movement and drug therapy, bed rest is often prescribed in the treatment of tuberculosis.

LUNG CANCER

The death rate due to cancer of the lungs has increased 500 per cent in males and has doubled in females during the last 25 years. It is considerably higher in urban and industrial areas than in rural districts. There are many possible causes, but which are most blameworthy is still controversial. Those factors which have been mentioned most frequently are the presence of foreign particles and other irritants in the air (smoke particles, smog, exhaust fumes, etc.), and the smoking of cigarettes and cigars.

Sometimes cases of lung cancer are discovered at the time an x-ray is taken for the purpose of detecting tuberculosis. Too often, however, a current emphasis upon the danger of exposure to radiation from x-ray machines can frighten people away from routine chest x-rays and thus prevent an early diagnosis of lung cancer. Early detection is absolutely essential if any possibility of a cure is to be maintained. Modern x-ray machines in competent hands pose such slight danger, at least to those over 40 years of age, that this would be much more than offset by the advantages of discovering a tumor while it is still small enough to be completely removed.

A common form of lung cancer is **bronchogenic** (brong-ko-jen'ik) **carcinoma,** so-called because the malignancy originates in a bronchus. The tumor may grow until the bronchus is blocked, cutting off the supply of air to that lung. The lung then collapses, and the secretions trapped in the lung spaces become infected, with a resulting pneumonia or the formation of a lung abscess. Such a lung cancer also can spread to cause secondary growths in the lymph nodes of the chest and neck as well as in the brain and other parts of the body. The only treatment that offers a possibility of cure, before secondary growths have had time to form, is to remove the lung completely. This operation is called a **pneumonectomy** (nu-mo-nek'to-me).

Malignant tumors of the stomach, the breast, the prostate gland and other organs may spread to the lungs, causing many secondary growths throughout the lung.

PLEURISY

Pleurisy (ploor'i-se) is inflammation of the pleura, and it usually accompanies a lung infection—particularly pneumonia and tuberculosis. This condition can be quite painful, because the inflammation produces a sticky exudate which roughens the pleura of both the lung and the chest wall; when the 2 surfaces rub together during respiration, the roughness causes acute irritation. If the 2 surfaces stick together, this condition is called an **adhesion** (ad-he'zhun). Infection of the pleura also causes an abnormal flow of pleural fluid. This may accumulate between the 2 layers in such large amounts that the lung will be compressed, so that the patient cannot obtain enough air. Removal of the fluid by means of a syringe is often necessary. An abnormal accumulation of pleural fluid is called a pleural effusion, as we saw in the discussion of tuberculosis.

HAY FEVER AND ASTHMA

Sensitivity to plant pollens, to dust, to certain foods, and to other allergens may lead to **hay fever** or **asthma** or both. Hay fever is characterized by a watery discharge from the eyes and nose, and about half of all hay fever attacks end in asthma. In asthma the symptoms usually are due to a spasm of the involuntary musculature of the bronchial tube walls. This spasm constricts the tubes so that the victim cannot exhale easily. He experiences a sense of suffocation and has labored breathing **(dyspnea).** Much has been written about the part that psychological factors play in the causation of asthma. It would seem advisable to leave the decision concerning the possible causes in the hands of the family physician or the specialist he may recommend. Individuals vary considerably, and most cases of asthma present a multiplicity of problems.

One great difficulty in the treatment of hay fever or asthma is to isolate the particular substance to which the patient is allergic. Usually a number of skin tests are given, but the results of these are far from conclusive in most cases.

SOME PRACTICAL ASPECTS OF VENTILATION

People usually devote a great deal of thought to the food that they take into their bodies but very little to the air that they breathe. Consideration of the latter will go a long way toward the maintenance of health. So many ideas concerning ventilation are erroneous. There are fresh-air fiends who open windows at night allowing cold air to chill their bodies unduly. This habit may be a carry-over from the days when wood stoves or gas heaters had no vent to the outside, and it was important to prevent an accumulation of deadly carbon monoxide and other gases in the room. On the other hand, there are others who seemingly are not happy outside of an unbearably stuffy, unventilated and overheated room. Scientific studies have shown that the factors that make air healthy and comfortable are:

1. Enough coolness to remove some body heat without chilling.

2. Avoidance of drafts, which have been shown to cause disturbances within the body that cause a predisposition to colds and other infections.

3. Enough circulation of air to remove unpleasant odors or other pollutants.

Various mechanisms for modifying or conditioning the air have been devised. Most of the emphasis has been on the alteration of temperature, the air being heated if the outside temperature is low and cooled if the outside air is too warm. Modern heaters are vented so that noxious gases do not enter the living quarters, and in many areas laws have been passed prohibiting the installation of unvented heaters. Nevertheless, deaths from the escape of poisonous gases from heaters still are all too common. The general public should be better informed on the whole field of ventilation and air conditioning.

Desirable modification of air includes more than merely heating or cooling it. The humidity should be maintained at the proper level, and some effective means of filtering the air should be provided. Air filters, needless to say, should be cleaned regularly; otherwise they are worse than useless. An acceptable air conditioner should be able to maintain adequate air circulation without blowing a gale and chilling everyone within its range.

SPECIAL EQUIPMENT FOR RESPIRATORY TRACT TREATMENTS

The **bronchoscope** (brong′ko-skope) is a tubular instrument containing tiny mirrors so arranged that the doctor can inspect the bronchi and the larger bronchial tubes. The bronchoscope is passed into the respiratory tract via the mouth and the pharynx. It may be used to remove foreign bodies or to inspect the tubes for tumors or other evidence of disease. Children inhale a variety of objects such as pins, beans, pieces of nuts, and small coins, all of which are removed with the aid of a bronchoscope. If such things are left in the lung, an abscess or other serious complication may cause death.

Oxygen therapy is employed to maintain life when some condition prevents adequate oxygenation of the blood by natural means. Oxygen tents are closed-circuit kinds of apparatus which often include all the benefits of air conditioning. Nursing care should be planned so that many tasks are performed at one time in order to prevent excessive loss of oxygen. The temperature, as in the case of the best air conditioning, should not be too many degress different from the surrounding atmosphere in order to avoid shock to the patient when the canopy is opened. Visitors must not be allowed to smoke nor have smoking materials in their possession, since the danger of an explosive fire is a serious hazard near the oxygen tent. A few sparks could ignite all combustible material. The manufacturer's directions should be most carefully followed.

Another type of oxygen equipment, a mask, includes intermittent positive pressure devices that exert positive pressure during inhalation and then allow an easy exhalation. These units provide an automatic cycle of pressure exertion and release that is adjusted to the patient's rate of breathing. It is just as important to provide ease of exhalation to remove carbon dioxide as it is to assure an adequate supply of oxygen.

Suction apparatus for removing mucus or other substances from the respiratory tract also may be required. Usually these devices take the form of a drainage bottle, with one tube from it leading to the area to be drained, and another tube from the bottle leading to a suction machine. When the suction is applied, the drainage is made to flow from the patient's respiratory tract into the bottle.

A **tracheostomy** (tra-ke-os′to-me) **tube** is used if the pharynx or the larynx is obstructed. This is a small metal tube which is inserted through a cut made in the trachea, and it acts as an artificial air intake as well as an exhaust duct for the carbon dioxide. The operation for the installation of such a tube is called a tracheostomy. The word **tracheotomy** (tra-ke-ot′o-me) is used to refer to the incision into the trachea for the purpose of removing a growth or a foreign body, or for obtaining a specimen for a biopsy. Very often emergency tracheotomies are performed on children who have inhaled something large enough to block the respiratory passages; otherwise they would die in a very short time.

Artificial respiration is resorted to in cases where an individual has either temporarily or permanently lost the capacity to perform the normal motions of respiration. Such emergencies include smoke asphyxiation, electric shock, or drowning. Every first-aid manual has step-by-step illustrations of the technique of maintaining the respiratory movements of the thorax by applying pressure with the hands. Another technique of artificial respiration is the mouth-to-mouth method. A mechanical device that pumps oxygen into the lungs under pressure is called a **pulmotor.**

Patients with poliomyelitis sometimes are left with permanently paralyzed muscles, so that a **respirator,** or "iron lung," is employed to provide an outside means of maintaining respiratory movements. This is a metal chamber, variations of which either cover the chest or else encompass all of the patient with the exception of his head. The pressure within the respirator is changed rhythmically, much as the diaphragm changes the pressure within the thoracic cavity, and with the same result. The patient breathes normally with no effort on his own part.

SUMMARY

1. **Respiration.**
   A. Purpose: supply oxygen to tissues, remove carbon dioxide.
   B. Aspects.
      (1) External: gas exchange in lungs.
      (2) Internal: gas exchange in tissues.

2. **Respiratory system as a whole.**
   A. Nasal cavities: include sinuses, nasolacrimal duct.
   B. Pharynx (throat): passageway for both food and air.
   C. Larynx (voice box).
   D. Trachea (windpipe): conducts air to bronchi, lungs.
   E. Bronchi: 2 tubes branching at end of trachea; each to a lung.
   F. Bronchial tubes: subdivisions of bronchi in lungs.
   G. Bronchioles: smallest subdivisions of bronchial tree.
   H. Alveoli: air sacs where gas exchange occurs. Connected to terminal bronchioles. Contain capillaries of pulmonary circulation.
3. **Lung cavities.** Lungs occupy most of thoracic cavity. Both lungs covered by, and thoracic cavity lined with, pleura. Diaphragm separates thoracic and abdominal cavities. Space between lungs is mediastinum, containing heart and other organs.
4. **Physiology of respiration.**
   A. Phases of breathing: inhalation, exhalation.
   B. Rate: 12 to 25 times a minute.
   C. Control: by respiratory center in medulla, through phrenic nerves to diaphragm.
5. **Abnormal respiration:** anoxia, asphyxia, dyspnea, Cheyne-Stokes, suffocation, cyanosis.
6. **Disorders of respiratory system.**
   A. Sinusitis: inflammation of membrane lining of sinuses; may cause obstructing tumors (polyps).
   B. Deviated septum: may cause closure of a nasal cavity in infection; aggravate sinusitis.
   C. Nosebleed (epistaxis): many causes. Failure to stop of own accord may indicate something more serious.
   D. Adenoids: cause mouth breathing, coughing, earache.
   E. Spread of infection: upper respiratory infection can spread down mucosa, develop into more serious diseases. Progression of inflammation: rhinitis, pharyngitis, laryngitis, tracheitis, bronchitis, pneumonia.
   F. Common cold: caused by a virus; no sure prevention.
   G. Influenza: caused by virus. Can develop into pneumonia.
   H. Pneumonia: inflammation of alveoli.
      (1) Kinds.
         (a) Lobar (usually caused by pneumococcus, involves entire lobe of lung).
         (b) Brochopneumonia (caused by staphylococcus or virus. Lung involvement patchy).
         (c) Atypical (may not be true pneumonia. Air sacs probably not involved).
      (2) Characteristics: alveoli fill with exudate; blood in sputum; responds well to antibiotics.

I. Tuberculosis.
    (1) Cause: bacillus *Mycobacterium tuberculosis.*
    (2) Inhalation main method of transmission.
    (3) Bacillus forms tubercles; may or may not destroy tissue.
    (4) Pleurisy common.
    (5) Treatment: drugs, immobilization of lung, rest.
J. Lung cancer.
    (1) Common form: bronchogenic carcinoma.
    (2) Pneumonectomy may halt progress if done early.
K. Pleurisy: inflammation of pleura. Adhesions, fluid accumulation.
L. Hay fever and asthma. Latter may follow the former. Difficult to identify allergen.
7. **Ventilation.** Good ventilation includes coolness without chilling, avoidance of drafts, adequate air circulation.
8. **Special equipment:** bronchoscope, oxygen equipment, suction apparatus, tracheostomy tube, respirator.

QUESTIONS AND PROBLEMS

1. What is the purpose of respiration, and what are its 2 aspects?
2. Trace the pathway of air from the outside into the blood.
3. What are the advantages of breathing through the nose?
4. What are some causes of mouth breathing, and what should be done about them?
5. Describe the lung cavities.
6. Describe normal breathing, including: 2 phases, respiratory rates, mechanism of breathing and nerve control.
7. Name and describe 6 types of abnormal respiration.
8. What are: sinusitis, polyps, deviated septum. Effect of each?
9. What are some causes of nosebleed?
10. Describe some possible developments and complications of upper respiratory infections. Trace the course of infection down the respiratory tract and give the name for the inflammation of each area.
11. Describe: common cold, influenza.
12. Name the principal types of pneumonia with the causative organism. Describe the general effect of pneumonia.
13. Describe tuberculosis with respect to: cause, method of spread, internal effect of the organism, and methods of treatment.
14. What are some possible causes of lung cancer?
15. What is pleurisy? Its complications?
16. What do hay fever and asthma have in common?
17. Name 3 characteristics of ideal ventilation.
18. Name and describe 5 devices used in treatments of the respiratory tract.

CHAPTER 17

THE URINARY SYSTEM
AND ITS DISORDERS

A secretion that is an excretion ▪ Excretions and their mechanisms ▪ Kidneys, inside and out ▪ Functions and disorders of the
kidneys ▪ Dialysis and transplants ▪ Tubes that carry urine to
the bladder ▪ Bladder location and structure ▪ Function and
disease of the bladder ▪ Excretory tube ▪ Disorders of the urethra ▪ Normal urine and what is in it ▪ Abnormal urine substances and their significance.

The **urinary system** also is called the **excretory system,** and its job is to remove
certain waste products from the blood and eliminate them from the body.
What does the name of this system mean? The terms "elimination" and
"excretion" often are used interchangeably. Actually, we usually think of excretion
as the function of removing useless substances (i.e., the waste products of cell
metabolism) from the blood and the lymph, often by a type of cellular activity
similar to that of gland cells producing a **secretion.** For example, we often speak
of the secretory function of the kidney cells along with their excretory function.
Urine, then, is both a secretion and an excretion. On the other hand, **elimination**
indicates the actual emptying of the hollow organs in which these waste substances
have been temporarily stored. The kidney would then excrete, while the urinary
bladder eliminates. In the digestive system the liver would excrete bile (again by
a process of secretion) while the large intestine would eliminate this bile in the feces.
Here it may be of interest to summarize the chief excretory mechanisms of the
body, along with the various substances which they eliminate:
1. The urinary system: water, waste products containing nitrogen, and salts.
These are all contained in the urine. $\left(CO_2 \rightarrow H_2O \right)$
2. The digestive system: water, some salts, bile, and the residue of digestion.
These are all contained in the feces. $H_2O \ \tau \ stool$
3. The respiratory system: carbon dioxide and water. The latter appears as
vapor, as breathing on a windowpane will prove.

258

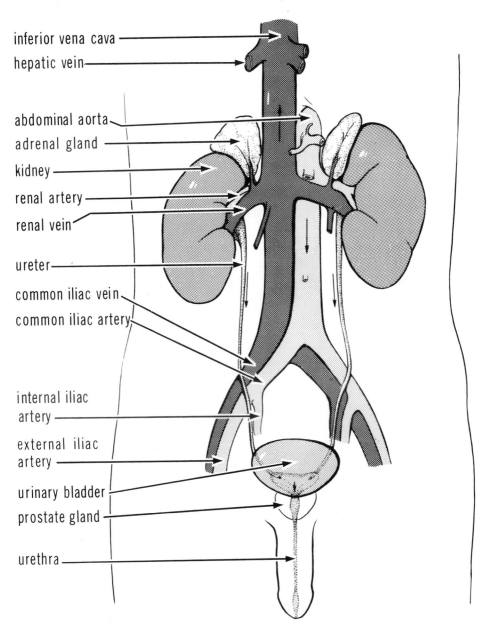

inferior vena cava

hepatic vein

abdominal aorta

adrenal gland

kidney

renal artery

renal vein

ureter

common iliac vein

common iliac artery

internal iliac
artery

external iliac
artery

urinary bladder

prostate gland

urethra

Fig. 66. The urinary system with blood vessels.

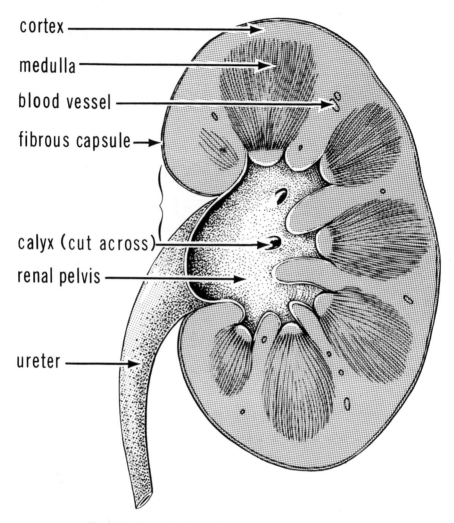

cortex

medulla

blood vessel

fibrous capsule

calyx (cut across)

renal pelvis

ureter

FIG. 67. Vertical (frontal) section through a kidney.

4. The skin, or integumentary system: water, small quantities of nitrogenous wastes and salts. These all appear in perspiration, though evaporation of water from the skin may go on most of the time without our being conscious of it.

This chapter will, of course, cover only the first of these systems. However, when we come to such a subject as the means by which the body maintains its delicate balance of water and various chemicals, other systems pertinent to the discussion will be referred to. No system of the body operates independently of the others, after all, in spite of its specialized functions. A study of the urinary system will reveal several of these interrelationships.

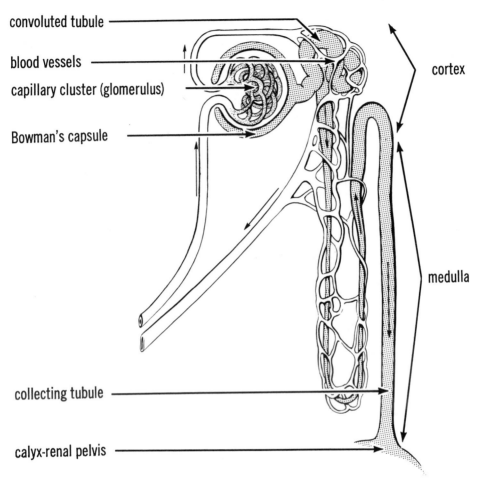

convoluted tubule

blood vessels

capillary cluster (glomerulus)

Bowman's capsule

cortex

medulla

collecting tubule

calyx-renal pelvis

FIG. 68. A simplified nephron.

ORGANS OF THE URINARY SYSTEM

The main parts of the urinary system are:

1. Two **kidneys,** which are glandular organs that are necessary for life. These are the organs which, in addition to other things, extract wastes from the blood.

2. Two **ureters** (u-re'ters), which conduct the secretion from the kidneys to the urinary bladder.

3. The single **urinary bladder,** a reservoir which receives the urine brought into it by the 2 ureters.

4. A single **urethra** (u-re'thrah), which is the excretory tube for the bladder. Through the urethra the urine is conducted to the outside of the body.

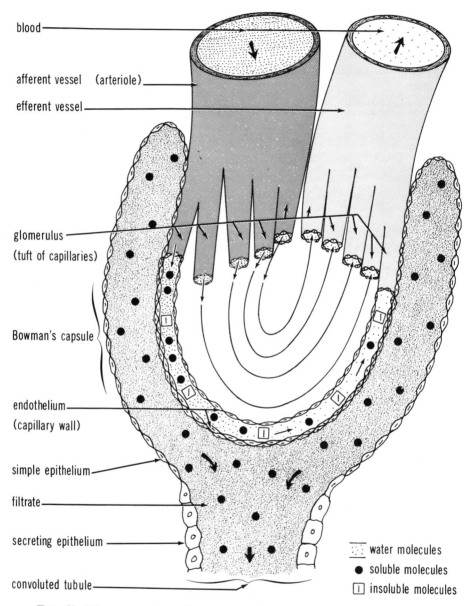

blood

afferent vessel (arteriole)

efferent vessel

glomerulus
(tuft of capillaries)

Bowman's capsule

endothelium
(capillary wall)

simple epithelium

filtrate

secreting epithelium

convoluted tubule

⬚ water molecules
● soluble molecules
☐ insoluble molecules

FIG. 69. Diagram to show the process of filtration in the formation of urine. The higher pressure inside the small capillaries (of the glomerulus) forces the dissolved substances (except the plasma proteins) and much water into the space inside Bowman's capsule.

THE KIDNEYS

LOCATION OF THE KIDNEYS

The 2 kidneys lie against the muscles of the back in the upper abdomen. They are protected by the ribs and their cartilages, since they are up under the dome of the diaphragm. Each kidney is enclosed in a membranous capsule that is made of fibrous connective tissue; it is loosely adherent to the kidney itself. In addition there is a circle of fat around the perimeter of the organ. It is called the adipose capsule and is one of the chief supporting structures. The peritoneum covers the front of the kidneys only, and so these and several other structures are not in the peritoneal cavity. This area is known as the **retroperitoneal** (re-tro-per-it-o-ne′al) **space,** indicating that it is behind the peritoneum.

Nephrons are in the cortex

STRUCTURE OF THE KIDNEYS

The kidney is a somewhat flattened organ about 4 inches long, 2 inches wide, and 1 inch thick. On the inner or medial border there is a notch called the **hilum** (hi′lum), at which region the artery, the vein and the ureter connect with the kidney. The outer or lateral border is convex (curves outward), giving the entire organ a bean-shaped appearance.

The kidney is a glandular organ; that is, most of the tissue is epithelium with just enough connective tissue to serve as a framework. As is the case with most organs, the most fascinating aspect of the kidney is too small to be seen with the naked eye. This basic unit of the kidney, where the kidney's business is actually done, is called a **nephron** (nef′ron); and a nephron is essentially a tiny coiled tube (called a **convoluted tubule)** with a bulb on one end containing a cluster of capillaries, the **glomerulus** (glo-mer′u-lus). A kidney is composed of over a million nephrons; if all these coiled tubes were separated, straightened out, and laid end to end, they would span some 75 miles!

The cluster of capillaries within the bulb of each nephron has 1 blood vessel (an arteriole) to supply it with blood, and another tiny vessel to drain it. As the blood passes through the capillary cluster, a mixture of water, useful materials, and dissolved waste materials passes directly from the blood (by filtration), through the capillary walls, and into **Bowman's capsule,** the beginning of the convoluted tubule (see Fig. 69). Now this mixture begins its journey through the coiled tube of the nephron. As it passes through the tube, most of the water, minus the waste materials but containing the useful substances that have escaped through the nephron capillaries, is *reabsorbed* through the walls of the nephron tube and sent back to the bloodstream. Thus we see that each nephron is able to "clean" or filter a very large volume of blood without causing the body to lose too much of its water or other essential materials. The water that the nephrons do retain becomes increasingly more concentrated with waste materials; and this concentrated mixture now is known as **urine.**

The nephron bulbs, with their blood vessels, are located in the **cortex,** or outer part of the kidney. The open ends of the nephron tubes come together at the **collecting tubules,** located within the **medulla,** or inner part of the kidney. Inside the kidney, toward the medial part, the ureter expands to form a basin which receives the urine collected by the collecting tubules in the medulla. This space is referred to as the **renal** (re'nal) **basin** (or, sometimes, the **pelvis** of the kidney). In order to increase the area for collection, tubelike extensions project from the renal pelvis into the active kidney tissue. These extensions are called **calyces** (kal'i-sez). The urine which collects in the renal basin passes down the ureters to the bladder.

THE KIDNEYS AND BODY CHEMISTRY

The kidneys have 3 main functions. The first, which has been discussed already to some extent, is **excretion.** The use of proteins by the body cells (in the form of amino acids) produces, among other waste materials, those containing the chemical element nitrogen; the chief waste product of this category is **urea** (u-re'ah). The urinary system is the specialized mechanism of excretion for this nitrogenous waste material. Certain salts from the blood plasma also are excreted.

A second function of the kidneys is as an aid in the maintenance of **water balance.** The average man takes in about 2½ quarts (about 2500 cc.) of water daily. About half of this usually comes from foods, some of which contain considerable amounts of water, such as fruits, many vegetables, soups, milk, etc. In addition to this, more than a tumblerful (about 300 cc.) of water is formed in the cells when their materials combine with oxygen. On the other hand, water is constantly being lost in a number of ways. About a quart and a half (1500 cc.) is lost through the urine each day. Considerable water is lost in fecal material, and every exhalation is accompanied by water loss. Even though the weather may be cool, some moisture is lost in the form of unnoticed perspiration. In spite of this great variation in the amount of water which the body takes in and gives off, the water in the tissues must be maintained at a constant quantity. The mechanism for accomplishing this is complicated, but the kidneys are an important part of it. It may be noted that the kidneys serve as a sort of "overflow" for water that the body does not need. If, for example, a person deliberately drinks a large amount of water even though he may not feel thirsty, most of this water will be very quickly excreted by the kidneys; and furthermore this water will contain only a small concentration of waste materials.

A third function of the kidneys is as an aid in regulating the **acid-base balance** of the body. Acids are a category of chemical substances which, in the body, are produced by cell metabolism. They may take the form of solids, liquids, or gases.

Bases, also called alkalies, are another category of chemicals; these have the effect of neutralizing acids (the product of an acid-base reaction is a salt). Certain foods can cause acids or alkalies to form in the body. In order that all the normal body processes may take place, a certain critical proportion of acids and bases must be maintained at all times—this despite the fact that the person may take in varying quantities of acid-forming and alkaline-producing substances as food. It is just as important for the blood and other tissues that an excess of alkalinity be avoided as it is to prevent too much acidity. In other words, there must be a balance. Acid substances are constantly being removed from the body in various ways, including the exhalation of carbon dioxide, which serves to remove carbonic acid. Both acid and alkaline substances which may be present in excess are constantly being removed by the kidneys. The kidneys also are able to manufacture ammonia at certain times. Ammonia neutralizes acids, and so we have another example of the kidneys' ability to help maintain the acid-base balance.

An interesting and equally important sidelight on the maintenance of the acid-base balance is the presence in the blood of certain mineral salts called "buffers," which maintain the blood in the nearly neutral, slightly alkaline state in spite of the varying character of the food that is taken in.

KIDNEY DISEASE

Nephritis (ne-fri'tis) means inflammation of the kidney tissue. The term includes not only the results of infection, but also the results of certain degenerative changes in the kidney that may occur, for example, as a part of a generalized arteriosclerosis. Sometimes this category of disorders is given the general name of **Bright's disease.** Bacteria or their toxins may involve the kidneys following such infections as "strep" sore throat, scarlet fever, or many of the other contagious diseases. Whatever the cause of the nephritis, the effects upon the kidney are similar. The tiny clusters of capillaries in the nephrons become inflamed and sometimes blocked, in the case of an infection. They may collapse for lack of blood, in the case of arteriosclerosis. Either condition can render the nephron useless. As more and more nephrons are destroyed, the kidney shrinks in size, and its efficiency is gradually decreased. One characteristic symptom of nephritis is **edema** (e-de'mah), meaning an abnormal accumulation of fluid in the body tissues or cavities, which shows up as a puffy, swollen condition of the area involved. In a generalized edema the patient can actually be considered waterlogged. In nephritis, one reason for the edema is that because of the destruction of the nephrons, a great deal of **albumin,** a blood protein, escapes in the urine. Because of the deficiency of albumin in the blood, the fluid part of the blood now can escape through the walls of the capillaries and into the tissues. Formerly, of course, the proper proportion of blood constituents guaranteed that only the normal amount of fluid would pass back and forth between the capillaries and the tissues. Besides nephritis, there are many other conditions causing edema: various infections, malnutrition, and certain other factors that upset the body's chemistry.

Chronic nephritis can lead to a sometimes fatal condition known as **uremia** (u-re'me-ah), which, as the name indicates, means an accumulation of urinary constituents in the blood. The cause of this is the inability of the kidneys to remove these poisonous substances from the blood. As we saw, a prolonged destruction of nephrons can ultimately render a kidney completely useless.

Some poisons such as mercury or arsenic cause degeneration of the epithelial cells of the coiled tubes of the kidney with a resulting kidney disease called **nephrosis** (ne-fro'sis). A gradual decrease in the size of the space (lumen) inside the renal artery supplying the kidney is a serious condition found in certain types of hypertension.

Infections of the kidney pelvis may be caused by a variety of bacteria such as the colon bacillus, streptococci, staphylococci, and others. The bacteria may reach the kidney via the bloodstream or as an ascending infection that travels along the lining membrane of the urinary tract. Any interference with the normal flow of urine, such as an enlarged prostate (a gland of the male reproductive system, that surrounds the urethra), or a developing pregnancy in the female, may cause stagnation of urine in the kidney pelvis; and this seems to greatly encourage **pyelitis** (pi-e-li'tis), inflammation of the renal basin. Extension of this inflammation into the kidney tissue is common, with a resulting **pyelonephritis** (pi-el-o-ne-fri'tis).

Tuberculosis of the kidney is usually a blood-borne infection which has originated in the lungs, the bones, or the lymph nodes. X-ray examination often shows destruction and abnormalities of the calyces which have given them a moth-eaten appearance. Inoculation of a guinea pig with urine from the sick person is a very helpful procedure in making a diagnosis. Expert care, sometimes including surgery, can do much for the person who suffers from tuberculosis of the kidney.

Tumors of the kidney usually grow rather slowly, but occasionally rapidly invading types are found. Blood in the urine and dull pain in the kidney region are warnings that should be heeded at once. Immediate surgery may be lifesaving. A **polycystic** (pol-e-sis'tik) kidney is one in which many fluid-containing sacs develop in the active tissue and gradually, by pressure, destroy the functioning parts. This disorder runs in families, and until now treatment has not proved very satisfactory.

Kidney stones, or **calculi** (kal'ku-li), are made of certain substances such as uric acid and calcium salts which precipitate out of the urine instead of remaining in solution. They usually form in the renal pelvis, although the bladder can be another site of formation. The causes of this precipitation of stone-building materials include infection of the urinary tract and stagnation of the urine. These stones may vary in size from tiny grains resembling bits of gravel up to large masses that fill the kidney pelvis and extend into the calyces. These are described as **stag-horn calculi.** There is no way of dissolving these stones, since substances that would be able to do so also would destroy the kidney tissue. Sometimes instruments can be used to crush smaller stones and thus allow them to be expelled with the urine, but more often surgical removal is required.

DIALYSIS MACHINES AND KIDNEY TRANSPLANTS

Dialysis (di-al'e-sis) means "the diffusion of dissolved molecules through a semipermeable membrane." These molecules tend to pass from the area of greater concentration to one of less concentration. In patients who have defective kidney function, the accumulation of urea and other nitrogen waste products can be reduced by passing the patient's blood through a dialysis machine. This is where the principle of "molecules leaving the area of greater concentration" operates to remove the excessive amounts of nitrogen waste products from the blood. The machines are being improved steadily, and larger numbers of them are being manufactured. Hopefully, in the near future, sufficient numbers of less expensive and less cumbersome machines will be available so that all persons who could benefit by dialysis would receive it. This could save the lives of many people who would otherwise die of kidney failure and fatal uremic poisoning.

Many hundreds of kidney transplants have been done successfully during the last several years. Kidneys have so much extra functioning tissue that in the normal individual no problem is posed by losing one kidney. Records show that the percentage of transplant successes is greatest when living, closely related donors are used. However, organs from a deceased donor have also proved satisfactory in many cases. The problem of tissue rejection (the rejection syndrome) is discussed in Chapter 20.

THE URETERS

STRUCTURE AND FUNCTION OF THE URETERS

The 2 ureters are long, slender, muscular tubes that extend from the kidney basin down to and through the lower part of the urinary bladder. Their length naturally varies with the size of the individual, and so may be anywhere from 10 to 13 inches long, including nearly an inch at its lower part that passes obliquely through the bladder wall. They are entirely extraperitoneal; that is behind and, at the lower part, below the peritoneum.

The wall of the ureter includes a lining of epithelial cells, a relatively thick layer of involuntary muscle, and finally an outer coat of fibrous connective tissue. The muscle of the ureters is capable of the same rhythmic contraction found in the digestive system and known as peristalsis. Urine is moved along the ureter from the kidneys to the bladder by peristalsis at frequent intervals. Because of the oblique direction of the last part of each ureter through the lower bladder wall, compression of the ureters by the full bladder prevents backflow of urine.

DISORDERS OF THE URETERS

Abnormalities in structure of the ureter include double portions at the pelvis and constricted or abnormally narrow parts, called **strictures** (strik'tures). Narrowing of the ureter also may be caused by abnormal pressures from tumors or other masses outside the tube. Obstruction of the ureters may be caused by stones from the kidneys or by a kinking of the tube due to a dropping of the kidney. This latter condition is called **ptosis** (to'sis).

The passage of a small stone along the ureter causes one of the most excruciating pains known to man. This intense pain is called **renal colic** and usually requires morphine for relief. The first "barber surgeons" operating without benefit of anesthesia were permitted by their patients to cut through the skin and the muscles of the back to remove stones from the ureters. "Cutting for stone" in this way was relatively successful, in spite of lack of sterile technique, because of the approach through the back and the avoidance of the peritoneal cavity, with the possibility of deadly peritonitis. Modern surgery for a kidney stone may cause very little temporary disability and a short convalescence.

THE URINARY BLADDER

CHARACTERISTICS OF THE BLADDER

The urinary bladder is located below the parietal peritoneum and behind the pubic joint when it is empty. When it is filled, it may extend well up into the abdominal cavity proper. The urinary bladder is a temporary reservoir for urine, just as the gallbladder is a storage bag for bile.

The bladder wall has many layers. It is lined with mucous membrane; the lining, like that of the stomach, is thrown into the folds called rugae when the receptacle is empty. Beneath the mucosa is a layer of connective tissue. Then follows a 3-layered coat of involuntary muscle tissue which is capable of stretching to a great extent. Finally there is an incomplete coat of peritoneum that covers only the upper portion of the bladder. When the bladder is empty, the muscular wall becomes thick and the entire organ feels firm. As the organ fills, the muscular wall becomes thinner and the organ may increase from a length of 2 or 3 inches to 5 or more inches. A moderately full bladder holds about a pint of urine.

Near the outlet of the bladder circular muscle fibers contract to prevent emptying, and form what is known as the **internal sphincter.** In the infant a center in the lower part of the spinal cord receives impulses from the bladder and sends motor impulses out to the bladder musculature; the organ is emptied in an action that is automatic (i.e., a **reflex** action). However, with training, the child learns to control this reflex.

DISORDERS INVOLVING THE BLADDER

A full (distended) bladder lies in an unprotected position in the lower abdomen, and a light blow may rupture it. Immediate surgical repair is required. Tumors and infections involve the urinary bladder fairly often; blood in the urine is a rather common symptom of these. Inflammation of the bladder is called **cystitis** (sis-ti'tis) and often is secondary to infection in some other part of the urinary tract. Obstruction by an enlarged prostate gland or from a pregnancy may lead to stagnation and cystitis. Reduction of the general resistance to infection, as in diabetes, may lead to cystitis.

THE URETHRA

LOCATION AND FUNCTION OF THE URETHRA

The **urethra** is the tube that extends from the bladder to the outside, and is the means by which the bladder is emptied. The urethra differs in men and women, since in men it is also a part of the reproductive system and it is much longer.

The female urethra is a thin-walled tube about 1½ inches long. It is located behind the pubic joint and is embedded in the muscle of the front wall of the vagina. The external opening is called the **urethral meatus** and is located just in front of the vaginal opening.

The male urethra is about 8 inches long. In the first part of its course it passes through the prostate gland, where 2 ducts carrying the male sex cells join it. From here it leads through the **penis** (pe'nis), the male organ of copulation, to the outside. The male urethra, then, serves the dual purpose of conveying the sex cells and draining the bladder, while the female urethra performs only the latter function.

The process of expelling urine through the urethra is called **urination** or **micturition** (mik-tu-rish'un). It is controlled by the action of circular muscles continuous with those in the walls of the bladder and in the urethra. These form valvelike structures that are aided by external muscles in the pelvic floor.

DISORDERS OF THE URETHRA

Congenital **anomalies** (ah-nom'ah-lees) (defects) present at birth involve the urethra as well as other parts of the urinary tract. The opening of the urethra to the outside may be too small, or the urethra itself narrowed. Occasionally it happens that there is an abnormal valvelike structure located at the point where the urethra enters the bladder. These valvelike folds of tissue can cause a back pressure of the urine, with serious consequences if they are not removed surgically. There is also a condition in the male in which the urethra opens on the under surface of the penis instead of at the end. This is called **hypospadias** (hi-po-spa'de-as).

Urethritis, in which inflammation of the mucous membrane and the glands of the urethra are involved, is much more common in the male than in the female and is often due to gonorrhea, although many other bacteria also may be responsible for the infection.

"Straddle" injuries to the urethra are common in men. This type of injury occurs when, for example, a man walking along a raised beam slips and lands with the beam between his legs. Such an accident may catch the urethra between the hard surfaces of the beam and the pubic arch, and rupture the urethra. In accidents in which the bones of the pelvis are fractured, rupture of the urethra is fairly common.

THE URINE

NORMAL CONSTITUENTS

In this chapter we have learned some of the main constituents of urine. Here they are summarized in a more detailed manner in order to complete the picture of the normal situation.

Urine is a yellowish liquid which is about 95 percent water. Dissolved in this water are a number of solids and a few gases, including:

1. Nitrogen waste products, which include urea, uric acid, and **creatinine** (kre-at'i-nin). These substances sometimes are classified as **organic** compounds because they are formed by the breakdown of cells in the body and from proteins of food, many of which originated from animal tissues. That is, they originated from living organisms.

2. Mineral salts, including compounds such as sodium chloride (as in common table salt), sulfates, and phosphates of different kinds. These substances are often classified as **inorganic** compounds because they do not originate in living organisms. They are excreted in appropriate amounts in order to keep the blood concentrations of mineral salts constant.

3. Yellow pigment, which is derived from certain bile compounds. The color of urine varies with the concentration, being lighter when more dilute, as a rule.

ABNORMAL CONSTITUENTS

Urine examination is one of the most important parts of an evaluation of an individual's physical state. Among the most significant abnormal substances found in urine are:

1. Simple sugar in the form of **glucose,** usually an important indication of the disease known as **diabetes mellitus,** in which the blood sugar is not "burned" in the body cells but is excreted in the urine instead. Tests for sugar in the urine

may be done at home with the use of a tablet provided by the physician or ordered by him. These help the diabetic to keep his urine sugar-free.

2. **Albumin,** a protein that is normally retained in the blood. It may indicate a kidney disorder; nephritis, for example.

3. **Blood,** an important indication of possible urinary tract disease. Its presence in the urine is known as **hematuria** (hem-ah-tu're-ah). Incidentally, compare this word with **uremia.**

4. **Acetone** (as'e-tone), a substance formed by the incomplete oxidation of fats. This is seen in diabetes, starvation, and other conditions.

5. **Pus cells,** which can be seen by using a microscope on a centrifuged specimen. These are evidence of infection.

6. **Casts,** which are really molds formed in the microscopic tubules of the kidney, evidence of nephritis.

SUMMARY

1. **Excretion and elimination.**
   A. Excretion: removal of useless substances from body structures.
   B. Elimination: emptying of organs in which waste products have been stored.
   C. Excretory mechanisms: digestive, urinary, respiratory, skin.
2. **Urinary system:** kidneys, ureters, bladder, urethra.
3. **Kidneys.**
   A. Location: retroperitoneal.
   B. Structure: largely epithelium in tiny tubes (nephrons) acting as filters. Nephrons lead to collecting tubules in medulla. Urine from collecting tubules collected in renal basin (pelvis) where ureters join.
   C. Functions: excretion; maintenance of water balance; regulation of acid-base balance.
   D. Diseases: nephritis (inflammation, destruction of nephrons); uremia; nephrosis; pyelitis; pyelonephritis; tuberculosis; tumors; calculi.
   E. Dialysis machines and transplants.
4. **Ureters.**
   A. Structure and function: muscular tubes that carry urine from kidney to bladder by peristalsis.
   B. Disorders: structures; kinking from ptosis of kidney; renal colic.
5. **Bladder.**
   A. Structure and function: muscular sac capable of stretching; reservoir for urine. Has internal sphincter; impulse to empty a controllable reflex.
   B. Disorders: injuries; tumors; stagnation and cystitis.
6. **Urethra.**
   A. Structure and function: tube leading from bladder to outside; longer in male than in female; in male is also part of reproductive system.

B. Disorders: congenital anomalies; urethritis; straddle injuries.
7. **Urine.**
   A. Normal constituents: water (95 per cent); nitrogenous wastes; mineral salts; pigment.
   B. Abnormal constituents: glucose; albumin; blood; acetone; pus cells; casts.

QUESTIONS AND PROBLEMS

1. In what way might secretions and excretions be the same, and how do these differ from each other?
2. How do the terms "elimination" and "excretion" differ from each other? Name the body systems which have an excretory function.
3. Where are the kidneys located?
4. Describe the external appearance of the kidneys and tell what tissues form most of the kidney structure. Name and describe the microscopic structure that is the basic kidney unit.
5. What structures empty into the kidney pelvis, and what drains this space?
6. In what 3 ways does the kidney adjust the body chemistry?
7. What are some of the infections that involve the kidney, and what parts are most often affected?
8. What are calculi, and what are some of the causes of this disorder?
9. What is meant by dialysis and how is this principle used for persons with kidney failure? What type of donors are best for kidney transplants?
10. Locate and describe the ureters.
11. What is renal colic?
12. Name and describe the layers of the bladder wall.
13. What is infection of the bladder called?
14. Describe the female urethra and tell how it differs from the male urethra in structure and function.
15. What is meant by a congenital anomaly and what is an example of such condition involving the urethra?
16. What are other disorders that affect the urethra?
17. What are some of the most important normal constituents of urine?
18. Define and tell the possible significance of 5 abnormal constituents of urine.

CHAPTER 18

GLANDS AND HORMONES

Glands, exocrine and endocrine ▪ Secretions, external and internal ▪ Structure of glands ▪ What hormones do ▪ The thyroid gland and its hormone ▪ Four parathyroids ▪ Multiple functions of the "master gland" ▪ The pancreas, insulin, and diabetes ▪ Two-part adrenals and their hormones ▪ The sex glands ▪ The placenta, the thymus, and the pineal body ▪ Hormones and treatment.

CLASSIFICATION OF SECRETIONS AND GLANDS

A gland as such is any organ that produces a certain secretion; and the secretions themselves are substances manufactured from blood constituents by the specialized cells of which the glands are made.

The secretions of the various glands may be divided into 2 main groups:

1. **External secretions,** which are carried from the gland cells to a nearby organ or to the body surface. These external secretions are effective in a limited area near their origin. We already have learned something of most of these secretions: digestive juices, the secretions from the sebaceous glands of the skin, tears from the lacrimal glands, and urine (both a secretion and an excretion).

2. **Internal secretions,** which are carried to all parts of the body by the blood or lymph. These substances often affect tissues a considerable distance from the point of origin. Internal secretions are known as **hormones;** and the hormones, with the glands that produce them, will be the subject of this chapter.

Glands, like secretions, also are divided into 2 categories:

1. **Exocrine** (ek′so-krin) **glands,** which have tubes (ducts) to carry the secretion from the gland to another organ or part of the body.

2. **Endocrine** (en′do-krin), or **ductless, glands,** which have no ducts, and so must depend upon the blood and the lymph to carry their secretions to various body tissues, via the capillaries of the glandular tissue.

Sometimes the lymph nodes are spoken of as glands (i.e., the "neck glands," which are actually nodes); but so far as is known the lymph nodes do not produce secretions.

The endocrine glands proper produce only internal secretions (hormones), but some organs contain both exocrine and endocrine gland tissue. The liver and the pancreas, for example, are combination glands, producing both external and internal secretions. The mucous membranes of the stomach and the small intestine produce both external secretions (mucus, digestive juices) and a hormone called **secretin** (se-kre′tin), which has the function of stimulating certain other digestive organs to produce *their* digestive juices.

STRUCTURE OF GLANDS

Exocrine glands vary in complexity from very simple depressions resembling tiny dimples to involved arrangements such as are found in the kidneys. Simple tube-like structures are found in the stomach wall and in the intestinal lining. Complex, treelike groups of ducts are found in the liver, the pancreas, and the salivary glands. Most glands are made largely of epithelial tissue with a framework of connective tissue. There may be a tough connective tissue capsule (a fibrous envelope) enclosing the organ, with extensions into the organ which form partitions. Between the partitions are groups of cells, and these units are called **lobes.**

Most endocrine glands, like exocrine glands, are made of epithelial tissue. However, since they have no ducts, they seem to make up for this lack by a most extensive blood vessel network. Operations on endocrine glands such as, for example, on the thyroid, require care in the control of bleeding. The organs believed to have the very richest blood supply of any in the body are the tiny **adrenal** (ad-re′nal), or **suprarenal** (su-prah-re′nal), **glands** which are located near the upper parts of the kidneys.

GENERAL FUNCTIONS OF HORMONES

Hormones are chemical substances manufactured by the endocrine glands, and their overall function is to regulate the activities of various body organs. In one sense, the action of hormones can be compared with that of the nervous system (in fact, in the chapter covering the nervous system, we saw how the hormone epinephrine acted in conjunction with the autonomic system in an emergency). Hormones sometimes are referred to as "chemical messengers." Some hormones stimulate exocrine tissues to produce their secretions, as in the example of secretin. Another category of hormone stimulates other endocrine glands to action. There are hormones that have a profound effect upon growth, development, and even the personality of the individual. Others regulate the body chemistry: for example, the metabolism of the cells. Still others regulate the contraction of muscle tissues. Finally, there are hormones which control various sex processes. The action of

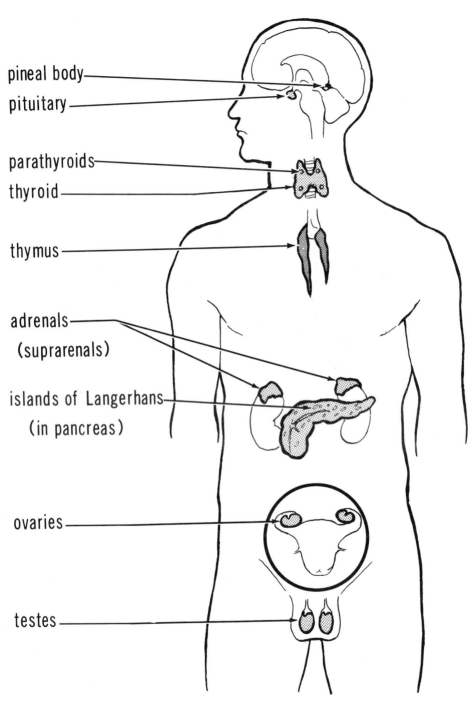

pineal body

pituitary

parathyroids

thyroid

thymus

adrenals
(suprarenals)

islands of Langerhans
(in pancreas)

ovaries

testes

FIG. 70. Endocrine system. Both the male and the female sex glands are shown.

each hormone is specific; that is, each has its particular, specialized job to do and no other.

ENDOCRINE GLANDS AND THEIR HORMONES

The Thyroid Gland and Thyroxine

The largest of the endocrine glands is the **thyroid,** which is located in the neck. It has 2 oval parts called the lateral lobes, one on either side of the voice box. A narrow band called the **isthmus** (is'mus) connects these 2 lobes. The entire gland is enclosed by a connective tissue capsule. This gland produces the hormone **thyroxine** (thi-rok'sin). The principal function of thyroxine is to regulate the production of heat and energy in the body tissues. In order that this hormone may be manufactured, there must be an adequate supply of iodine in the blood. The iodine content may be maintained by eating vegetables grown in iodine-containing soils, or by eating sea foods. In some parts of the United States, as well as in certain regions of Italy and Switzerland, the soil is so deficient in iodine that serious defects may result in the inhabitants of these districts. The use of iodized salt may prevent difficulties.

One result of a deficiency of iodine in the blood is the formation of a **goiter,** which is a swelling of the neck due to an enlarged thyroid. As will be seen, there are other causes of goiter as well; but in this first-mentioned case, known as **simple goiter,** the thyroid becomes enlarged simply because it must work overtime to compensate for the lack of iodine. This form of goiter, also called **adolescent goiter,** sometimes appears in adolescent girls, because of the particularly heavy stresses imposed upon the thyroid by the body at puberty. This condition usually disappears in time. Simple goiter also is known as **endemic goiter,** meaning that it is common to the inhabitants of a particular region—in this instance, of course, to the people living in those areas in which there is little iodine in the soil.

Another form of goiter is **adenomatous** (ad-e-no'mah-tus), or **nodular, goiter;** and, as the name would indicate, the goiter has an accompanying tumor formation which comes about through the overgrowth of the cells of the thyroid tissue. In nodular goiter the tumor formation may be single or multiple; the former condition appears to be more likely to become malignant.

For various reasons the thyroid gland may become either underactive or overactive. Underactivity of the thyroid is known as **hypothyroidism** (hi-po-thi'roi-dizm) and shows up as 2 characteristic states:

1. **Cretinism** (kre'tin-izm), a condition in which there is a serious lack of thyroid activity from the beginning of the individual's life. It is sometimes due to the complete absence of thyroid tissue. The infant becomes dwarfed and mentally deficient because of failure of physical growth and mental development. Only if continuous thyroid replacement is begun early is there any hope of altering the

outlook. This disorder is fortunately rather rare in the United States, though endemic in certain regions where iodine is lacking.

2. **Myxedema** (mik-se-de′mah), the result of atrophy of the thyroid in the adult. The patient becomes sluggish both mentally and physically. The skin and the hair become dry, and there develops a peculiar swelling of the tissues of the face. Since thyroid extract or the hormone itself may be administered by mouth, the victim of myxedema can be restored to health very easily, though treatment must be maintained throughout the remainder of his life.

Hyperthyroidism is the opposite of hypothyroidism: overactivity of the thyroid gland. The development of a simple goiter might suggest hyperthyroidism, but there is a difference. In a simple goiter the thyroid is usually normal, but enlarges because it has more work to do, just as the heart will enlarge if something causes its work load to increase. Hyperthyroidism, however, is abnormal activity of the thyroid without an accompanying need of it by any other part of the body. A common form of hyperthyroidism is **exophthalmic** (ek-sof-thal′mik) **goiter,** or **Graves' disease,** in which there is a goiter, bulging of the eyes, a strained appearance of the face, intense nervousness, weight loss, a rapid pulse, sweating, and a tremor. Metabolism is stepped up to a terrific rate; it would seem that the victim had a fire raging within him. In many cases the administration of drugs, or surgical removal of a part of the thyroid gland, will remedy the condition.

Tests for Thyroid Function. The 2 tests most commonly used in evaluating thyroid function are:

1. The **basal metabolism test,** in which the amount of oxygen a person uses is determined while the individual is at rest. It must be carefully supervised and be performed in the morning before breakfast. It is preferable that a person have this test done after having stayed in the hospital overnight, since conditions can be more closely controlled by hospital personnel prior to the test.

2. The **blood iodine test,** in which blood is taken from a vein and then tested for the amount of so-called protein-bound iodine present. This is a much simpler test, and in most cases is very helpful in determining the activity of the thyroid.

A third test involves the use of radioactive iodine, in which excretion of iodine is studied following the ingestion of a measured amount. The collection of every specimen of urine is mandatory if the test is to be accurate. Radioactive substances are used also in the treatment of some cases of hyperthyroidism.

THE PARATHYROID GLANDS AND PARATHORMONE

Behind the thyroid glands, and embedded in its capsule, are 4 tiny epithelial bodies called the **parathyroid glands.**

The hormone produced by these glands regulates the amount of calcium dissolved in the circulating blood. If these glands are removed, there will follow a series of muscle contractions involving particularly the hand and the

THE ENDOCRINE GLANDS AND THEIR HORMONES

GLANDS	HORMONES	PRINCIPAL FUNCTIONS
anterior pituitary (adenohypo- physis)	ACTH (adrenocortico- trophic)	stimulates adrenal cortex, which aids in protecting the body in stress situations (injury, pain, etc.) as well as in normal body chemistry
	TH or TSH (thyroid stimulating)	energizes thyroid gland (to produce thy- roxine)
	FH or FSH (follicle stimulating)	stimulates growth and hormone activity of ovarian follicles
	H (growth hormone)	causes growth of all tissues that can grow, most noticeably bones
	LH (luteinizing) a gonadotropin	causes development of corpus luteum at site of ruptured ovarian follicle
	LTH (luteotropic) (a gonadotropin)	stimulates hormone activity of luteal cells, which produce progesterone
posterior pituitary (neurohypo- physis)	ADH (antidiuretic) or vasopressin	promotes resorption of water in kidney tubules; stimulates involuntary muscle tissue
	oxytocin	causes contraction of pregnant uterus
adrenal cortex	cortisol (95% of glucocorticoids)	aids in metabolism of food components (proteins, carbohydrates, and fats); ac- tive during stress
	aldosterone (95% of mineralocor- ticoids)	aids in regulating mineral salts (electro- lytes) ↓ sodium Retention
adrenal medulla	epinephrine (adrenaline) and norepi- nephrine	increases blood pressure and heart rate, activates cells influenced by the sym- pathetic nervous system plus many not affected by sympathetics
pancreatic islets	insulin	required for glucose metabolism, for the use of glucose within body cells
	glucagon	maintains amount of glucose in blood ade- quate for brain and other organs to which glucose is so vital
parathyroids	parathormone	increases the amount of calcium ion in the blood ↓ phosphate
	calcitonin	produces rapid increase in calcium ion in emergencies

in thyroid gland

LoweRS plasma calcium

THE ENDOCRINE GLANDS AND THEIR HORMONES (*Continued*)

GLANDS	HORMONES	PRINCIPAL FUNCTIONS
thyroid gland	thyroxine	increases metabolic rate, influencing both physical and mental activities; required for normal growth and catabolism
	triiodothyronine	potent activator of all metabolic activities
ovarian follicle	estrogen	stimulates growth of primary sexual organs (uterus, tubes, etc.) and development of secondary sexual organs, such as breasts, plus change in pelvis to ovoid broader shape
corpus luteum (in ovaries)	progesterone	stimulates development of secretory parts of mammary glands; prepares uterine lining for implantation of fertilized ovum; aids in maintaining pregnancy; enhances reabsorption of water and salt (NaCl) from kidney tubules
testes	testosterone	stimulates growth and development of sexual organs (testes, penis, etc.) plus development of secondary sexual characteristics such as hair growth on body and face, deepening of voice, and increase in development and strength of muscles
placenta	chorionic gonadotropin	causes continued growth and secretory activity of corpus luteum (of ovary)
	estrogens	stimulate growth of mother's reproductive organs, cause relaxation of pelvic ligaments (to make childbirth easier)
	progesterone	aids in maintaining nutrition of embryo (due to effects on uterine lining cells)
stomach lining (mucosa)	gastrin	stimulates secretion of HCl and some enzymes
intestinal mucosa	prosecretin (becomes secretin)	activates the pancreas to produce an alkaline watery pancreatic juice (to neutralize HCl), and stimulates intestinal glands and liver to produce their digestive juices
	cholecystokinin	cooperates with peristalsis of small intestine to cause contraction and emptying of gallbladder

face muscles. These spasms are due to a low concentration of blood calcium, and the condition is called **tetany** (tet'ah-ne), which must *not* be confused with the infection called tetanus (lockjaw). On the other hand, if there is an excess production of the secretion of these glands, called **parathormone** (par-ah-thor'mone), as may happen in tumors of the parathyroids, calcium (normally stored in the bones for use by the tissues as needed) is removed from its storage place and is poured into the bloodstream, whence it finally is excreted by the kidneys. Because of the outpouring of calcium from the bones, they become soft and easily bent. It is believed that the excess of calcium in the blood is one cause of kidney stones.

THE PITUITARY, OR "MASTER GLAND"

The **pituitary** (pi-tu'i-tar-e) is a small gland about the size of a cherry. It is nearly surrounded by bone except for its area of connection with the brain. The pituitary is located in a saddlelike depression just behind the point of optic nerve crossing, in the midline. It has 2 important parts called the **anterior** and the **posterior lobes,** each of which produces several different hormones.

The **Anterior Lobe.** This lobe produces a large number of hormones. Many of them stimulate other glands, and it is for this reason that the pituitary is known as the master gland. Its main hormones are:

1. The **growth-promoting,** or **somatotropic** (so-mah-to-trop'ik), **hormone.** If a human is born with a deficiency of this hormone, he will remain a dwarf (of the type often referred to as a midget).

2. The **gonadotropic** (gon-ad-o-trop'ik) **hormones,** which control the development of the reproductive systems in both the male and the female. This action includes the stimulation of the monthly menstrual cycle of the female.

3. The **thyrotropic** (thi-ro-trop'ik) **hormone,** which stimulates the thyroid gland to activity.

4. The **adrenocorticotropic** (ah-dre-no-kor-ti-ko-trop'ik) **hormone,** abbreviated ACTH, which stimulates the cortex of the adrenal gland (to be discussed in this chapter).

5. The **lactogenic** (lak-to-jen'ik) **hormone,** which stimulates the production of milk in the female.

The **Posterior Lobe.** This lobe of the pituitary gland produces 3 hormones. Their functions are:

1. To stimulate the smooth muscle of the blood vessels.
2. To promote reabsorption of water in the tubules of the kidney.
3. To stimulate the contraction of the muscles of the uterus.

An extract containing these hormones, called **pituitrin** (pi-tu'i-trin), is given in various forms to produce these effects. For example, a type of this extract known as obstetrical pituitrin is given to induce uterine contractions at one of the stages of childbirth.

Tumors of the Pituitary. The effects of pituitary tumors depend upon what types of cells the new or excess tissue contains. Some of these tumors contain the cells that produce the growth hormone. If this occurs in childhood, the person will become abnormally tall, resulting in a condition called **gigantism** (ji-gan'tizm). Although these people are large, they are usually very weak. If the growth-producing cells become overactive in the adult, a disorder known as **acromegaly** (ak-ro-meg'ah-le) develops. In acromegaly the bones of the face, the hands, and the feet widen. The fingers resemble a spatula, and the face takes on a grotesque appearance: the nose widens, the lower jaw protrudes, and the forehead bones may bulge. Often these pituitary tumors involve the optic nerves and cause blindness.

Tumors or disease may destroy the secreting tissues of the gland so that signs of underactivity develop. Such a patient often becomes obese and sluggish, and may exhibit signs of underactivity of other endocrine glands such as the ovaries, the testes or the thyroid. Evidences of tumor formation in the pituitary gland may be obtained by x-ray examinations of the skull. The saddlelike space for the pituitary body is distorted by the pressure of the tumor.

THE PANCREAS, INSULIN AND DIABETES

Scattered throughout the **pancreas** are small groups of specialized cells called **islets** (i'lets), which are also known as the **islands of Langerhans** (lahng'er-hanz). They function independently, and are *not* connected with the ducts with which the exocrine part of the pancreas is so well supplied. These islands manufacture a hormone known as **insulin.** Insulin is necessary for the normal use of sugar in the body tissues. If for some reason the pancreatic islets fail to produce enough insulin, sugar is not "burned" in the tissues for transformation into energy; instead, the sugar is simply excreted along with the urine. This condition is called **diabetes mellitus** (di-ah-be'teez mel-li'tus). In order that the diabetic patient may lead a normal life, he must help to restore and to maintain proper utilization of his body's fuel. In mild cases of diabetes this can be achieved by a modification of the diet. In severe cases, however, the patient must also receive insulin from an outside source, in periodic doses. Insulin must be given by injection because it is destroyed by the action of digestive juices. This poses the problem of daily injections for the diabetic patient. As a rule it is considered desirable for the patient to learn to give the injections to himself. He should learn to adjust his diet, his exercise, and his other activities in order to maintain the proper balance between the intake of insulin and sugar needs. He should also carry a special identification card to let people know that he is a diabetic taking insulin, and that a dazed condition might indicate a need for some sugar.

A further understanding of the far-reaching effects of insulin may be obtained by noting certain other medical uses for this hormone. Some of these are:

1. As an aid in weight gain, when accompanied with a high caloric diet.

2. As an agent to relieve vomiting in pregnancy, when administered with sugar (glucose).

3. As a helpful treatment in certain mental disorders.

Mild cases of diabetes mellitus can be controlled by several drugs that can be taken by mouth. Examples of these drugs are chlorpropamide (klor-pro'pah-mid) and tolbutamide (tol-bu'tah-mid). The trade names for these agents are Diabinese and Orinase, respectively. They are not forms of insulin but act by stimulating the pancreas to produce more insulin.

THE ADRENAL GLANDS AND THEIR HORMONES

The **adrenals,** or **suprarenals** (su-prah-re'nals), are 2 small glands, each one situated above a kidney. An adrenal gland is made of 2 different parts each of which acts as a separate gland. The inner area is called the **medulla,** while the outer portion is the **cortex.**

The Hormones from the Medulla. The principal hormone produced by the medulla is one which we already have learned something about: **epinephrine,** also called **adrenaline** (ad-ren'al-in). Another hormone, **norepinephrine** (nor-ep-e-nef'rin), is closely related chemically and is similar but not identical in its actions. These are referred to as the "fight and flight" hormones because of their effects during emergency situations. Some of these effects are:

1. Stimulation of the sympathetic nerves which supply the involuntary muscle in the walls of the arterioles, causing these muscles to contract and the blood pressure to rise accordingly.

2. Conversion of the glycogen of the liver into sugar, which is poured into the blood and brought to the voluntary muscles, permitting them to do an extraordinary amount of work.

3. Increase of the heartbeat rate.

4. Dilation of the bronchioles, through relaxation of the smooth muscle of their walls.

The Hormones from the Adrenal Cortex. This group of hormones has 3 main functions:

1. To control the reabsorption of sodium in the kidney tubules, and the excretion of potassium. The principal hormone responsible for this electrolyte-regulating function is called **aldosterone** (al-do-ster'one).

2. To maintain the carbohydrate reserve of the body by changing amino acids to sugar instead of to protein, whenever the needs of the body call for such action. The hormone that does this is **cortisol** (a glucocorticoid). (This hormone is also produced in larger amounts in times of stress and so aids the body in responding to some unfavorable situations.)

3. To govern certain secondary sexual characteristics, particularly in the male. For example, these hormones are responsible in some ways for the muscular vigor

that is typically masculine. One of these hormones is sometimes referred to as **adrenosterone** (ad-re-no'ster-one).

It should be mentioned once again that production of these hormones from the adrenal cortex is stimulated by ACTH from the "master gland" (pituitary) which is in turn stimulated by impulses from the hypothalamus. Not only are endocrine glands interrelated so they affect each other, but recent research indicates complex nervous and hormone connections.

The adrenal cortex is essential to life because it is largely by means of this part of the adrenal glands that the body succeeds in adapting itself to the constant changes in the environment. Hypofunction of the adrenal cortex gives rise to a condition known as **Addison's disease.** The original cause of this condition usually is destruction of the adrenals by tuberculosis. Addison's disease is characterized chiefly by inability of the body to withstand the stresses of both internal and external environmental changes. For instance, the victim has practically no resistance to infection, and also suffers from chronic disturbances in salt and water balance.

Tumors of the Adrenal Gland. The symptoms produced by tumors of the adrenal gland will depend upon whether the cortex, the medulla, or both are affected. Tumors of the adrenal cortex in young children have caused rapid sexual development, while those in adult women have led to the development of masculine characteristics, such as growth of hair on the face, deepening of the voice, and increase in the size of the voluntary muscles. In these cases the cells of the new growth, have caused an increase of the hormones related to sex functions. Tumors associated with the medulla have been known to produce great increases in blood pressure, abnormally rapid heart rate, and profuse sweating, all of which are evidences of excessive production of the hormone epinephrine.

THE SEX GLANDS

The sex glands, including the ovaries of the female and the testes of the male, are important endocrine structures. The hormones produced by these organs play an important part in the development of the sexual characteristics, usually first appearing in the early teens, and in the maintenance of the reproductive apparatus once full development has been attained. The hormone produced by the male sex glands is called **testosterone** (tes-tos'ter-one), and is responsible for such secondary sexual characteristics as the deep voice and the growth of facial hair, and also for the functioning of certain of the reproductive organs themselves. Those structures which are directly concerned with reproduction are considered the **primary** sexual characteristics.

In the female, the hormone which most nearly parallels testosterone in its action is **estrone** (es'trone), which besides being concerned with the development of the female secondary sexual characteristics, also stimulates the development of the mammary glands, the onset of menstruation, and the development and functioning of the female reproductive organs.

There is one other hormone produced by the female sex glands, and it is called **progesterone** (pro-jes'ter-one). This hormone assists in the normal development of the pregnancy; its action will be explained in the next chapter.

THE PLACENTA, THE THYMUS, AND THE PINEAL BODY

The **placenta** (plah-sen'tah) produces several hormones during pregnancy (see Chap. 19). These cause changes in the uterine lining, and later in pregnancy they help to prepare the breasts for lactation. The tests for pregnancy are based on the presence of placental secretions.

The **thymus** (thi'mus) and the **pineal** (pin'e-al) **body** are being studied intensively, and the results of research indicate the possibility that they both produce hormones or hormonelike substances. The thymus apparently produces a substance that stimulates the production of small lymphocytes (see Chaps. 14 and 20).

The pineal body, a small flattened cone-shaped structure located between the 2 parts of the thalamus, produces a hormone in a number of animals, and possibly also in the human. The hormone, **melatonin** (mel-ah-to'nin), acts on the pigment cells of the skin in certain animals. The human pineal body may be invaded by tumor tissue, and the symptoms produced are probably due to pressure on nearby structures. It is hoped that we will soon have more definite answers concerning the function of the pineal body.

HORMONES AND TREATMENT

Many hormones have been extracted from animal tissues for use as medication to treat those persons who may lack them or to bring about desired temporary effects. By careful processing, hormones have been obtained in pure form. A few examples of the use of hormones in treatment include:

1. Insulin, some clinical uses of which already have been noted.

2. ACTH and cortisone for rheumatic fever; rheumatoid arthritis and other pathology involving the joints; various skin and eye diseases.

3. Epinephrine (adrenaline), the many uses of which include: to stimulate the heart muscle, when rapid action is required; to decrease bleeding by constricting small blood vessels; to prevent too rapid absorption of local anesthetics, again by constricting blood vessels; to treat asthmatic attacks by relaxing the muscles of the small breathing tubes; to counteract insulin shock by increasing the amount of sugar released by the liver into the bloodstream.

4. Thyroid extract (thyroxine) for treatment of such hypothyroid conditions as cretinism and myxedema.

5. Pituitrin, used to contract the uterine muscle, as has been mentioned.

SUMMARY

1. **Secretions.**
   A. External: carried from gland to nearby organ or body surface.
   B. Internal: carried to all parts of body by blood or lymph. Called hormones.
2. **Glands:** mostly epithelial, connective tissue framework, fibrous capsule; divided into lobes.
   A. Exocrine: have ducts to carry secretions.
   B. Endocrine: ductless; secretions reach blood via capillaries.
3. **Hormones:** "chemical messengers" regulating activities of various body systems.
4. **Thyroid gland.**
   A. Location and function: in neck. Produces thyroxine; regulates heat and energy generated in tissues; iodine a necessary constituent of thyroxine.
   B. Disorders: simple goiter (lack of iodine); hypothyroidism (cretinism, myxedema); hyperthyroidism (Graves' disease).
5. **Parathyroid glands.**
   A. Location and function: 4 bodies behind thyroid gland. Regulate calcium content of blood.
   B. Disorders: tetany, bone decalcification.
6. **Pituitary gland.**
   A. Location and structure: in skull below brain; 2 lobes.
      (1) Anterior lobe. Hormones: somatotropic; gonadotropic; thyrotropic; adrenocorticotropic; lactogenic.
      (2) Posterior lobe. Hormone functions: stimulate smooth muscle of blood vessels; reabsorption of water; stimulate uterine contraction.
   B. Effect of tumors: dwarfism; gigantism; acromegaly; obesity with underactivity of other endocrine glands.
7. **Pancreas:** islets (or islands) of Langerhans produce insulin.
   A. Function: necessary for proper use of sugar in tissues.
   B. Disorder: diabetes mellitus (caused by insufficient production of insulin).
8. **Adrenal** (or suprarenal) **glands:** 2 of these; each has medulla and cortex.
   A. Adrenal medulla: produces epinephrine (adrenaline). Effects: contraction of arteriole walls; conversion of glycogen to sugar; increased heartbeat; dilation of bronchioles.
   B. Adrenal cortex: hormones control sodium reabsorption, change amino acids to sugar, govern certain secondary sexual characteristics (mostly in male).
   C. Disorders: Hypofunction of cortex (Addison's disease). Tumors of cortex (rapid sexual development in children, masculinity in adult women). Tumors of medulla (symptoms of excess epinephrine).
9. **Sex glands:** govern development of secondary sexual characteristics and maintain operation of reproductive system.

    A. Testosterone: male hormone.

    B. Estrone and progesterone: female hormones.

10. Placenta, thymus, and pineal body: research continuing.

QUESTIONS AND PROBLEMS

1. What is a gland? What is the usual glandular structure? What are the 2 types of glands?
2. What is a secretion? Name the 2 types of secretions.
3. Name some general functions of hormones.
4. Where is the thyroid gland located? What is its hormone and what does it do?
5. What is the cause of simple goiter?
6. Describe the effects of hypothyroidism and hyperthyroidism.
7. Name and describe briefly 3 tests for thyroid function.
8. What is the main purpose of the parathyroid hormone? What are the effects of removal of these glands? Of excess secretion?
9. Name the 2 divisions of the pituitary and describe the effects of the various hormones of each.
10. Name 4 effects of pituitary tumors.
11. What is the purpose of insulin in the body? Name and describe the condition characterized by insufficient production of insulin.
12. Name the 2 divisions of the adrenal glands and the effects of the hormones of each.
13. What are the results of hypofunction of the adrenal cortex?
14. Describe some effects of tumors of the adrenal gland.
15. Name the male and female sex hormones and briefly describe what each does.
16. What is the present status in research on the thymus and the pineal body?
17. Describe some uses of hormones in treatment.

CHAPTER 19

REPRODUCTION

Specialized reproductive cells ▪ Male reproductive system and its disorders ▪ Female reproductive system and its disorders ▪ Pregnancy, normal and abnormal ▪ The menopause.

This chapter will concern itself with what is certainly one of the most interesting and mysterious attributes of living matter: the ability to reproduce. The lowest forms of life, the one-celled organisms, usually need no partner in order to reproduce; they simply divide by themselves. This form of reproduction is known as **asexual** (nonsexual) reproduction.

In higher animals, however, reproduction is **sexual,** meaning that there is a differentiation in the individuals: they are male or female, and both have their own specialized cells designed specifically for the perpetuation of the species. These specialized sex cells are known as **spermatozoa** (sper-mah-to-zo′ah) in the male and **ova** (o′vah) in the female. In spite of the differentiation of the reproductive apparatus in man and woman, both systems have these 3 broad characteristics in common:

1. Sex glands, or **gonads** (gon′ads or go′nads), which produce the sex cells and manufacture hormones. The sex glands include the **testes,** which are the male gonads, and the **ovaries,** which are the female gonads. Other names for sex cells are **germ cells** and **gametes** (gam′etes).
2. The tubes and passageways for the sex cells.
3. The accessory organs, which include various exocrine glands.

MALE REPRODUCTIVE SYSTEM
THE TESTES

The male gonads (testes) are normally located outside the body proper in a sac called the **scrotum** (skro′tum), suspended between the thighs. The testes are egg-

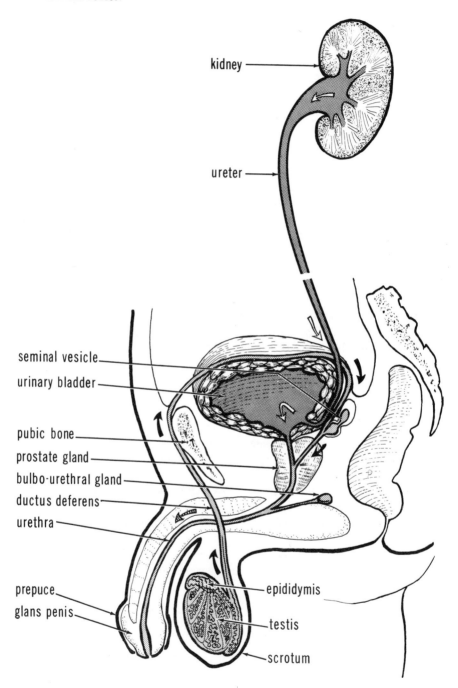

FIG. 71. Male genitourinary system.

shaped organs measuring about 1½ to 2 inches in length and approximately one inch in each of the other 2 dimensions. The bulk of the specialized tissue of the testes is arranged in tubules in the walls of which the spermatozoa are produced. Between these tiny tubes are small groups of cells that secrete the hormone testosterone.

THE MALE TUBES

The tubes for carrying the spermatozoa begin with the tubules inside the testis itself. From these tubes the spermatozoa are collected by a much-coiled 20-foot long tube called the **epididymis** (ep-e-did'e-mis), which is located inside the scrotal sac. While they are temporarily stored in the epididymis, the spermatozoa mature and become motile; that is, they become able to move or "swim" by themselves. The epididymis finally extends upward, and then this straighter part becomes the **ductus deferens** (def'er-enz). The ductus deferens continues through a small canal in the abdominal wall and then curves behind the urinary bladder. There each ductus deferens (also called the **vas deferens**) joins with a seminal vesicle (ves'e-kal), one on each side of the midline (see Fig. 71). The combination of ductus deferens, nerves and blood and lymph vessels extending from the scrotum and testis on each side through the abdominal wall is called the **spermatic cord.**

SEMINAL VESICLES

The **seminal vesicles** are tortuous muscular tubes with small outpouchings. They are about 3 inches long and are attached to the connective tissue at the back of the urinary bladder. The glandular lining produces a thick yellow secretion that forms much of the volume of the ejaculated semen. The glucose and other substances in this secretion aid in nourishing the spermatozoa.

THE PROSTATE GLAND

From the ductus deferens and the seminal vesicles the spermatozoa are carried in the vesicle secretion through the **ejaculatory** (e-jak'u-lah-to-re) **ducts,** which are located inside the prostate gland. About 40 tiny tubes from the prostate gland enter these ejaculatory ducts adding the **prostatic** (pros-tat'ik) **secretion** to the sex cells, which is another secretion that maintains the motility of the spermatozoa. The prostate gland also is supplied with muscular tissue which, upon the order of the nervous system, contracts to aid in the **ejaculation,** the expulsion of the **semen** (the mixture of spermatozoa and secretions) into the urethra and thence to the outside.

THE URETHRA AND THE PENIS

The male urethra, as we saw earlier, serves the dual purpose of conveying urine from the bladder and carrying the reproductive cells and their accompanying secretions to the outside. The ejection of semen into the receiving canal (vagina) of the female is made possible by the **erection,** or stiffening and enlargement, of the penis, through which the longest part of the urethra extends. The penis is made of a spongelike tissue in which are many blood spaces that are relatively empty when the organ is flaccid but filled with blood and distended when the penis is erect. The penis and the scrotum are referred to as the external genitalia of the male.

MUCUS-PRODUCING GLANDS

The largest of the mucus-producing glands in the male reproductive system are a pair of pea-sized organs located in the pelvic floor tissues just below the prostate gland. They are called the **bulbourethral** (bul-bo-u-re′thral), or **Cowper's, glands.** Their ducts extend for about an inch from each side and then empty into the urethra just before it extends within the penis. Other very small glands secrete mucus into the urethra as it passes through the penis. The mucus from all these glands helps to provide ideal conditions for the spermatozoa to maintain themselves. However, according to some authorities, the prostatic secretion and the mucus serve mainly as lubricants.

THE SPERMATOZOA

The spermatozoa themselves are tiny detached cells. The fact that at least 200 million spermatozoa are contained in the average ejaculation may give some idea of their size. The individual sperm cell is egg-shaped and has a tail which enables it to make its way through the various passages until it reaches the ovum of the female. It is interesting to note that out of the millions of spermatozoa in an ejaculation, only one of these actually fertilizes the ovum. The remainder of the spermatozoa perish within a short time.

DISORDERS OF THE MALE REPRODUCTIVE SYSTEM

Cryptorchidism. Cryptorchidism (krip-tor′ki-dizm) means "hidden testes," and is a disorder characterized by failure of the testes to descend to the scrotum. During embryonic life the gonads of both male and female develop from tissue near the kidney. In both sexes the gonads descend to a region considerably lower than the areas of origin. The female gonad descends only as far as the pelvic part of the abdomen, while the testis continues down through the abdominal wall and into the scrotum. This complete descent of the testis is necessary if it is to function normally, the reason being that in order to produce spermatozoa, the testes must be kept at the temperature of the scrotum, which is lower than that of the abdominal cavity. Undescended testes also are particularly subject to tumor formation. A rupture (hernia) is usually present, requiring surgery, which preferably should be done in childhood. In some cases hormonal treatment may stimulate descent of the testes (or testis, depending upon whether one or both testes are undescended).

Rupture. During embryonic life the testis pushes through the muscles and connective tissues of the abdominal wall, carrying with it the blood vessels and the other structures that later form the spermatic cord. This region in the abdominal wall is called the **inguinal** (ing'gwi-nal) **canal.** In the normal adult this area is fairly well reinforced with connective tissue, and there is no direct connection between the abdominal cavity and the scrotal sac. However, this area, as well as some other regions in which openings permit the passage of various structures to and from the abdominal cavity, constitute weak places at which a rupture in the wall may occur. The scientific name for rupture is **hernia** (her'ne-ah), and the most common type is inguinal hernia. Often surgical repair is required.

Infections. Infections of various kinds may involve the male reproductive organs, but by far the most common is **gonorrhea.** This disease manifests itself by a discharge from the urethra, which may be accompanied by burning and pain, especially during urination. The infection may travel along the mucous membrane into the prostate gland and into the epididymis; and if both sides are affected and enough scar tissue is formed to destroy the tubules, sterility may be the result.

Other infectious agents that sometimes invade the reproductive organs include the tubercle bacillus and various staphylococci. The testes may be involved in mumps with a resulting **orchitis** (or-ki'tis), which is inflammation of the testes.

Tumors. Tumor formation may involve the male reproductive organs, most commonly the prostate, and is quite common in elderly men. Such growths may be benign or malignant. Both cause such pressure on the urethra that urination becomes difficult, and back pressure often causes destruction of kidney tissue, as well as permitting stagnation of urine in the bladder with a resulting tendency to infection. Removal of the prostate or parts of it should be done early in order to prevent serious damage to the urinary system.

Phimosis. Phimosis (fi-mo'sis) refers to a tightness of the foreskin (prepuce) so that it cannot be drawn back. This may be remedied by circumcision by which part or all of the foreskin is removed. This operation is often done on very young male infants as a routine measure, either for hygienic reasons or because of religious principles.

Sterility. Sterility means inability to reproduce. The proportion of sterile marriages due to defects involving the male has been estimated variously from one third to one half. The tubules of the testes are very sensitive to x-rays, to infections, to toxins and to malnutrition, all of which bring about degenerative changes in the tubules. Sometimes sterilization is performed deliberately by operation, a

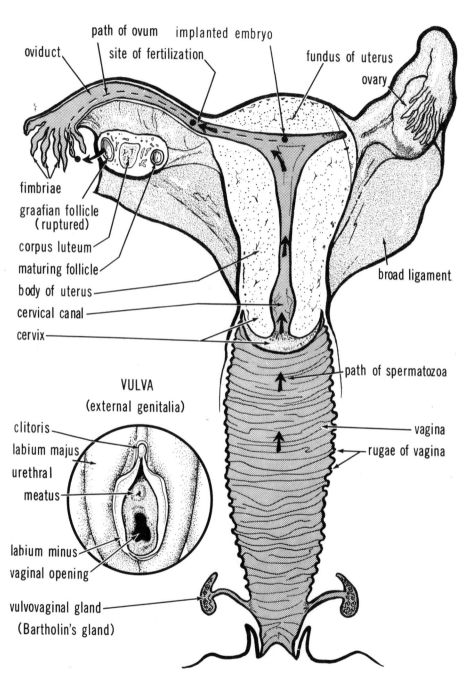

FIG. 72. Female reproductive system.

portion of the ductus deferens on each side being removed to keep the spermatozoa from reaching the urethra. These tiny cells are absorbed without injury, and the individual retains the ability to produce hormones as well as to perform the sex act.

FEMALE REPRODUCTIVE SYSTEM

THE OVARIES, OR FEMALE GONADS

In the female the counterparts of the testes are the 2 **ovaries,** and it is within the ovaries that the female sex cells, or **ova,** are formed. The ovaries are small bodies located in the pelvic part of the abdomen, and are attached to the back of structures made of 2 layers of peritoneum (called broad ligaments).

The outer layer of each ovary is made of a special epithelium, and it is within this tissue that the ova are produced. The ova are formed and begin a complicated process of maturation in small sacs called **ovarian follicles** (o-va're-an fol'e-kls). When an ovum has "ripened," the ovarian follicle literally ruptures, and the ovum is discharged from the surface of the ovary, whence it makes its way to the duct known as the **fallopian** (fah-lo'pe-an) **tube,** of which there is one for each ovary. The rupture of a follicle allowing the escape of the egg cell is called **ovulation** (ov-u-la'shun), and it occurs regularly once a month, probably about halfway between menstrual periods. Although the ovaries produce a vast number of ova, usually only one ovum at a time is released. The regularity of this occurrence is apparently due to the hormones from the pituitary gland.

THE FALLOPIAN TUBES

The egg-carrying tubes of the female reproductive system are variously called **oviducts, uterine** (u'ter-in) **tubes,** or **fallopian tubes.** They are small, muscular structures, nearly 5 inches long, extending from near the ovaries to the uterus (womb). There is no direct connection between the ovaries and these tubes. The ova are swept into the tubes by a current in the peritoneal fluid produced by small fringelike extensions from the edges of the abdominal openings of the tubes. These extensions are called **fimbriae** (fim'bre-e). Once inside the tubes, the ova, which—unlike the spermatozoa—cannot move by themselves, are kept moving toward the uterus by the action of the cilia in the lining of the tubes as well as by peristalsis. It takes about 5 days for the ovum to reach the uterus from the ovary.

THE UTERUS

The organ to which the fallopian tubes lead is the **uterus** (u'ter-us), and it is within this structure that the fetus grows until it is ready to be born.

The uterus is a muscular pear-shaped organ located between the urinary bladder and the rectum. It is approximately 3 inches long, 2 inches wide, and about 1 inch deep. The upper portion is the larger and is called the body, or **corpus,** while the lower smaller part is called the **cervix (ser'viks), meaning** "necklike." The small rounded part above the level of the tubal entrances is known as the **fundus** (fun'dus). The cavity inside the uterus is shaped somewhat like a tiny capital T, but is capable of changing shape and dilating as the embryo (later called the fetus) develops. The cervix leads to the **vagina** (vah-ji'nah), the lower part of the birth canal, which opens to the outside of the body.

The interior layer of the uterus is a specialized epithelium known as **endometrium** (en-do-me'tre-um), and it is this layer which is concerned with the phenomenon of menstruation. In order to see the whole picture of this cycle, let us return to the ovaries for a moment.

Remember that the ovum is released about halfway between menstrual periods. While the ovum is still ripening in its follicle, it is surrounded by a fluid which contains the hormone **estrone.** This hormone is carried by the blood to the uterus, where it prepares the endometrium for a possible pregnancy. These preparations include thickening of the endometrium and elongation of the glands that produce the uterine secretion.

The ovum is released, to begin its journey to the uterus. It may or may not become fertilized while passing through the fallopian tube. If it is not fertilized, it disintegrates soon after it reaches the uterus. Also, if fertilization does not occur, the endometrium of the uterus begins to deteriorate. Small hemorrhages appear in this lining, producing the bleeding known as the **menstrual flow.** Bits of the endometrium come away and accompany the menstrual flow. This discharge lasts from 1 to 5 days on the average.

Before the flow ceases, the endometrium begins to repair itself through the growth of new cells from the underlying layer of tissue. Within the ovaries a new ovum is ripening, and the cycle begins anew.

THE VAGINA

The vagina is a muscular tube about 3 inches long connecting the uterine cavity with the outside. It receives the cervix, which dips into the upper vagina in such a way that a circular recess is formed, giving rise to areas known as **fornices** (for'ne-sez). The deepest of these spaces is behind the cervix and is called the **posterior fornix** (for'niks). This recess in the posterior vagina is separated from the lowest part of the peritoneal cavity by a rather thin layer of tissue, so that abscesses or tumor cells in the peritoneal cavity sometimes can be detected by vaginal examination.

The lining of the vagina is a folded type of mucous membrane something like that found in the stomach. These folds (rugae) permit of enlargement so that childbirth will not tear the lining (as a rule). In addition to being a part of the birth canal, the vagina is the organ which receives the penis during sexual intercourse. At or near the vaginal (vaj′i-nal) canal opening to the outside there sometimes may be found a more or less definite fold of membrane called the **hymen.**

THE VULVOVAGINAL GLANDS

Just above and to each side of the vaginal opening are the mucus-producing **vulvovaginal** (vul-vo-vaj′i-nal), or **Bartholin's, glands.** These paired structures are also called the **greater vestibular** (ves-tib′u-lar) **glands** because they open into an area near the vaginal opening known as the **vestibule.** These glands may become infected, then painfully swollen and finally abscessed. A surgical incision to promote drainage may be required (see Fig. 72).

THE VULVA AND THE PERINEUM

The external parts of the female reproductive system form the **vulva** (vul′vah). These include 2 pairs of lips, or **labia** (la′be-ah), the **clitoris** (kli′to-ris), which is a small organ of great sensitivity, and related structures. Although the entire pelvic floor is properly called the **perineum** (per-i-ne′um) in both the male and the female, those who care for the pregnant woman usually refer to the limited area between the vaginal opening and the anus. The pelvic floor tissues may be torn during childbirth. Such a tear does not heal readily; and after it does, it often leaves a weakened area in the pelvic floor. Because of this the physician often cuts the perineum just before the child is born and then repairs this clean cut immediately after childbirth. Such an operation is called an **episiotomy** (e-piz-e-ot′o-me).

DISORDERS OF THE FEMALE REPRODUCTIVE SYSTEM

Leukorrhea. A nonbloody vaginal discharge, usually whitish in color, is called leukorrhea (lu-ko-re′ah). It is not a disease but rather a symptom of infection or congestion of some part of the reproductive tract, usually the cervix or vagina, and is one of the most common disorders of the female reproductive system. The usual causative organism is a protozoan called the *Trichomonas* (tri-kom′o-nas) *vaginalis.* There may be other causes so that a microscopic examination of the discharge should be done in order to make a diagnosis. In some cases the cervical glands may habitually produce larger than average amounts of colorless mucus, especially during the time of ovulation, halfway between menstrual periods.

Damage to the cervix during childbirth is a common factor in infections of the cervix resulting in leukorrhea. A variety of organisms may then invade the injured cervix. This is one of the reasons for examinations following childbirth. Such a diseased cervix, if neglected, may become cancerous.

Menstrual Disorders. Absence of the menstrual flow is known as **amenorrhea** (a-men-o-re′ah). This condition can be symptomatic of such a disorder as insufficient hormone secretion, or of a congenital abnormality of the reproductive organs. Very often psychological factors play a part in stoppage of the menstrual flow. For example, a change in the pattern of living such as a shift in working hours can cause a woman to miss a period. Any significant change in the general state of health can cause this also. The most common cause of amenorrhea (except, of course, for the menopause) is pregnancy.

Dysmenorrhea (dis-men-o-re′ah) means painful or difficult menstruation. It may be classified as primary in cases in which the cause is unknown, or as secondary if it is caused by pathology involving the pelvic organs. The pain may be mild, or it may be so severe that it resembles the colic found in the case of a stone in the ureter or in a bile duct. More common causes include pelvic congestion, endocrine disturbances, faulty position of the uterus, nervous upsets, or some type of obstruction that prevents the free flow of the menstrual discharge. In many cases women have been completely relieved of menstrual cramps by the first pregnancy. Apparently the cervical openings are thus enlarged adequately. Artificially dilating the cervical openings may alleviate dysmenorrhea for several months. Often such health measures as sufficient rest, a well-balanced diet, and appropriate exercises will remedy dysmenorrhea. During the attack the application of heat over the abdomen usually relieves the pain, just as it may ease other types of muscular cramps.

Premenstrual tension is a condition in which nervousness, irritability, and depression precedes the menstrual period. It is thought to be due to fluid retention in various tissues, including the brain. Sometimes a low salt diet and appropriate medication for the 2 weeks before the menses prevents this disorder. This treatment also may avert dysmenorrhea.

Abnormal uterine bleeding includes excessive menstrual flow, too-frequent menstruation, and nonmenstrual bleeding. Any of these may cause serious anemias and deserve careful medical attention. Nonmenstrual bleeding may be an indication of a tumor, possibly cancer.

Tumors. Fibroids, which are more correctly called myomas (see Chap. 4), are common tumors of the uterus. Studies indicate that about 50 per cent of women who reach the age of 50 have one or more of these growths in the walls of the uterus. Very often they are small, and usually they remain benign and produce no symptoms. They develop between puberty and the menopause and ordinarily stop growing after 50. In some cases these growths interfere with pregnancy and if the patient is under 40, the surgeon may simply shell out the tumor and leave the uterus fairly intact. Normal pregnancy has developed after such surgery.

Fibroids may become so large that pressure on adjacent structures causes grave disorders. In some cases invasion of blood vessels near the uterine cavity causes serious hemorrhages. For these and other reasons it may be necessary to remove the entire uterus or the larger part of it. Surgical removal of the uterus is called a **hysterectomy** (his-ter-ek'to-me).

Cancer of the uterus is relatively common. It involves the body of the organ in about 1 in 7 cases and there is some evidence that this type of cancer is on the increase. However, most uterine cancers originate in the cervix, and these occur in younger women than do those that begin in the body of the uterus. It has been thought that injuries sustained during childbirth may be one of the predisposing causes, since nearly all of the victims have had children. However, about 80 per cent of all women have had children by the time they reach middle age and most of them do not have cancer. Therefore some investigators question the assumption that there is this definite relationship between childbearing and cancer of the cervix.

Abnormal discharge or irregular bleeding are among the first symptoms noted by the patient who has cancer of the uterus. Routine cancer detection studies, including particularly the **Papanicolaou's** (pap-ah-nik-o-la'ooz) **stain** of material from the upper vagina, are now responsible for saving many lives. All women should be encouraged to request these studies each year, since waiting until symptoms appear may be courting disaster.

Cancer of the breast is one of the most common malignancies, being third in frequency in the female. The growth is usually painless and so often is not discovered; or if it is noted, it is too frequently ignored. Films are now being shown for the purpose of teaching techniques that will help future victims to find these growths early. Any lump, be it ever so small, should be reported to a physician at once. Total removal of the affected breast together with the axillary lymph nodes is the usual and most effective treatment at the present time. This operation is known as a **radical mastectomy** (mas-tek'to-me), and is often followed by radiation treatments in order to insure the destruction of any stray cancer cells that might remain after surgery.

Salpingitis (sal-pin-ji'tis) means "inflammation of a tube," and is used most often to refer to disease of the fallopian tubes. Infection of the fallopian tubes is caused by gonorrhea in most cases, though other bacteria (including the tubercle bacillus) can bring it about. Salpingitis may cause sterility by obstructing the tubes and thus preventing the passage of the ovum.

Sterility. In the female sterility is much more difficult to diagnose and evaluate than it is in the male. Whereas a microscopic examination of properly collected seminal fluid may be all that is required to determine the presence of abnormal or too few spermatozoa, no such simple study can be made relative to the female. Sterility may be relative or absolute, as is also true in the male. Causes of female sterility include infections, endocrine disorders, psychogenic factors, and abnormalities in the structure and function of the reproductive organs themselves. In all cases the male partner should be investigated first, since the procedures for determining sterility in the male are much simpler, less costly, and in any case essential for the evaluation.

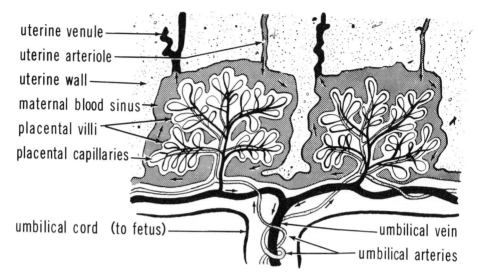

uterine venule
uterine arteriole
uterine wall
maternal blood sinus
placental villi
placental capillaries

umbilical cord (to fetus)
umbilical vein
umbilical arteries

FIG. 73. Section of the placenta.

PREGNANCY

FIRST STAGES OF PREGNANCY

The sperm cells are injected by the male into the vagina, and they immediately begin their journey into the uterus and the fallopian tubes. When a sperm cell encounters the ovum, it penetrates the cell membrane of the ovum; and the result of the union of these 2 cells is a cell which now can divide and grow into a new individual. The new cell formed by this union is called the **zygote** (zi′gote). It immediately begins a process of cell division by which a ball of simple cells is formed, and during this time the cilia of the fallopian tube lining are pushing these cells toward the uterine cavity.

As soon as fertilization has taken place, a second female hormone, normally produced to some extent after ovulation has occurred, is manufactured in a greatly increased quantity. To find its origin, let us have another look at the ovary. Once the ovum has left the follicle, the follicle is transformed into a solid glandular mass called the **corpus luteum** (lu′te-um), meaning "yellow body." This yellow body produces its own hormone known as **progesterone** (pro-jes′ter-one), a word meaning roughly "for pregnancy." Normally this hormone takes up where the estrone left off in preparing the endometrium for pregnancy. Now that the ovum has been fertilized, the corpus luteum is much increased in size and its production of progesterone stepped up accordingly. Since the prepared endometrium now is to be put to use in containing the growing embryo, menstruation ceases. The increased quantity of progesterone brings about the final changes in the endometrium which enable the embryo to be "planted" and nourished within this layer of tissue.

As the pregnancy progresses, the progesterone-forming tissue continues to be stimulated by yet other hormones manufactured by an organ known as the **placenta** (plah-sen'tah), which will be discussed in a moment.

After reaching the uterus, the little ball of cells becomes imbedded in the now greatly thickened uterine lining. Then there begins a process of invasion into maternal blood vessels by projections (villi) made of embryonic cells from the ball-like mass. A flat, circular organ called the **placenta** eventually is formed by this process, serving as the organ of nutrition, respiration, and excretion for the developing individual. The new human being is called an **embryo** (em'bre-o) until the third month; and after that the term **fetus** (fe'tus) is used until birth.

DEVELOPMENT OF THE EMBRYO

Embryology (em-bre-ol'o-je) is the study of the development of the embryo. This science begins with the fertilization of the ovum and includes a complex series of changes about which many books have been written. It is important in understanding the human body, but it is too complex and involved for a short book of this nature. Actually the embryo develops from but a very small part of the original ball of simple cells. The placenta and the sac that surrounds the embryo as well as the **umbilical** (um-bil'e-kal) **cord** also are structures that originate largely from some of the simple primitive cells of this ball. Among the first organs to develop in the embryo are the heart and the brain. By the end of the first month the embryo is about a fourth of an inch long with 4 small swellings at the sides called **limb buds,** which will develop into the 4 extremities. At this time the heart produces a prominent bulge at the front of the embryo. By the end of the second month the embryo takes on an appearance that is recognizably human.

THE FETUS

By the end of the third month the new individual, now known as a fetus, has reached a length of nearly 4 inches, including the legs. By the seventh month the fetus is usually about 14 inches long, while at the end of pregnancy the normal length is around 18 to 20 inches and the weight varies from 6 to 9 pounds.

Since the ball of cells became attached to the wall of the uterus, various auxiliary organs designed to serve the fetus have been developing as well. Two of these are the placenta and the umbilical cord, the latter connecting the fetus with the placenta. The cord contains 2 arteries and a vein. The fetus is encased in a membrane called the **amniotic** (am-ne-ot'ik) **sac,** and this sac is filled with a clear liquid, **amniotic fluid,** which serves as a protective cushion for the fetus. The

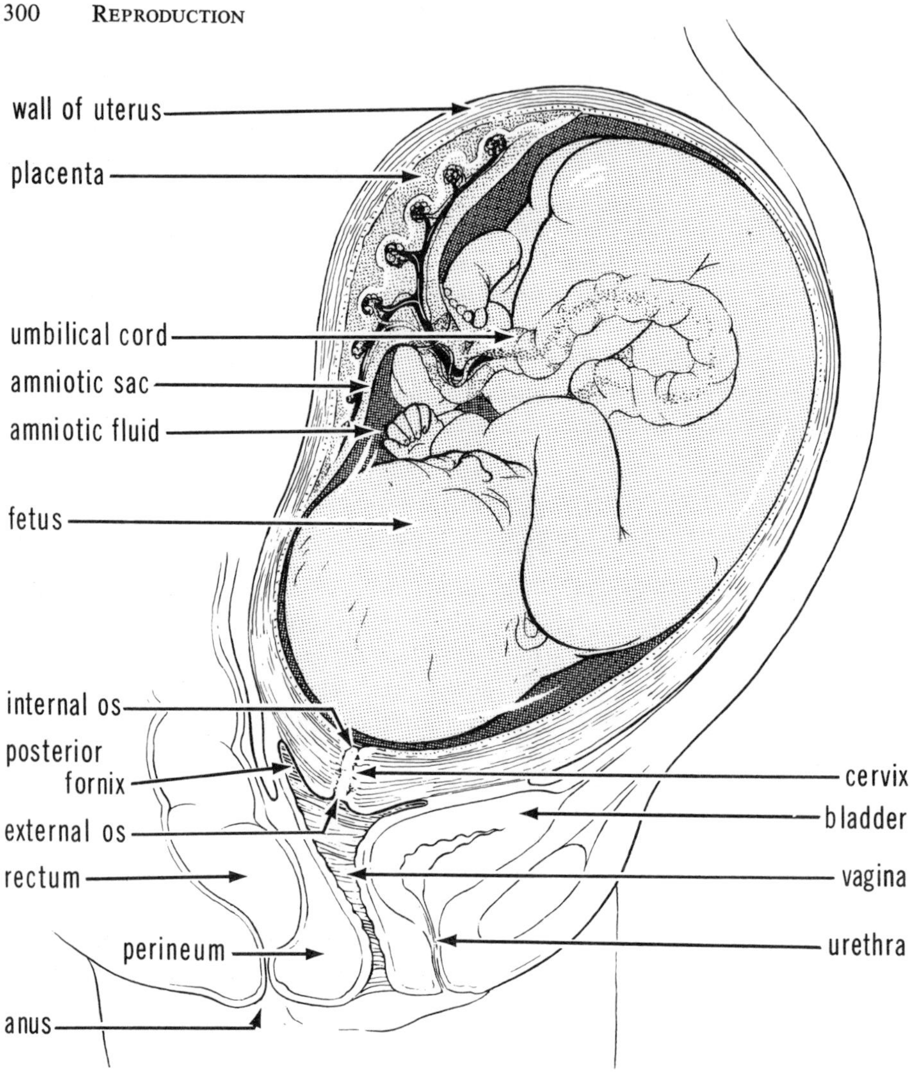

wall of uterus

placenta

umbilical cord

amniotic sac

amniotic fluid

fetus

internal os

posterior fornix

external os

rectum

perineum

anus

cervix

bladder

vagina

urethra

FIG. 74. Midsagittal section of the pregnant uterus.

amniotic sac, which ruptures at birth, is popularly known as the bag of waters. The skin of the fetus is protected by a layer of cheeselike material called **vernix caseosa** (ver′niks ka-se-o′sah).

THE MOTHER

The total period of pregnancy, from fertilization of the ovum to birth, is about 280 days. During this period the mother must supply all the food and oxygen for the fetus, and eliminate its waste materials as well. She must certainly "eat for two," and the calcium intake should be especially high, since the developing bones and teeth of the fetus call for great quantities of this element. The kidneys of the mother have an especially heavy burden imposed upon them because of the larger amount of nitrogenous waste to be eliminated. For this reason and others it is important that the kidneys function normally.

Nausea and vomiting are present in nearly half of all pregnancies, especially during the early months. These symptoms may be due to a temporary imbalance in body chemistry. There may be a lack of certain hormones or vitamins, a sensitivity to progesterone, or possibly some disturbance of carbohydrate metabolism. Most frequently nausea appears about the 5th week of pregnancy and lasts for a few weeks. In many cases the patient awakes in the morning feeling nauseated and is unable to retain her breakfast, but by noon she feels better and usually to able to retain other meals without any difficulty.

Toxemias of pregnancy are serious disorders, usually metabolic, that can develop in the latter part of the pregnancy. The patient may have convulsions and the condition can end fatally. Hypertension and albumin in the urine are evidences of this disorder and may be present before definite symptoms are noted by the patient. Regular visits to the physician for checks of the blood pressure and the urine are the best preventive measures. Early treatment of toxemias will usually avert disastrous results.

Frequency of urination and constipation are often present during the early stages of the pregnancy and then usually disappear as the pregnancy progresses. Late in the pregnancy these symptoms may reappear because the head of the fetus often drops from the abdominal region down into the pelvis where it may press on the rectum and the urinary bladder.

CHILDBIRTH

The process of giving birth to a child is known medically as **parturition** (par-tu-rish'un), and as a rule it is divided into 3 stages:

1. In the first stage, the muscles of the uterus begin the contractions known as **labor pains.** During this process the amniotic sac is forced into the cervix, serving to dilate it. This stage usually requires several hours, at the end of which time the amniotic sac usually ruptures.

2. This stage involves the passage of the fetus, head first as a rule, through the cervical canal and the vagina to the outside.

3. During the third stage, usually 15 or 20 minutes after the child is born, the **afterbirth** is expelled. The afterbirth includes the placenta, the membranes of the amniotic sac, and the umbilical cord, except for a small portion remaining attached to the baby's navel, or **umbilicus** (um-bi-li'kus or um-bil'e-kus).

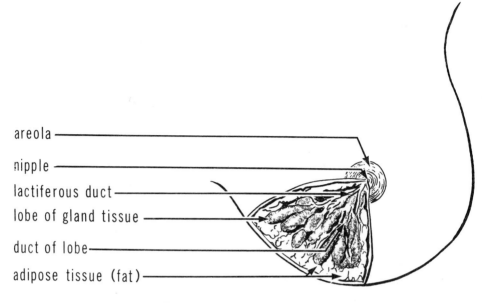

areola ————————————

nipple ————————————

lactiferous duct————————

lobe of gland tissue ————

duct of lobe————————

adipose tissue (fat)————————

FIG. 75. Section of the breast.

THE MAMMARY GLANDS AND LACTATION

The **mammary glands,** or the breasts of the female, are accessories of the reproductive system. They are designed to provide nourishment for the baby after its birth; and the secretion of milk at this period is known as **lactation** (lak-ta'shun).

The mammary glands are constructed in much the same manner as are the sweat glands. Each of these glands is divided into a number of lobes composed of glandular tissue and fat, and each lobe in turn is subdivided. The secretions from the lobes are conveyed through **lactiferous** (lak-tif'er-us) **ducts,** all of which converge at the nipple (see Fig. 75).

Although the mammary glands begin development during puberty, they do not become functional until at the end of pregnancy. A lactogenic hormone **(prolactin),** produced by the anterior lobe of the pituitary, stimulates the secretory cells of the mammary glands. The first of the mammary gland secretions is a thin liquid called **colostrum** (ko-los'trum). It is nutritious but has a somewhat different composition from milk. Within a few days milk is secreted, and it will continue for several months if frequently removed by the suckling baby or by pumping.

The digestive tract of the newborn baby is not ready for the usual mixed diet of an adult. The mother's milk is more desirable for the young infant than is that from other animals for several reasons. Some of these are:

1. Infections that may be transmitted by foods exposed to the outside air are avoided by nursing the baby.

2. The psychological and emotional satisfactions of nursing the infant are thought to be of infinite value to both the mother and the child.

3. Antibodies may be unaffected by the less potent digestive juices found in the infant. Thus these antibodies may help to protect the baby against pathogens.

4. The particular proportion of the various nutrients and other substances in human milk are believed to be especially well suited to the human infant. While substitutes are made to imitate as nearly as possible the qualities of human milk, it is not likely that every detail of the content of human milk is well enough known to make an exact replica possible. Nutrients are present in more desirable amounts if the mother's diet is well balanced.

MULTIPLE BIRTHS

Statistics indicate that twins occur in about 1 in every 80 to 90 births, varying somewhat in different countries. Triplets occur much less frequently, usually once in several thousand births, while quadruplets occur very rarely indeed, and the birth of quintuplets represents an historical event.

Twins originate in 2 different ways, and on this basis are divided into 2 groups:

1. **Fraternal** twins are formed as a result of the fertilization of 2 different ova by 2 spermatozoa. Two completely different individuals, as different from each other as other brothers and sisters, except in age, are produced. Each fetus has its own placenta and surrounding sac.

2. **Identical** twins develop from a single zygote formed from a single ovum fertilized by a single spermatozoan. Sometime during early stages of development the simple embryonic cells separate into 2 (or more) groups. Usually there is a single placenta, although there naturally must be an umbilical cord for each individual.

Other multiple births may be fraternal, identical, or combinations of these. The tendency to multiple births seems to be hereditary.

Fertility drugs have increased the number of multiple births. These drugs stimulate the ovary either directly or indirectly (via the pituitary). The usual prematurity of multiple births causes a very high death rate. Newer drugs that will cause less drastic stimulation are being investigated, with the hope that single births and more living children will be the end result.

DISORDERS OF PREGNANCY

Ectopic Pregnancy. A pregnancy that develops in a location outside the uterine cavity is said to be an **ectopic** (ek-top'ik) pregnancy, "ectopic" meaning "out of its normal place." The most common type is the **tubal** ectopic pregnancy, in which the growth of the embryo takes place inside the fallopian tube. Sometimes the tube ruptures, causing internal hemorrhage, in which case surgery must be done to save the mother's life.

Placenta Previa (pre'via). This is an abnormal condition in which the placenta is attached at or near the internal opening of the cervix. Whereas the placenta is usually attached to the upper part of the uterus, in placenta previa it becomes attached to the lower segment of the organ. This condition can cause a separation of the placenta from the uterine wall, resulting in hemorrhage as well as in interference with the fetal oxygen supply. Sometimes placenta previa calls for a **cesarean section,** which is delivery of the fetus by way of an incision made in the abdominal wall and the wall of the uterus.

LACTATION DISTURBANCES

Lactation disturbances may be due to a variety of reasons, including:

1. Malnutrition or anemia, which may prevent lactation entirely.

2. Emotional disturbances, which may affect lactation (as they may other glandular activities).

3. Abnormalities of parts of the mammary glands or injuries to these organs, which may cause interference with their functioning.

4. **Mastitis** (mas-ti'tis), which means inflammation of the breast, and which would make nursing the child inadvisable.

FETAL DEATHS AND LIVE BIRTHS

Because of the confusion concerning the meanings of the words "abortion" and "miscarriage," another set of terms, recommended by a World Health Committee, was approved by the World Health Assembly in June of 1950. Most records concerning fetal deaths and live births now use this terminology, which is as follows:

Group I.   Early fetal death, when the embryo or fetus is less than 20 weeks old.

Group II.   Intermediate fetal death, when the fetus is more than 20 but less than 28 weeks old.

Group III. Late fetal death, when the fetus is more than 28 weeks old.

Group IV. Not classifiable under Groups I, II, or III.

The classification **Live Birth** is used if the baby breathes or shows any evidence of life such as a heart beat, definite movement of voluntary muscles, or pulsation of the umbilical cord. The term **Immature Infant** is used (instead of premature infant) if the baby weighs less than 5½ pounds (2,500 grams), or if the pregnancy has been of less than 37 weeks duration.

In the recent past, efforts at clarifying the words "abortion" and "miscarriage" led to many definitions, still being used considerably, such as the following:

I. Abortion, the loss of the embryo or fetus during the first 20 weeks for any reason. These may be considered in 2 categories:

1. **Spontaneous abortions,** which are due in the great majority of cases to some abnormality of the embryo, and may represent a way by which nature expels undesirable products of conception. Abortions may also be caused by infections in the mother, chronic disorders such as kidney disease or diabetes, or certain abnormalities of the uterus.

2. **Induced abortions,** which represent termination of pregnancy through artificial means. This classification includes **criminal abortions,** which are performed illegally and which are the cause of many tragic and unnecessary deaths each year.

II. Miscarriage, the loss of the fetus between 20 and 28 weeks.

III. Premature birth, the birth of the baby between 28 and 40 weeks (approximately 9 months).

It should be mentioned that the fetus stands little or no chance of survival if he is expelled before the 6th or 7th month, while after the 7th month the fetus is **viable,** that is, capable of living outside the uterus. The nearer the fetus comes to being the full 9 months of age, the better are its chances of survival. The belief that a 7-month fetus may be more likely to live than the 8-month fetus is without basis in fact. **Immaturity** (prematurity) is one of the most common causes of death in the newborn.

THE MENOPAUSE

The **menopause** (men'o-pawz), popularly called the change of life, is that period at which menstruation ceases altogether. It ordinarily occurs between the ages of 42 and 54, the average being about 48, and is caused by cessation of ovarian activity. The ovary becomes chiefly scar tissue and no longer produces either ova or estrone. Because of the lack of this hormone, the uterus, the fallopian tubes, the vagina and the vulva all gradually become atrophied.

Although the menopause is an entirely normal condition, its onset sometimes brings about effects that are temporarily disturbing. The absence of estrone can cause such nervous symptoms as irritability, "hot flashes," and extreme excitability. Sometimes these symptoms are relieved through the administration of estrone or one of its derivatives. As a rule, the better a woman's state of health, the less traumatic this period will be.

SUMMARY

1. **Reproduction.**
   A. Asexual in lowest forms of life.
   B. Sexual in higher forms. Specialized cells: ova in female, spermatozoa in male.

C. Reproductive systems in human male and female have in common: gonads, passageways for sex cells, accessory organs.

2. **Male reproductive system.**

A. Parts and functions: testes (produce spermatozoa and testosterone); tubes (epididymis, ductus deferens); seminal vesicles (form bulk of secretion in semen); prostate gland (contains ejaculatory ducts, produces secretion, muscle produces ejaculation); penis (organ of copulation, contains urethra, erectile tissue); bulbourethral glands (mucus).

B. Disorders: cryptorchidism, hernia, gonorrhea, tumors of prostate, phimosis, sterility (can be caused by degenerative changes in tubules of testes).

3. **Female reproductive system.**

A. Parts and functions: ovaries (produce ova and estrone; progesterone from corpus luteum); fallopian tubes (convey ova; fertilization occurs here); uterus (lined with endometrium which is prepared by hormones for pregnancy; embryo grows here); vagina (part of birth canal); vulva (labia, clitoris); greater vestibular glands; perineum.

B. Disorders: leukorrhea, menstrual disorders (amenorrhea, dysmenorrhea), tumors (fibroids, cancer of uterus and breast), salpingitis, sterility.

4. **Pregnancy.**

A. First stages: ovulation; sperm cell fertilizes ovum in fallopian tube; zygote divides, moves to uterus; implanted in uterus; progesterone production increased; menstruation ceases; placenta formed.

B. Development of embryo: heart and brain develop early; limb buds after first month; human appearance after second month.

C. Fetus: weighs 6-9 pounds at birth; is in amniotic sac with amniotic fluid; covered with vernix caseosa; umbilical cord connects fetus and placenta.

D. Mother: supplies food and oxygen for fetus; high calcium intake required; kidneys heavily worked.

E. Childbirth. Sequence: labor pains, dilation of cervix, rupture of amniotic sac, passage of the fetus, expulsion of afterbirth.

F. Lactation: secretion of milk by mammary glands (divided into lobes with lactiferous ducts).

G. Multiple births. Twins: fraternal (fertilization of 2 ova by 2 spermatozoa); identical (formed from single zygote).

H. Disorders: ectopic pregnancy, placenta previa, disorders of lactation.

I. Fetal deaths and live births: preferred method of recording fetal deaths is Groups I, II, III, and IV. Immaturity (prematurity) causes many deaths.

5. **The Menopause:** final cessation of menstruation, sometimes causing nervous symptoms. These may be relieved by hormone administration.

QUESTIONS AND PROBLEMS

1. In what fundamental respect does reproduction in the lowest animals differ from that of the higher?

2. Name the sex cells of both the male and the female.
3. Name all the parts of the male reproductive system and describe the function of each.
4. What is cryptorchidism? Why does this condition cause sterility?
5. Name and describe a disorder of the male reproductive system that is common in elderly men.
6. Name the principal parts of the female reproductive system and describe the function of each.
7. Describe the process of ovulation.
8. Describe the processes that occur in menstruation.
9. Name 2 principal female hormones. Where are they produced, and under what circumstances? What does each do?
10. Outline briefly the following processes: conception; development of the embryo and fetus; parturition.
11. Give some reasons for both dysmenorrhea and amenorrhea.
12. Name and describe 3 common tumors of the female reproductive system.
13. What are some causes of sterility in both the male and the female?
14. What are some reasons why a mother should nurse her baby?
15. Define: ectopic pregnancy; placenta previa; abortion (2 categories); miscarriage; immaturity (prematurity).
16. Name some disturbances of lactation.
17. What is the new and preferred terminology for records of fetal deaths and live births as approved by the World Health Assembly?
18. What is the menopause? What can be done to relieve some of its distressing effects?

CHAPTER 20

IMMUNITY,
VACCINES AND SERUMS

Conditions for infection ▪ Defenses of the body ▪ What immunity means ▪ Antigens and antibodies ▪ Immunity, inborn and acquired ▪ Vaccines and booster shots ▪ Serums and borrowed antibodies ▪ Allergy ▪ Transplants and the rejection syndrome.

THE OCCURRENCE OF INFECTION

This chapter will concern itself primarily with the various defenses which the body brings to bear against parasitic invasion or other injury, with particular emphasis upon the most complex of these defenses: that series of chemical processes producing what is known as **immunity.**

It should be repeated that although the body is constantly being exposed to pathogenic invasion, a large number of conditions determine whether or not an infection will actually occur. Many pathogens have a decided preference for certain body tissues. For example, some viruses will attack only nerve tissue, as is the case with the poliomyelitis pathogen. Even though it may be inhaled or swallowed in large numbers and therefore may be in direct contact with the mucous membrane, no apparent disorder of these respiratory or digestive system linings occurs. On the other hand, such pathogens as the influenza and cold viruses do attack these mucous membranes.

The respiratory tract is a common **portal of entry** for many pathogens. Other important avenues of entry include the digestive system and the tubes that open into the urinary and the reproductive systems. Any break in the· skin or in a mucous membrane allows organisms such as staphylococci easy access to the deeper tissues and nearly always leads to infection, while the unbroken skin or membrane usually is not affected at all. The portal of entry, then, is an important condition influencing the occurrence of infection.

The **virulence** (vir'u-lens), or the power of an organism to overcome the defenses of its host, must also be considered. Virulence has 2 aspects: one may be thought of as "aggressiveness," or invasive power; and the other as the ability of the organism to produce **toxins,** or poisons, which damage the body. The virulence of different organisms varies, and the virulence of a specific organism also can change. In other words, an organism can be more dangerous at some times than at others. As a rule, organisms which come from an already infected host are more "vicious" than, say, the same type of organism grown under laboratory conditions.

The number of pathogens which invade the body also has much to do with whether or not an infection develops. Even if the virulence of a particular organism happens to be low at the moment, if a large number of them enter the body, infection has a better chance of occurring than if the number were small.

Finally, there are the defenses of the body itself, considered in sum as its **resistance.** There are certain protective devices common to all living things, effective against any harmful agent. These devices might be classified as the body's **nonspecific resistance.** Then there are devices which act against a certain specific agent and no other. These defenses are referred to as **specific resistance,** or **immunity.**

THE BODY'S DEFENSES AGAINST DISEASE

The devices which protect the body against disease usually are considered as successive "lines of defense," beginning with the relatively simple first, or outer, line and proceeding through the progressively more complicated lines until the ultimate defense mechanism—immunity—is reached.

The first line of defense against invaders is the combination of the skin and mucous membranes, which serve as mechanical barriers as long as they remain intact, by virtue of their thickness alone. Certain other properties of the skin and the mucous membranes help to discourage parasites; for example, their acid secretion. The cilia of some mucous membranes serve to keep their surfaces swept clean.

Included in this first line are other defenses of a mechanical or chemical nature. Certain reflexes aid in the removal of pathogens. Sneezing and coughing, for instance, are reflexes that tend to remove foreign matter, including microorganisms, from the upper respiratory tract. In the digestive tract the acid stomach juice destroys many organisms. Vomiting and diarrhea are ways in which toxins (poisons) and bacteria may be expelled.

The second great line of defense is the process of **inflammation,** which is the body's effort to get rid of anything that irritates it (or, if this proves impossible, to minimize the harmful effects of the irritant). Inflammation can occur as a result of any irritant, not only bacteria. Friction, fire, chemicals, x-rays and cuts or blows all can be classed as irritants. If the irritant is due to pathogenic invasion, the resulting inflammation is termed an **infection.** With the entrance of pathogens and their subsequent multiplication a whole series of defensive processes begins.

This is called an **inflammatory reaction,** and accompanying it are the 4 classic symptoms: heat, redness, swelling and pain. What takes place in the course of an inflammatory reaction is briefly this. When the parasite enters the tissues, the small blood vessels dilate, admitting more blood into the area. This is the basis of the heat, redness and swelling.

With the increased blood flow come a vast number of leukocytes. Now a new phenomenon occurs: the walls of the tiny blood vessels become "coarsened" in their texture (as a piece of cloth will do when stretched), the blood flow slows down, and the leukocytes move through these altered walls and into the tissue, where they can get at the irritant directly. Accompanying the leukocytes through the vessel walls is fluid from the blood plasma, and the mixture of white cells and this fluid is the **inflammatory exudate.** The pressure of this material, as well as that of the increased amount of blood in the vessel walls, on the nerve endings causes the pain of an inflammation.

The leukocytes now proceed to surround, engulf and digest the invaders. As was mentioned in Chapters 7 and 14, this process is called **phagocytosis** (fag-o-si-to′sis), meaning (roughly) "cell-eating" (see Fig. 21).

The bacteria fight back. They discharge their poisons (toxins) and destroy large numbers of leukocytes, so that eventually the area becomes filled with dead white cells. The mixture of exudate, living and dead white cells and pathogens plus destroyed tissue is **pus.**

Meanwhile the regional lymph nodes become enlarged and tender, a sign that they are performing their own protective function in working overtime to produce phagocytic cells which "clean" the lymph drained from the inflamed area, as well as in manufacturing lymphocytes at an accelerated rate. These cells figure in the production of **antibodies,** to be discussed shortly.

Finally we arrive at the ultimate defense against disease, immunity, to which most of this chapter will be devoted.

THE PROCESSES OF IMMUNITY

Immunity can be defined as the power of an individual to resist or overcome the effects of a particular disease or other harmful agent. Sometimes the words "immunity" and "resistance" are used interchangeably; but it is more accurate to think of the immune process as one which nullifies the effect of the invading bacteria *before* they have had a chance to set up an infection. Also, it is useful to consider immunity as a selective process; that is, a person may be immune to measles but not to diphtheria, or vice versa. This selective characteristic has a name: **specificity** (spes-i-fis′i-te).

The chemical processes that produce immunity can be described briefly as follows. Every pathogenic microorganism that enters the body carries within itself a substance known as an **antigen** (an′te-jen). When the antigen is introduced into the body, it causes certain of the body cells to produce protein compounds called

antibodies. These antibodies destroy the toxins or the pathogens, or else act on them in a way that will make the microorganisms more susceptible to the action of the white blood cells or other phagocytes. Antigens vary in their chemical structure, and a specific antigen will stimulate the body to produce only a specific antibody in response to it. The antibody, then, will react only with the kind of antigen that caused its production, and no other. This is the reason for the selective nature of immunity; so that immunity to one disease does not necessarily cause a person to be immune to another. Indeed, it is possible to have immunity to one disease and **susceptibility,** its opposite, to a different disease.

KINDS OF IMMUNITY

There are 2 main categories of immunity: **inborn** (or inherited) **immunity** and **acquired immunity.** This second type may be acquired by **natural** or **artificial** means. In addition, an acquired immunity may be either **active** or **passive.** Let us investigate each category in turn.

INBORN IMMUNITY

Although certain diseases found in animals may be transmitted to man, many infections such as chicken cholera, hog cholera, distemper in dogs, and various other animal diseases do not affect man. On the other hand, the constitutional differences that make man immune to these disorders also make him susceptible to others that do not affect the lower animals. Such infections as measles, scarlet fever, diphtheria, and influenza do not seem to affect the animals contacted by man during the time he is suffering from the contagion. Both men and animals have what is called a **species immunity** to many of each other's diseases.

Another form of inborn immunity is termed **racial immunity.** Indications seem to be that some racial groups have a greater inborn immunity to certain diseases than other racial groups. For instance, in our own country Negroes are apparently more immune to poliomyelitis, malaria, and yellow fever than are members of the white race. Jewish people seem to be more resistant to tuberculosis than are most other groups. Of course, it is often difficult to tell how much of this variation in resistance to infection is due to environment and how much is due to actual inborn traits of the particular racial or national group.

Some members of a given group have a more highly developed **individual immunity** than the other members. Newspapers and magazines sometimes feature the words of advice given by an elderly person who is asked to give his secret for living to a ripe old age, and his answer may be that he practiced temperance and lived a carefully regulated life with the right amount of rest, exercise and work. The next oldster interviewed may boast of his use of alcoholic beverages, his constant smoking, his lack of exercise, and other kinds of reputedly unhygienic behavior. Could it be that the latter oldster has lived through the onslaughts of toxins and disease organisms, resisting infection and maintaining health in spite of his environment rather than because of it, thanks to the resistance factors and immunity to disease that he inherited?

ACQUIRED IMMUNITY

The difference between an inborn immunity and an acquired immunity is that in the latter case the immunity is not due to inheritance factors. An immunity can be **naturally acquired** before birth through the transmission of antibodies from the mother by way of the placenta. An immunity also may be naturally acquired by contracting the disease itself.

On the other hand, an immunity can be **artificially acquired** by the administration of a vaccine or an immune serum.

An acquired immunity also can be classed as **active** or **passive**. The difference is that in an actively acquired immunity the antibodies are made "on the premises" —in the person's own tissues. In a passively acquired immunity, the antibodies come from some outside source. Let us look more closely at typical active and passive situations.

Active Immunity. In actively acquired immunity the person's tissues and cells *actively* manufacture antibodies by themselves which then act against the infecting agent or its toxins. Each time that a person is invaded by the organisms of a disease, his cells may manufacture antibodies that give him immunity against that particular infection for years, and in some cases for life. Sometimes a small number of relatively nonvirulent organisms may cause so little disturbance that the host is not conscious of the invasion. His tissues nevertheless may produce antibodies which give an active immunity of a natural type.

Now suppose that for one reason or other a person fails to be exposed to repeated small doses of a particular organism. Having no antibodies, he would be defenseless against a heavy onslaught of that certain pathogen, and the result might be disastrous. Therefore, artificial measures are taken to cause the person's tissues to actively manufacture antibodies. One could inject the virulent pathogen into the person's tissues, but obviously this would be dangerous. What is done, then, is to take some of the pathogen (or toxin), treat it to reduce its virulence (that is, **attenuate** it), and then inject it. In this way the tissues are made to produce antibodies without causing a serious illness. This process is known as **vaccination** or **inoculation,** and the solution containing the pathogen (with reduced virulence) is a **vaccine.** By means of vaccination an active immunity of the artificially acquired type is accomplished.

Passive Immunity. In a passively acquired immunity, it was noted, the antibodies are borrowed, not made by the person's own tissues. We already have seen an example of this in the case of the fetus, which receives antibodies from the mother's blood via the placenta. The result of this borrowing (or rather, donation) of antibodies is that at birth the infant has much more resistance to contagious diseases than he does when he is several months old. The antibodies borrowed from the mother do not last as long as those actively produced by the child himself, but they serve to "tide him over" during the period when the child's constitution might not otherwise withstand exposure to various infections. Some think it is possible that nursing the infant may lengthen the period of this immunity. These are the only known examples of naturally acquired passive immunity.

If a person receives a large dose of virulent organisms with no established immunity to them, he stands in great danger since it takes several weeks to produce a naturally acquired active immunity, and even longer to produce an artificial active immunity through the administration of a vaccine. In order to prevent catastrophe, then, the victim must receive a counteracting dose of borrowed antibodies in a hurry. This is accomplished through the administration of a **serum,** the nature and origin of which will be explained shortly. The serum gives a short-lived but effective protection against the invaders, and its action is an example of an artificially acquired passive immunity.

VACCINES AND SERUMS

VACCINES

The purpose of a vaccine, we learned, is to provide an artificially acquired active immunity to a specific disease. A vaccine is a preparation made of the actual cause of the disease—the organism or its toxin—treated in such a way that it will not cause the disease when injected but nevertheless will stimulate antibody formation. Ordinarily the administration of a vaccine is a preventive measure, designed to provide protection in anticipation of an invasion by a certain disease organism.

Sometimes the terms "vaccine" and "antigen" are confused, understandably since both are concerned with antibody formation. Think of it this way: all vaccines are antigens, but not all antigens are vaccines. Actually, the word "antigen" includes a much broader area of biologic activity. Antigens include many protein substances, such as the Rh factor in blood, the A and B proteins which are in part responsible for the 4 blood groups, as well as such toxins as snake venon and many other materials. The Rh factor from an Rh positive baby, entering the bloodstream of the Rh negative mother causes in some cases, the production of antibodies against itself. This Rh factor is an antigen, but we would not think of it as a vaccine. Vaccines, then, are merely one small group of a large number of antigenic substances, and should be thought of only as agents given to prevent disease.

Examples of Vaccines. To nearly everyone the word "vaccination" means the inoculation for smallpox. The smallpox vaccine is actually the virus of cowpox, a much less severe form of smallpox than the human form. Cowpox virus is grown on the skin of a calf for the purpose of manufacturing this vaccine.

Because of the seriousness of whooping cough in the young infant, early inoculation with whooping cough or **pertussis** (per-tus'is) vaccine, made from heat-killed whooping cough bacteria, is recommended. This vaccine sometimes is given in conjunction with diphtheria toxoid and tetanus toxoid, all in one mixture (a **toxoid** is a form of vaccine containing the weakened toxin of the disease organism instead of the organism proper). This combination, often referred to as D.P.T., may be given as early as the second month, and should be followed by additional injections at the time the child enters a school, a nursery or any other situation in which he might be exposed to one of these contagions. It is also recommended that smallpox vaccination be done in infancy.

Typhoid vaccine, made of killed typhoid bacilli, sometimes is given as part of another combination preventive inoculation, the other elements consisting of 2 different related **paratyphoid** bacteria.

A great deal of intensive research in viruses has led to the development of vaccines for an increasing number of virus diseases. Spectacular results in preventing poliomyelitis have been obtained by the use of a variety of vaccines. The first of these was the Salk vaccine. Now the more convenient oral vaccines, such as the Sabin, are used the most. A number of vaccines have been developed for influenza, this disease being caused by several different strains of virus. The measles (rubeola) and whooping cough (pertussis) vaccines are proving to be very effective. The use of German measles (rubella) vaccine will lower the number of birth defects. Although the disease itself is very mild, this vaccine is one all children might very well take in order to reduce the possibility of a pregnant woman contracting the disease. See Appendix, Table 4.

An exception to the usual rule of a vaccine being given before the invasion of the disease organism is the rabies vaccine. Rabies is a virus disease transmitted by the bite of such animals as dogs, cats, wolves, coyotes, foxes and bats. There is no actual cure for rabies; it is fatal in exactly 100 per cent of cases. However, the disease develops so slowly following the transmission of the organism that the "treatment" consists of the administration of a vaccine, there being time enough to develop an active immunity. Anyone bitten by an animal suspected of having rabies should begin this **Pasteur treatment** at once. The most desirable method of controlling rabies is to immunize all dogs.

A final word regarding the long-time efficacy of vaccines: in many cases an active immunity acquired by artificial (or even natural) means does not last a lifetime. Repeated inoculations, called booster shots, administered at relatively short intervals, help materially in maintaining a high level of immunity. The number of such booster injections recommended varies with the disease and with the environment or exposure of the individual. Anyone planning a trip into a foreign country in which smallpox is uncontrolled should be revaccinated.

SERUMS

A serum that is given for the purpose of producing an immunity should properly be called an **immune serum,** but in this discussion it will be referred to simply as a serum for the sake of convenience.

There are a number of differences between vaccines and serums. When a vaccine is given, it results in antibody formation by the body tissues. In the administration of a serum, the antibodies are supplied "ready made." The administration of a serum produces immediate immunity, but this passive immunity does not last as long as that actively produced by the body tissues.

There is a basic difference, too, in the content of vaccines and serums. Whereas the principal element of a vaccine is a weakened form of the disease organism or its toxin, a serum contains neither of these. In an earlier chapter we saw that serum as such consists of blood plasma minus the fibrinogen content. An immune serum is this basic serum with the addition of antibodies.

A serum prepared for immune purposes usually is derived from animals, mainly horses. It has been found that the tissues of the horse produce large quantities of antibodies in response to the injection of organisms or their toxins. After repeated injections the horse is bled, using careful sterile technique; and because of the size of the animal it is possible to remove large quantities without injury. The blood is allowed to clot, the serum is removed, and it is packaged in sterile glass vials or other appropriate containers. It is then sent to the hospital, clinic, or doctor's office for use. In most cases the use of a serum is in the nature of an emergency; that is, there is no time to wait until an active immunity has developed.

Examples of Serums. Most immune serums are of the type known as **antitoxins;** that is, they neutralize the toxins but have no effect upon the toxic organisms themselves. The following are a few typical immune serums obtained from horses or other animals:

1. Diphtheria serum, which contains large amounts of antitoxin.

2. Tetanus serum, which contains antitoxin against tetanus toxin, and is very valuable in preventing lockjaw (tetanus), usually a complication of neglected wounds.

3. Antiplague serum, effective against the plague bacillus (fortunately a rarity in the United States).

4. Anti-snake-bite serum, or **antivenin** (an-te-ven'in), which is used to combat the effects of bites by certain poisonous snakes.

Not all serums are derived from animals; some are of human origin. An example of this latter category is gamma globulin, a fraction of human blood serum which is very rich in antibodies. Gamma globulin is effective against measles, which by itself or because of its complications (pneumonia, for one) can be dangerous, particularly in children. If gamma globulin does not actually prevent measles, it at least will reduce the seriousness of the disease.

Another example of the use of human serum is in **convalescent** serum therapy, in which the serum (or whole blood) of an individual who is recovering from a certain disease is given to another person to provide a passive immunity. The reason for this is, of course, that the convalescent's blood is rich in antibodies. The advantage of human serum over horse serum is that administration of the former avoids the complications that can arise if one happens to be allergic to the proteins in horse serum.

ALLERGY

This is as appropriate a place as any to discuss the subject of **allergy,** since it has been touched upon several times without benefit of adequate explanation; moreover, allergy involves antigens and antibodies, and its chemical processes are much like those of immunity.

Allergy (a broader term for it is hypersensitiveness) can be defined informally as the tendency of some unlucky individuals to react unfavorably to the presence of certain substances that are normally harmless to most people.

These substances are called **allergens** and, like any antigen, are often of a protein nature. Examples of typical allergens are pollens, house dust, horse dander (dander is the term for the minute scales that are found on hairs and feathers), and certain food proteins. When the tissues of a susceptible person are repeatedly exposed to an allergen—for example, the nasal mucosa to pollens—these tissues become **sensitized;** that is, antibodies are produced in them. When the next invasion of the allergen occurs, there is an antigen-antibody reaction. Now, normally this type of reaction takes place in the blood without harm, as it does in immunity. In allergy, however, the antigen-antibody reaction takes place within the cells of the sensitized tissues, with results that are disagreeable and sometimes dangerous. In the case of the nasal mucosa that has become sensitized to pollen, the allergic manifestation is **hay fever,** with symptoms much like those of the common cold.

An important allergic manifestation that may occur in connection with serums is **serum sickness.** Some people are allergic to the proteins in serum derived from the horse or some other animal, and show such symptoms as fever, vomiting, joint pain, enlargement of the regional lymph nodes, and hives or **urticaria** (ur-ti-ka're-ah). This type of allergic reaction can be severe, but is rarely fatal.

Many drugs can bring about the allergic state, particularly aspirin, barbiturates and the antibiotics (especially penicillin). In some cases of allergy it is possible to desensitize a person by means of repeated injections of the offending allergen at short intervals. This form of protection, unfortunately, does not last long.

It is believed that one reason for the irritating effects of an allergic response is that the antigen-antibody reaction liberates from the tissues a substance called a **histamine** (his'tah-min) which purportedly does a great deal of the damage. Sometimes a group of drugs called **antihistamines** are effective in treating certain cases of allergy.

An interesting sidelight on some allergic disorders is that they are strongly associated with emotional disturbances. Asthma and **migraine** (mi'grane), or sick headache, are 2 good examples of this type. In such disorders the interaction of body and mind still is not fully understood.

TRANSPLANTS AND THE REJECTION SYNDROME

The hope that organs and tissues could be obtained from animals or other human beings to replace injured or incompetent parts of the body has long been under discussion. Much experimental work with **transplantation** (grafting) of organs and tissues in animals has preceded transplant operations in the human. Replacement by grafting of bone marrow, lymphoid tissue, skin, eye corneas, parathyroid glands, ovaries, kidneys, lungs, heart, liver, and uterus are among those that have been attempted. The natural tendency for every organism to reject foreign substances, especially tissues from another person or any other animal, has been the most formidable obstruction to complete success. This normal quality, an antigen-antibody reaction, has been called the **rejection syndrome.**

In all cases of transplanting or grafting, the tissues of the donor, the person donating the part, should be typed in much the same way that blood is typed whenever a transfusion is given. Blood types are much fewer in number than tissue substances, and the process of obtaining matching blood is much less involved than is the process of trying to match the latter. Tests are being done in a number of laboratories and an effort is made to obtain donors whose tissues contain relatively few antigens that might cause transplant rejection.

Because it has been impossible to completely match all the antigens of a donor with those of the recipient (the person receiving the part), drugs that suppress the action of antibodies against the transplanted organ are given to the recipients. The goal is to avoid suppressing the action of antibodies against organisms that might cause infection at the same time as rejection of the transplant is prevented. Much of the reaction against the foreign material in transplants is believed to be by small lymphocytes. It is hoped that drugs can be obtained to suppress the action of these cells without preventing the action of humoral antibodies against pathogens. Humoral antibodies are those in the tissue fluids, such as the blood and lymph, and they are thought to be most important in preventing infections.

SUMMARY

1. **Influences on the occurrence of infection.**
   A. Portal of entry of pathogen.
   B. Virulence of pathogen.
   C. Number of pathogens.
   D. Resistance of the body.

2. **Defenses against disease.**
   A. Skin and mucous membranes.
   B. Reflex actions.
   C. Inflammation (phagocytosis).
   D. Immunity (antibodies).
3. **Immune process.**
   A. Pathogen contains antigens which stimulate antibody formation.
   B. Antibodies destroy pathogens or neutralize toxins.
   C. Immunity process is specific.
4. **Kinds of immunity.**
   A. Inborn (inherited): species, racial, individual.
   B. Acquired.
      (1) Naturally acquired: active or passive.
      (2) Artificially acquired: active or passive.
5. **Acquired immunity.**
   A. Naturally acquired.
      (1) Active (by contracting disease).
      (2) Passive (by transmission of antibodies through placenta).
   B. Artificially acquired.
      (1) Active (by administration of vaccine).
      (2) Passive (by administration of serum).
6. **Vaccines and serums.**
   A. Vaccines: cause tissues to produce antibodies; contain organism or toxoid. Examples: D.P.T., typhoid, smallpox, Sabin (for polio), rabies. Booster inoculations supplement vaccines, maintain immunity. Effects of vaccines long-lasting.
   B. Serums: provide antibodies directly; derived from blood serum of humans or horses and other animals. Examples: diphtheria, tetanus, antiplague, antivenin. Gamma globulin (human) sometimes given for measles. Human serum administration avoids allergic reactions to animal proteins. Effects of serums are of short duration.
7. **Allergy.**
   A. Some individuals are susceptible to allergens (usually foreign protein).
   B. Allergens cause antigen-antibody reaction in tissues, with accompanying irritation or other symptoms.
   C. Desensitization sometimes done. Antihistamines sometimes useful in treatment.
   D. Some allergies associated with nervous disturbances.
8. **Transplants and the rejection syndrome.**
   A. Normal antigen-antibody reaction.
   B. Suppress undesirable antibodies without injury to those needed to resist infection.

QUESTIONS AND PROBLEMS

1. Name 4 conditions which determine whether or not an infection will occur in the body.
2. What are the body's "lines of defense" against disease?
3. Describe the process of inflammation.
4. Define immunity and describe its basic process.
5. Give 3 examples of inborn immunity.
6. What is the basic difference between inborn and acquired immunity?
7. Outline the various categories of acquired immunity and give an example of each.
8. What is a vaccine? A toxoid? Give examples of each. What is a booster shot?
9. What is a serum? Give examples. Define an antitoxin.
10. Name 2 origins of serums. Why is one sometimes used in preference to another?
11. Define allergy. How is its process like that of immunity, and how do they differ?
12. What is an allergen? Name some examples.
13. Name and describe some typical allergic disorders. Why would the diagnosis of some of these be especially difficult?
14. What is meant by the rejection syndrome and what is being done to offset it?

SUGGESTIONS FOR FURTHER STUDY

Note: The titles marked with an asterisk (*) are
standard medical texts suitable for reference use.

*Anderson, W. A.: Pathology, ed. 5, St. Louis, Mosby, 1966.
*Anson, B. L.: Morris' Human Anatomy, ed. 12, McGraw-Hill, New York, 1966.
 Anthony, C. P.: Textbook of Anatomy and Physiology, ed. 7, St. Louis, Mosby, 1967.
*Arey, L. B.: Developmental Anatomy (Embryology), ed. 7, Philadelphia, Saunders, 1965.

*Bard, P.: Medical Physiology, ed. 11, St. Louis, Mosby, 1961.
*Bartalos, M.: Genetics in Medical Practice, Philadelphia, Lippincott, 1968.
 Bevelander, G.: Essentials of Histology, ed. 5, St. Louis, Mosby, 1965.
*Beeson, P. B., and McDermott, W. (eds.): Cecil-Loeb Textbook of Medicine, ed. 12, Philadelphia, Saunders, 1967.
*Best, C. H., and Taylor, N. B.: The Physiological Basis of Medical Practice, ed. 8, Baltimore, Williams & Wilkins, 1966.
 Borek, E.: The Atoms Within Us, New York, Columbia, 1961.
 Boyd, W.: Introduction to the Study of Disease, ed. 5, Philadelphia, Lea and Febiger, 1962.
 Brooks, S. M.: Basic Facts of Body Water and Ions, ed. 3, New York, Springer, 1968.
 Brooks, S. M.: Integrated Basic Science, ed. 3, St. Louis, Mosby, 1970.
 Brunner, L., et al.: Textbook of Medical-Surgical Nursing, ed. 2, Philadelphia, Lippincott, 1970.

 Carlson, A. J., et al.: The Machinery of the Body, ed. 5, Univ. Chicago Press, 1961.
 Chaffee, E. E., and Gresheimer, E. M.: Basic Physiology and Anatomy, ed. 2, Philadelphia, Lippincott, 1969.

 DeCoursey, R. M.: The Human Organism, ed. 3, New York, McGraw-Hill, 1968.
 Diehl, H. S.: Textbook of Healthful Living, ed. 7, New York, McGraw-Hill, 1964.
 Dorland's Illustrated Medical Dictionary, ed. 24, Philadelphia, Saunders, 1965.

*Elliott, H. C.: Textbook of Neuroanatomy, ed. 2, Philadelphia, Lippincott, 1969.

 Flitter, H.: An Introduction to Physics in Nursing, ed. 5, St. Louis, Mosby, 1967.
 Frohse, F., et al.: An Atlas of Human Anatomy, ed. 6, New York, Barnes and Noble, 1969.
 Frobisher, M., et al.: Microbiology in Health and Disease, ed. 12, Philadelphia, Saunders, 1969.

Ganong, W. F.: Review of Medical Physiology, ed. 4, Los Altos, Calif., Lange, 1969.

Garb, S.: Laboratory Texts in Common Use, ed. 4, New York, Springer, 1967.

*Goss, C. M. (ed.): Gray's Anatomy, ed. 28, Philadelphia, Lea and Febiger, 1966.

Grant, J. C. B.: An Atlas of Anatomy, ed. 5, Baltimore, Williams & Wilkins, 1962.

*Grollman, S.: The Human Body, ed. 2, New York, Macmillan, 1969.

*Guyton, A. C.: Textbook of Medical Physiology, ed. 3, Philadelphia, Saunders, 1966.

*Ham, A. W.: Histology, ed. 6, Philadelphia, Lippincott, 1969.

Holum, J. R.: Elements of General and Biological Chemistry, ed. 2, New York, Wiley, 1968.

Hopps, H. C.: Principles of Pathology, ed. 2, New York, Appleton, 1964.

Jensen, J. T.: Introduction to Medical Physics, Philadelphia, Lippincott, 1960.

Kimber, et al.: Anatomy and Physiology, ed. 15, New York, Macmillan, 1966.

*Lockhart, et al.: Anatomy of the Human Body, Philadelphia, Lippincott, 1965 Printing with Revisions.

*MacBryde, C. M.: Signs and Symptoms, ed. 4, Philadelphia, Lippincott, 1964.

Metheny, N. M., and Snively, W. D.: Nurses' Handbook of Fluid Balance, Philadelphia, Lippincott, 1967.

Mitchell, et al.: Cooper's Nutrition in Health and Disease, ed. 15, Philadelphia, Lippincott, 1968.

Moyer, C. A., et al.: Surgery: Principles and Practice, ed. 3, Philadelphia, Lippincott, 1965.

Pansky, B. and House, E. L.: Review of Gross Anatomy, ed. 2, Macmillan, London, 1969.

Robinson, C.: Proudfit-Robinson's Normal and Therapeutic Nutrition, ed. 13, New York, Macmillan, 1967.

Rodman, M. J., and Smith, D. W.: Pharmacology and Drug Therapy in Nursing, Philadelphia, Lippincott, 1968.

Sackheim, G., and Schultz, R.: Chemistry for the Health Sciences, New York, Macmillan, 1969.

Schifferes, J.: Essentials of Healthier Living, ed. 3, New York, Wiley, 1967.

Snively, W. D.: Sea Within, Philadelphia, Lippincott, 1960.

*Thompson, R. B.: Haematology, ed. 2, Philadelphia, Lippincott, 1965.

*Tuttle, W. W., and Schottelius, B. A.: Textbook of Physiology, ed. 15, St. Louis, Mosby, 1965.

Wheeler, M. F., and Volk, W. A.: Basic Microbiology, ed. 2, Philadelphia, Lippincott, 1969.

MEDICAL TERMINOLOGY

You can build many hundreds of medical words if you learn a relatively few basic parts which can be combined in a variety of ways. A complicated medical word will seem less difficult if you analyze it after you learn the meaning of these fundamental parts. Remember to look at the word carefully and say it out loud several times, so that each new word will become familiar to you.

The foundation of a word is the "word root." Examples of word roots are *abdomin-*, referring to the belly region; and *aden-*, pertaining to a gland. A word root is often followed by a vowel to facilitate pronunciation, as in *abdomino-* and *adeno-*. We then refer to it as a "combining form." The hyphen appended to a combining form indicates that it is not a complete word, and if the hyphen precedes the combining form, then it commonly appears as the terminal element or the word ending, as in *-algia,* meaning "a painful condition."

A "prefix" is a part of a word which precedes the word root and changes its meaning. For example, the prefix *mal-* in *malunion* means "an abnormal" union. A "suffix" or word ending is a part that follows the word root and adds to or changes its meaning. The suffix *-rrhea* means "profuse flow" or "discharge," as in *diarrhea,* a condition in which there is excessive discharge of liquid stools.

Many medical words are "compound" words; that is, they are made up of more than one root or combining form. Examples of such compound words are *erythrocyte* (red blood cell) and *hydrocele* (a fluid-containing sac); and many more difficult words, such as *sternoclavicular* (indicating relationship to both the sternum and the clavicle).

A general knowledge of language structure and spelling rules is also helpful in mastering medical terminology. For example, adjectives include words that end in *-al,* as in *sternal* (the noun is sternum), and words that end in *-ous,* as in *mucous* (the noun is mucus).

The following list includes some of the most commonly used word roots, combining forms, prefixes and suffixes. To help clarify their usage, it is suggested that you refer to the Glossary that follows (p. 329) for a definition of the examples given for each.

a-, an- absent, deficient, lack of: *atrophy, anemia, anuria.*

ab- away from: *abduction, aboral.*

abdomin-, abdomino- the belly or abdominal area: *abdominalgia, abdominocentesis, abdominoscopy.*

acou-, acu- hearing, sound: *acoustic, acumeter.*

acr-, acro- extreme ends of a part, especially of the extremities: *acral, acromegaly, acromion.*

actin-, actini-, actino- a relationship to raylike structures or, more commonly, to light or roentgen (x) rays, or some other type of radiation: *actiniform, actinodermatitis.*

ad- (sometimes converted to ac-, af-, ag-, ap-, as-, at-) toward, added to, near: *adrenal, accretion, agglomerated.*

aden-, adeno- gland: *adenectomy, adenitis, adenocarcinoma.*

-agogue inducing, leading, stimulating: *cholagogue, galactagogue.*

alge-, algo-, algesi- pain: *algetic, algophobia, algesia, analgesic.*

-algia pain, painful condition: *myalgia, neuralgia.*

amb-, ambi-, ambo- both, on two sides:

ambidexterity, ambivalent, amboceptor.

ambly- dimness, dullness: *amblyacousia, amblyopia.*

ant-, anti- against; to prevent, suppress, or destroy: *antarthritic, antibiotic, anticoagulant.*

ante- before, ahead of: *antenatal, antepartum.*

antero- a position ahead of or in front of (i.e., anterior to) another part: *anterolateral, anteroventral.*

arthr-, arthro- joint or articulation: *arthral, arthrolysis, arthrostomy.*

-asis see **-sis.**

audio- sound, hearing: *audiogenic, audiometry, audiovisual.*

aut-, auto- self: *autistic, autodigestion, autointoxication, autoplasty.*

bi- two, twice: *bifurcate, bisexual.*

bio- life, a living organism: *biopsy, antibiotic.*

blast-, blasto-, -blast an early stage, an immature cell or a bud: *blastula, blastophore, erythroblast.*

blenn-, blenno- mucus: *blennuria, blennogenic, blennorrhea.*

bleph-, blephar-, blepharo- eyelid, eyelash: *blepharism, blepharitis, blepharospasm.*

brachi- arm: *brachial, brachiocephalic, brachiotomy.*

brachy- short: *brachydactylia, brachyesophagus.*

brady- slow: *bradycardia.*

bronch- windpipe or other air tubes: *bronchiectasis, bronchoscope.*

bucc- cheek: *buccally.*

carcin- cancer: *carcinogenic, carcinoma.*

cardi-, cardia-, cardio- heart: *carditis, cardiac, cardiologist.*

-cele swelling; an enlarged space or cavity: *cystocele, meningocele, rectocele.*

centi- relating to 100 (used in naming units of measurement): *centigrade, centimeter.*

cephal-, cephalo- head: *cephalalgia, cephalopelvic.*

cheil-, cheilo- lips; a brim or an edge: *cheilitis, cheilosis.*

cheir-, cheiro- (also written **chir-, chiro-**) hand: *cheiralgia, cheiromegaly, chiropractic.*

chol-, chole-, cholo- bile, gall: *chologogue, cholecyst, cholecystitis, cholochrome.*

chondr-, chondri-, chondrio- cartilage: *chondric, chondrocyte, chondroma.*

chrono- time: *chronograph, chronology, chronophobia.*

-cid, -cide to cut, kill or destroy: *bactericidal, germicide, suicide.*

circum- around, surrounding: *circumoral, circumorbital, circumrenal.*

colp-, colpo- vagina: *colpectasia, colposcope, colpotomy.*

contra- opposed, against: *contraindication, contrastimulus.*

cost-, costa-, costo- ribs: *costiform, intercostal, costosternal.*

counter- against, opposite to: *counterirritation, countertraction.*

crani-, cranio- skull: *craniectomy, craniotomy.*

cry-, cryo-, crymo- low temperature: *cryalgesia, cryogenic, crymotherapy.*

crypt-, crypto- hidden, concealed: *cryptic, cryptogenic, cryptorchidism.*

cut- skin: *cutization, subcutaneous.*

cysti-, cysto- sac, bladder: *cystitis, cystoscope.*

cyt-, cyto-, -cyte cell: *cytemia, cytolytic, cytoplasm, erythrocyte.*

dacry-, dacryo- lacrimal glands: *dacryagogue, dacryocyst.*

dactyl-, dactylo- digits (usually fingers, but sometimes toes): *dactylitis, dactylology.*

derm-, derma-, dermo-, dermat-, dermato- skin: *dermic, dermatitis, dermatology, dermatosis.*

di-, diplo- twice, double: *diglossia, dimorphism, diplopia.*

dia- through, between, across, apart: *diaphragm, diaphysis.*

dis- apart, away from: *disarticulation, distal.*

dolicho- long: *dolichocephalic, dolichomorphic.*

dorsi-, dorso- back (in the human, this combining form refers to the same region as **postero-**): *dorsiflexion, dorsonuchal.*

-dynia pain, tenderness: *myodynia, neurodynia.*

dys- disordered, difficult, painful: *dysentery, dysphagia, dyspnea.*

-ectasis expansion, dilation, stretching: *angiectasis, bronchiectasis.*

ecto- outside, external: *ectoderm, ectogenous.*

-ectomize, -ectomy surgical removal or destruction by other means: *thyroidectomize, appendectomy.*

-emia blood: *glycemia, hyperemia.*

encephal-, encephalo- brain: *encephalitis, encephalogram.*

end-, endo- within, innermost: *endarterial, endocardium.*

enter-, entero- intestine: *enteritis, enterocolitis, enteroptosis.*

epi- on, upon: *epicardium, epidermis.*

eryth-, erythro- red: *erythema, erythrocyte.*

-esthesia sensation: *anesthesia, paresthesia.*

eu- well, normal, good: *euphoria, eupnea.*

ex-, exo- outside, out of, away from: *exanthem, excretion, exocrine.*

extra- beyond, outside of, in addition to: *extracellular, extrasystole, extravasation.*

-ferent to bear, to carry: *afferent, efferent.*

fibr-, fibro- threadlike structures, fibers: *fibrillation, fibroblast, fibrositis.*

galact-, galacta-, galacto- milk: *galactemia, galactagogue, galactocele.*

gastr-, gastro- stomach: *gastritis, gastroenterostomy.*

-gen an agent which produces or originates: *allergen, pathogen.*

-genic produced from, producing: *endogenic, pyogenic.*

genito- organs of reproduction: *genitoplasty, genitourinary.*

geno- a relationship to reproduction or sex: *genodermatology, genotype.*

geny- jaw: *genyantrum, genyplasty.*

-geny manner of origin, development or production: *ontogeny, progeny.*

glio-, -glia a gluey material; specifically, the connective tissue of the brain: *glioma, neuroglia.*

gloss-, glosso- tongue: *glossitis, glossopharyngeal.*

gly-, glyco- sweet, relating to sugar: *glycemia, glycosuria.*

gon- seed; knee: *gonad, gonarthritis.*

-gram a record, that which is recorded: *electrocardiogram, electroencephalogram.*

-graph an instrument for recording: *electrocardiograph, electroencephalograph.*

gyn-, gyne-, gyneco-, gyno- female sex (women): *gynatresia, gynecology, gynecomastia, gynoplasty.*

hem-, hema-, hemato-, hemo- blood: *hematoma, hematuria, hemorrhage.*

hemi- one half: *hemianopia, heminephrectomy, hemiplegia.*

hepat-, hepato- liver: *hepatitis, hepatogenous.*

heter-, hetero- other, different: *heteradenoma, heterocrine, heterogeneous, heterosexual.*

hist-, histio- tissue: *histology, histiocyte.*

homeo-, homo- unchanging, the same: *homeostasis, homosexual.*

hydr-, hydro- water: *dehydration, hydrocele, hydrocephalus.*

hyper- above, over, excessive: *hyperesthesia, hyperglycemia, hypertrophy.*

hypo- deficient, below, beneath: *hypochondrium, hypodermic, hypogastrium.*

hyster-, hystero- uterus: *hysterectomy, hysterodynia.*

-iatrics, -trics medical practice specialties: *pediatrics, obstetrics.*

idio- self, one's own, separate, distinct: *idiopathic, idiosyncrasy.*

ilio- flank, ilium (part of os coxae or hip bone): *iliocolotomy, iliotibial.*

im-, in- in, into; lacking: *implantation, inanimate, infiltration.*

inter- between: *intercostal, interstitial.*

intra- within a part or structure: *intracranial, intracellular, intraocular.*

-itis inflammation: *dermatitis, keratitis, neuritis.*

kerat-, kerato- cornea of the eye, certain horny tissues: *keratin, keratitis, keratoplasty.*

lact-, lacto- milk: *lactation, lactogenic.*

leuk-, leuko- (also written as **leuc-, leuco-**) white: *leukocyte* or *leucocyte, leukoplakia.*

lith-, litho- stones (also called calculi): *lithiasis, lithopedion.*

-logy, -ology the study of: *graphology, gynecology.*

lyso-, -lysis: flowing, loosening, dissolution (dissolving of): *lysobacteria, hemolysis.*

macro- large, abnormal length: *macroblast, macrocolon.* See also **mega-, megalo-.**

mal- disordered, abnormal: *malnutrition, malocclusion, malunion.*

malac-, malaco-, -malacia softening: *malacoma, malacosarcosis, osteomalacia.*

mast-, masto- breast: *mastectomy, mastitis, mastocarcinoma.*

meg-, mega-, megal-, megalo- unusually or excessively large: *megacolon, megalencephalon, megaloblast.*

men-, meno- physiologic uterine bleeding: *menses, menorrhagia.*

mening-, meningo- membranes covering the brain and spinal-cord: *meningitis, meningocele.*

ment-, mento- mind, chin: *menticide. dementia, mentolabial, mentum.*

mes-, mesa-, meso- middle, midline: *mesencephalon, mesaortitis, mesoderm.*

meta- a change, beyond, after, over, near: *metabolism, metacarpus, metaplasia.*

micro- very small: *microabscess, microbiology, microcyte.*

my-, myo- muscle: *myenteron, myocardium, myometrium.*

myc-, mycet-, myco- fungi: *mycid, mycete, mycology, mycosis.*

myel-, myelo- marrow (often used in reference to the spinal cord): *myeloid, myeloblast, osteomyelitis, poliomyelitis.*

necr-, necro- death, corpse: *necrectomy, necropsy, necrosis.*

neo- new, strange: *neopathy, neoplasm.*

neph-, nephro- kidney: *nephrectomy, nephritis, nephron.*

neur-, neuro- nerve: *neuralgia, neuroma.*

noct-, nocti- night: *noctambulation, nocturia, noctiphobia.*

nos-, noso- disease: *nosema, nosophilia, nosophobe.*

nyct-, nycto- night, darkness: *nycturia, nyctophobia.*

ocul-, oculo- eye: *oculist, oculomotor, oculomycosis.*

odont-, odonto- teeth: *odontalgia, odontiasis, odontology.*

-oid likeness, resemblance: *lymphoid, myeloid.*

olig-, oligo- few, a deficiency: *oligemia, oligospermia, oliguria.*

-oma tumor, a swelling: *hematoma, sarcoma.*

onych-, onycho- nails: *paronychia, onychoma.*

oo-, ovi-, ovo- ovum, egg: *oocyte, oviduct, ovoplasm* (do not confuse with **oophor-**).

oophor-, oophoro- ovary: *oophorectomy, oophoritis, oophorocystectomy.* See **ovar-.**

ophthalm-, ophthalmo- eye: *ophthalmia, ophthalmologist, ophthalmoscope.*

orth-, ortho- straight, normal: *orthesis, orthodontist.*

oss-, osseo-, ossi-, oste-, osteo- bone, bone tissue: *ossature, osseous, ossicle, osteitis, osteomyelitis.*

-ostomy creation of a mouth or opening by surgery: *colostomy, gastroenterostomy.*

ot-, oto- ear: *otalgia, otitis, otomycosis.*

-otomy cutting into: *iliocolotomy, phlebotomy.*

ovar-, ovario- ovary: *ovariectomy, ovariorrhexis.* See **oophor-.**

para- near, beyond, apart from, beside: *paramedical, parametrium, parathyroid.*

path-, patho-, -pathy disease, abnormal condition: *pathema, pathogen, pathognomonic, pathology, endocrinopathy.*

ped-, pedia- child; foot: *pedialgia, pedophobia, pediatrician.*

-penia lack of: *leukopenia, thrombocytopenia.*

per- through, excessively: *peracidity, percutaneous, perfusion.*

peri- around: *pericardium, perichondrium, periostitis.*

-pexy fixation: *nephropexy, proctopexy.*

phag-, phago- to eat, to ingest: *phage, phagocyte.*

-phagia, -phagy eating, swallowing: *aphagia, dysphagia, aerophagy.*

-phasia speech, ability to talk: *aphasia, dysphasia.*

-phil, -philic to be fond of, to like (have an affinity for): *eosinophilia, hemophilic.*

phleb-, phlebo- vein: *phlebitis, phleboclysis, phlebotomy.*

phob-, -phobia fear, dread, abnormal aversion: *phobic, acrophobia, hydrophobia, photophobia.*

pile-, pili-, pilo- hair, resembling hair: *pileous, piliation, pilonidal.*

-plasty molding, surgical formation: *gastroplasty, kineplasty.*

pleur-, pleuro- side, rib, the serous membrane covering the lung and lining the chest cavity: *pleurisy, pleurotomy.*

-pnea air, breathing: *dyspnea, eupnea.*

pneum-, pneuma-, pneumo- pneumon-, pneumato- lung, air: *pneumectomy, pneumatics, pneumograph, pneumonia, pneumatocardia.*

pod-, podo- foot: *podiatry, pododynia.*

-poiesis making, forming: *erythropoiesis, hematopoiesis.*

polio- gray: *polioclastic, polioencephalitis, poliomyelitis.*

poly- many: *polyarthritis, polycystic.*

post- behind, after, following: *postnatal, postocular, postpartum.*

pre- before, ahead of: *precancerous, preclinical, prepatellar.*

presby- old age: *presbyophrenia, presbyopia.*

pro- in front of, before: *prodromal, prosencephalon, provitamin.*

proct-, procto- rectum: *proctitis, proctocele, proctologist, proctopexy.*

pseud-, pseudo- false: *pseudarthrosis, pseudomania.*

psych-, psycho- mind: *psychasthenia, psychosomatic, psychotherapy.*

-ptosis downward displacement, falling, prolapse: *enteroptosis, nephroptosis.*

pulmo-, pulmono- lung: *pulmonic, pulmonology, pulmotor.*

py-, pyo- pus: *pyuria, pyogenic, pyorrhea.*

pyel-, pyelo- kidney pelvis: *pyelitis, pyelogram, pyelonephrosis.*

rachi-, rachio- spine: *rachicentesis, rachischisis, rachiocentesis.*

ren- kidney: *renal, renopathy.*

retro- backward, located behind: *retrocecal, retroperitoneal.*

rheo- flow of matter, or of a current of electricity: *rheology, rheoscope.*

rhin-, rhino- nose: *rhinitis, rhinophyma.*

-rrhage, -rrhagia excessive flow: *hemorrhage, menorrhagia.*

-rrhaphy suturing of or sewing up of a gap or defect in a part: *enterorrhaphy, perineorrhaphy.*

-rrhea flow, discharge: *diarrhea, gonorrhea, seborrhea.*

salping-, salpingo- tube: *salpingitis, salpingoscopy.*

scler-, sclero- hardness: *scleredema, scleroderma, sclerosis.*

scolio- twisted, crooked: *scoliosis, scoliosometer.*

-scope an instrument used to look into or examine a part: *bronchoscope, cystoscope, endoscope.*

semi- mild, partial, half: *semicanalis, semicoma.*

sep-, septic- poison, rot, decay: *sepsis, septicemia.*

-sis condition or process, usually abnormal: *dermatosis, enteroptosis.*

somat-, somato- body: *somatalgia, somatotype.*

splanchn-, splanchno- internal organs: *splanchnic, splanchnoptosis.*

sta-, stat- stop, stand still, remain at rest: *stasis, static.*

sten-, steno- contracted, narrowed: *stenosis, stenostomia.*

sthen-, stheno-, -sthenia, -sthenic strength: *sthenometry, sthenophotic, asthenia, asthenic.*

sub- under, below, near, almost: *subclavian, subcutaneous, subluxation.*

super- over, above, excessive: *superego, supernatant.*

supra- location above or over: *supranasal, suprarenal.*

sym-, syn- with, together: *symbiosis, symphysis, synapse.*

syring-, syringo- fistula, tube, cavity: *syringectomy, syringomyelia.*

tacho-, tachy- rapid, fast, swift: *tachogram, tachycardia.*

tars-, tarso- eyelid, foot: *tarsitis, tarsoplasty, tarsoptosis.*

-taxia, -taxis order, arrangement: *ataxia, chemotaxis, thermotaxis.*

tens- stretch, pull: *extension, tensor.*

therm-, thermo-, -thermy heat: *thermalgesia, thermocautery, diathermy.*

tox-, toxic-, toxico- poison: *toxemia, toxicology, toxicosis.*

trache- windpipe: *trachea, tracheitis, tracheotomy.*

trans- across, through, beyond: *transorbital, transpiration, transplantation.*

tri- three: *triad, triceps.*

trich-, tricho- hair: *trichiasis, trichocardia, trichosis.*

-trophic, -trophy nutrition (nurture): *atrophic, hypertrophy.*

-tropic turning toward, influencing, changing: *adrenotropic, gonadotropic, thyrotropic.*

uni- one: *unilateral, uniovular.*

-uria urine: *glycosuria, hematuria, pyuria.*

vas-, vaso- vessel, duct: *vascular, vasectomy, vasodilation.*

viscer-, viscero- internal organs: *viscera, visceroptosis.*

xero- dryness: *xeroderma, xerophthalmia, xerosis.*

GLOSSARY

abatement (ah-bate'ment): a decrease in the seriousness of a disorder; a decreasing severity of pain or other symptoms.

abdomen (ab-do'men): the part of the body located between the diaphragm and the pelvis; the cavity that contains the abdominal organs (viscera). It is also called the **venter.**

abdominalgia (ab-dom-i-nal'je-ah): pain in the abdomen.

abdominocentesis (ab-dom-i-no-sen-te'sis): a surgical puncture of the abdomen to remove fluid, as may be done in ascites. It is also called **paracentesis** (par-ah-sen-te'sis) of the abdomen.

abdominoscopy (ab-dom-i-nos'ko-pe): examination of the organs of the abdomen using an instrument (endoscope) which is inserted through the abdominal wall. It is also called a **peritoneoscopy** (per-i-to-ne-os'ko-pe).

abduction (ab-duk'shun): a movement away from the axis or midline of the body; the act of turning outward. The opposite is **adduction.**

aboral (ab-o'ral): away from the mouth.

abortion (ah-bor'shun): the premature loss of the embryo, or of the nonviable fetus (the fetus that is not capable of living outside the uterus); any failure in the normal process of developing or maturing.

abscess (ab'ses): an area of tissue breakdown; a localized space in the body containing pus and liquefied tissue.

abscission (ab-sish'un): the surgical removal of a part by cutting (especially the removal of part of the cornea of the eye).

acapnia (ah-kap'ne-ah): a decrease in the normal amount of carbon dioxide in the blood.

acatalepsia (ah-kat-ah-lep'se-ah): a lack of understanding; doubtfulness of a diagnosis.

acataleptic (ah-kat-ah-lep'tik): referring to a doubtful diagnosis, and also to mental deficiency.

acclimation (ak-li-ma'shun), **acclimatization** (ah-kli-mah-ti-za'shun): to become adjusted or to become accustomed to a different environment, a new climate or other varying conditions.

accommodation (ah-kom-o-da'shun): a change in the shape of the eye lens so that vision is more acute; an adjustment of the eye lens for various distances; the focusing process.

accouchement (ah-koosh-mon'): a French word meaning labor; the process of delivering the baby.

accretion (ah-kre'shun): a mass of material that has accumulated in a space or cavity; the adhesion of parts; the normal growth of organs or other structures.

acetabulum (as-e-tab'u-lum): the cup-shaped socket that receives the head of the thigh bone (femur).

acetone (as'e-tone): an organic compound that may be found in abnormal amounts in the urine of diabetics. Acetone bodies, which are also called ketone bodies, include several intermediate compounds occurring in fat metabolism.

acetonuria (as-e-to-nu're-ah): abnormal amounts of acetone (or ketone) bodies in the urine (found in fevers, cancers, digestive disorders, and diabetes).

achlorhydria (ah-klor-hid're-ah): lack of hydrochloric acid in the gastric juice.

achondroplasia (ah-kon-dro-pla'ze-ah): a disorder that causes the most common type of dwarfism, with relatively large head and short extremities.

acidosis (as-i-do'sis): a serious disorder of body chemistry in which the normal alkaline substances of the blood (such as sodium bicarbonate) are reduced in amount.

acinus (as'i-nus): any small saclike dilatation, such as is found in many glands. It is also called an **alveolus** (al-ve'o-lus).

acne (ak'ne): a skin disease in which the sebaceous (oil) glands become inflamed. A common type often forms elevations called papules (pimples).

acoustic (ah'koos-tik): pertaining to sound or the sense of hearing.

acral (ak'ral): affecting or pertaining to the extremities.

acromegaly (ak-ro-meg'ah-le): a disorder in which there is enlargement of the nose, jaw, and extremities; often due to a pituitary tumor that produces excessive growth hormone in an adult.

acromion (ah-kro'me-on): the flattened projection that extends from the shoulder blade (scapula) to form the top of the shoulder itself; also called the **acromial process.**

acronyx (ak'ro-niks): an ingrowing nail.

acrophobia (ak-ro-fo'be-ah): a great dread of high places.

actiniform (ak-tin'i-form): resembling a ray of light.

actinodermatitis (ak-ti-no-der-mah-ti'tis): a skin disorder due to exposure to roentgen rays (x-rays).

acumeter (ah-koo'me-ter): an instrument used to test hearing.

adduction (ah-duk'shun): a movement toward the body, or toward the midline of the body; the act of turning inward. The opposite is **abduction.**

adenectomy (ad-e-nek'to-me): the removal of a gland; also may refer to removal of the adenoids (pharyngeal tonsil).

adenitis (ad-e-ni'tis): inflammation of a gland; frequently refers to inflammation of lymph nodes.

adenocarcinoma (ad-e-no-kar-si-no'mah): a malignant growth of glandlike cells; a cancerous adenoma.

adenoma (ad-e-no'mah): a tumor with glandlike structure, usually benign, but may become malignant (i.e., adenocarcinoma).

adipose (ad'e-pose): fat; containing fat, as adipose tissue.

adiposity (ad-i-pos'i-te): the condition of being fat; overweight.

adrenal (ad-re'nal): located near the kidney; specifically the endocrine gland near the kidney. It is also called the **suprarenal gland.**

adrenotropic (ad-ren-o-trop'ik): having an influence over the adrenal (suprarenal) glands; also written **adrenotrophic.**

aerobic (a-er-o'bik): requiring free oxygen for growth as in the case of certain bacteria (called aerobes).

aerophagy (a-er-of'ah-je): spasmodic swallowing of air followed by eructation (belching); often seen in hysterical patients.

afferent (af'er-ent): carrying toward a center or main part; nerves that carry impulses toward the central nervous system, or toward ganglia.

agglomerated (ah-glom'er-at-ed): collected into a mass; gathered into a ball or cluster.

agglutination (ah-gloo-ti-na'shun): a process by which cells (bacteria, blood cells, etc.) are collected in groups or clumps; a kind of immunity response; clumping; a kind of antigen-antibody reaction.

agnosia (ag-no'se-ah): a loss of the ability to recognize the meaning of stimuli from the various senses (visual, auditory, touch, etc.).

aldosterone (al-do-ster'on): a hormone produced by the adrenal cortex; a steroid that regulates electrolytes.

algesia (al-je'ze-ah): sensitivity to pain; hyperesthesia.

algesiogenic (al-je-ze-o-jen'ik): causing or producing pain.

algetic (al-jet'ik): painful.

algophobia (al'go-fo'be-ah): an abnormal

fear of pain, or of seeing others in pain.

allergen (al'er-jen): a substance that causes sensitivity; something that induces allergy.

ambidextrous (am-bi-dek'strus): pertaining to or characterized by the ability to perform manual skills equally well with either hand.

ambivalent (am-biv'ah-lent): having opposite attitudes toward the same object or person, such as love and hate.

amblyacousia (am-ble-ah-koo'se-ah): dullness of hearing.

amblyopia (am-ble-o'pe-ah): dimness of vision, without a notable lesion of the eye.

amboceptor (am-bo-sep'tor): a substance believed to aid in destroying disease organisms or other foreign cells by connecting them to another element called the complement.

ameba (ah-me'bah): a 1-celled protozoan animal organism; a minute irregular mass of protoplasm which propels itself by extending a branch as a "false foot" and then flowing over it.

ameboid (ah-me'boid): resembling an ameba in appearance, or more especially in movement (by means of protoplasmic flowing and "false feet"). See **pseudopodia.**

amorphous (ah-mor'fus): without shape or form; pertaining to solids without crystalline structure.

analgesic (an-al-je'zik): insensitive to pain; a pain relieving agent that does not cause loss of consciousness.

anaphylaxis (an-ah-fi-lak'sis): a severe reaction caused by extreme sensitivity to a foreign protein or other substance. The adjective is **anaphylactic** (an-ah-fi-lak'tik).

anastomosis (ah-nas-to-mo'sis): a connection between blood vessels; a surgical formation of a passage between 2 distinct spaces or 2 organs (or their parts). See **gastroenterostomy.**

anatomy (ah-nat'o-me): the science of the structure of the body and the relationship of its parts to each other.

anemia (ah-ne'me-ah): a decrease in certain elements of the blood, especially red cells and hemoglobin.

anesthesia (an-es-the'ze-ah): the loss of feeling or sensation, particularly pertaining to loss of the sensation of pain.

aneurysm (an'u-rizm): a saclike enlargement of a blood vessel caused by a weakening of the wall.

angiectasis (an-je-ek'tah-sis): the dilation of a blood vessel, caused by an aneurysm, a varicosity, a muscle paralysis in the wall of the vessel, etc.

angina (an'ji-nah or an-ji'nah): a severe choking pain; a disease or condition producing such a pain. Angina pectoris is an agonizing pain in the chest which may or may not involve heart or artery disease.

angioma (an-je-o'mah): a tumor made of lymph or blood vessels; certain "birthmarks."

anomaly (ah-nom'ah-le): an abnormality which may be a developmental (congenital) defect; a variant from the usual standard.

anorexia (an-o-rek'se-ah): loss of appetite. (Anorexia nervosa is a nervous condition in which a person may become seriously weakened from lack of food intake.)

antarthritic (ant-ar-thrit'ik): an agent that relieves arthritis.

anteflexion (an-te-flek'shun): an abnormal forward curvature; a bending forward of the upper part of an organ, usually abnormal, but regarded as normal for the uterus.

antenatal (an-te-na'tal): formed or present (in the baby) before birth; prenatal.

antepartum (an-te-par'tum): before delivery of the child; occurring (to the mother) before childbirth.

anterolateral (an-ter-o-lat'er-al): located in front of and to one side.

anteroventral (an-ter-o-ven'tral): located in front of and toward the ventral surface.

antiamebic (an-ti-ah-me'bik): destroying or acting against amebae.

antibiotic (an-ti-bi-ot'ik): destructive of living things, especially chemicals produced by living organisms that act against disease-producing organisms.

anticoagulant (an-ti-ko-ag'u-lant): a substance that prevents the clotting (coagulation) of blood.

anuria (ah-nu're-ah): lack of urine excretion.

aphagia (ah-fa'je-ah): not eating; refusing to take food because it produces pain.

aphasia (ah-fa'ze-ah): the loss of power of expression by speech, writing, etc., or of comprehending what is said or spoken as a result of brain disease or brain injury.

aplastic (ah-plas'tik): relating to a failure in normal development; lacking the ability to form new cells or tissues.

aponeurosis (ap-o-nu-ro'sis): a sheetlike layer of connective tissue connecting a muscle to the part that it moves, or acting as a sheath enclosing a muscle.

appendectomy (ap-en-dek'to-me): the surgical removal of an appendage, especially the removal of the vermiform appendix.

arrhythmia (ah-rith'me-ah): a lack of normal rhythm, especially of the heart beat.

arteriole (ar-te're-ole): the smallest artery, one that branches into the microscopic capillaries.

arthral (ar'thral): pertaining to a joint.

arthrodynia (ar-thro-din'e-ah): pain in a joint.

arthrolysis (ar-throl'i-sis): the operative loosening of adhesions in an abnormally immobilized joint.

arthrostomy (ar-thros'to-me): production of a surgical opening into a joint.

ascaris (as'kah-ris): a kind of intestinal parasitic worm; a roundworm.

ascites (ah-si'tez): an abnormal collection of fluid in the abdominal cavity.

aseptic (ah-sep'tik): free from any infectious or septic material.

asthenia (as-the'ne-ah): weakness; loss of energy; lack of strength.

asthenic (as-then'ik): pertaining to asthenia.

astigmatism (ah-stig'mah-tizm): an irregularity of the cornea or the lens of the eye, causing the image to be out of focus and resulting in faulty vision.

astringent (as-trin'jent): causing contraction of tissues; a substance that decreases or arrests discharges.

ataxia (ah-tak'se-ah): the lack of muscular coordination; lack of orderly motion.

atheroma (ath-er-o'mah): a fatlike cyst or tumor; a yellowish plaque that may be deposited in an artery wall decreasing the size of the lumen (or channel). See **atherosclerosis.**

atherosclerosis (ath-er-o-skle-ro'sis): a disorder involving the lining (intima), mostly of larger arteries, in which yellowish patches of fat are deposited, forming plaques that decrease the size of the lumen. See **atheroma.**

atom (at'om): any one of the ultimate units of an element that can exist and still have the properties of the element; the particles that together form a molecule in a compound.

atresia (ah-tre'ze-ah): the abnormal closure of a passage or the absence of a normal body opening.

atrophic (ah-trof'ik): related to or characterized by lack of nutrition resulting in a wasting away or decrease in size. See **atrophy.**

atrophy (at'ro-fe): a wasting away or decrease in size of a part, due to a failure or abnormality of nutrition. The adjective is **atrophic.**

audiogenic (aw-de-o-jen'ik): produced or caused by sound.

audiometry (aw-de-om'e-tre): the process of testing hearing. The instrument used is an **audiometer** (aw-de-om'e-ter), and the specialist who measures hearing ability is an **audiometrician** (aw-de-o-me-trish'an).

audiovisual (aw-de-o-vizh'u-al): stimulating the senses of both hearing and sight (said of aids such as slides and motion pictures used in teaching).

aura (aw'rah): a feeling or sensation that precedes an epileptic seizure, or any paroxysmal attack (such as one of bronchial asthma).

auscultation (aws-kul-ta'shun): a method of examination by listening to sounds within the body. (A stethoscope may or may not be used.)

autistic (aw-tis'tik): self-centered.

autodigestion (aw-to-di-jest'yun): the softening and dissolving of one's own tissues, most often occurring after death.

autohypnosis (aw-to-hip-no'sis): self-induced hypnotism.

autointoxication (aw-to-in-tok-se-ka'shun): poisoning by some substance within the body.

automaticity (au-to-mah-tis'e-te): a characteristic whereby there is action without an outside stimulus. (An example is the contraction of the heart muscle.)

autoplasty (aw'to-plas-te): a surgical reconstruction using parts from the patient's own body; in psychoanalysis, an adaptation to reality.

autopsy (aw'top-se): the examination of the body after death; a postmortem study of the corpse. See **necropsy.**

axilla (ak-sil'ah): the small hollow beneath the arm where it joins the body at the shoulder; the armpit.

axillary (ak'si-lar-e): related to or located in the armpit.

bactericide (bak-ter'i-side): a substance that destroys bacteria. The adjective is **bactericidal.**

bacteriology (bak-te-re-ol'o-je): the study of the many beneficial as well as disease-producing plantlike organisms called bacteria. See **microbiology.**

bacteriolysis (bak-te-re-ol'i-sis): the disintegration or dissolving of bacteria.

bacteriophage (bak-te're-o-faj): a bacterial virus; an ultramicroscopic agent that eats or dissolves bacteria. See **phage.**

bacteriostasis (bak-te-re-os'tah-sis): a condition in which bacteria are inhibited in their growth, but not killed.

basal ganglia (ba'sal gang'le-ah), **basal nuclei:** masses of gray matter within the lower part of the forebrain which aid in maintaining muscle coordination and steadiness of muscle contraction.

bifurcate (bi-fur'kate): to divide into 2, forming 2 branches or subdivisions.

biliary (bil'e-a-re): relating to bile, the gallbladder or the bile ducts.

biopsy (bi'op-se): removal of tissue or other material from the living body for purposes of examination. (It is usually a microscopic study.)

bisexual (bi-seks'u-al): having elements of both sexes; having both male and female gonads.

blastophore (blas'to-for): the part of the sperm cell that does not become converted into spermatozoa.

blastula (blas'tu-lah): the somewhat spherical structure formed by the division of the fertilized ovum, made up of a layer of cells around a fluid-filled cavity.

blennogenic (blen-no-jen'ik): producing mucus.

blennorrhea (blen-no-re'ah): a profuse discharge from a mucous surface, particularly the membranous lining of the urethra and vagina.

blennuria (blen-nu're-ah): the presence of mucus in the urine.

blepharism (blef'ah-rizm): spasm of the eyelids; continuous blinking.

blepharitis (blef-ah-ri'tis): inflammation of the eyelid. See **tarsitis.**

blepharospasm (blef'ah-ro-spazm): spasm of the muscle that closes the eyelids, producing almost complete closure.

brachial (bra'ke-al): pertaining to the arm (the part between the shoulder and elbow).

brachiocephalic (brak-e-o-se-fal'ik): relating to the arm and the head, as for example, the brachiocephalic artery (formerly called the innominate artery).

brachiotomy (bra-ke-ot'o-me): the removal or cutting of an arm.

brachydactylia (brak-e-dak-til'e-ah): an abnormal shortness of the fingers and toes.

brachyesophagus (brak-e-e-sof'ah-gus): an abnormally short esophagus.

bradycardia (brad-e-kar'de-ah): an abnormal slowness of the heart beat with a slowing of the pulse rate to 60 or less a minute.

bronchiectasis (brong-ke-ek'tah-sis): a chronic disorder in which there is loss of the normal elastic tissue and dilation of lung air passages, characterized by difficulty in breathing, coughing, expectoration of pus, and unpleasant breath.

bronchiole (brong'ke-ole): a very small

subdivision of the lung tubes; a microscopic bronchial tube; also called a **bronchiolus** (brong-ki'o-lus).

bronchium (brong'ke-um): a smaller subdivision of the main bronchi; one of the bronchial tubes that is larger than the bronchioles. The plural is **bronchia** (brong'ke-ah).

bronchoscope (brong'ko-skope): an instrument used to examine the interior of the large tubes of the lungs (bronchi).

bronchus (brong'kus): a main division of the trachea (windpipe); one of the larger air passages in the lungs. The plural is **bronchi** (brong'ki).

bubo (bu'bo): an enlarged, inflamed lymph node (especially an inguinal node in the groin), usually due to absorption of infected material (seen in syphilis and gonorrhea).

buccal (buk'al): referring to the cheek.

buccally (buk'al-le): toward the cheek.

buffer (buf'er): any compound that prevents appreciable changes in the acidity (hydrogen ion concentration) in a liquid upon the addition of an acid or a base.

bulla (bul'ah): a large blister filled with fluid; also a bubblelike cavity.

bursa (bur'sah): a fluid-filled sac or space located in areas where friction may develop between moving parts, as near joints, under muscles, and over bony projections.

calcification (kal-si-fi-ka'shun): the process of hardening by deposits of calcium compounds.

calculus (kal'ku-lus): a stone formed within the body, as in the kidney, urinary bladder, or gallbladder. The plural is **calculi** (kal'ku-li).

calorie (kal'o-re): a unit of heat. (The small calorie is the amount of heat required to raise the temperature of 1 gram of water 1 degree centigrade. The large calorie or kilocalorie is the one used in nutrition and metabolic studies, and is the amount of heat necessary to raise 1 kilogram of water 1 degree centigrade.)

calyx, calix (ka'liks): an extension from the renal pelvis into the kidney tissue. The plural is either **calyces** or **calices** (kal'i-sez).

carbohydrate (kar-bo-hi'drate): a starch, sugar, cellulose, or gum; a compound containing carbon, hydrogen, and oxygen in a particular amount and arrangement.

carbuncle (kar'bungk'l): a serious infection involving the skin and underlying connective tissues, tending to spread under the skin and to surface at various points.

carcinogenic (kar-si-no-jen'ik): stimulating or causing the growth of a malignant tumor (cancer).

carcinoma (kar-si-no'mah): a malignant spreading growth made of epithelial cells; a kind of cancer.

cardiac (kar-de-ak'): a person with a heart disorder; pertaining to the heart.

cardiologist (kar-de-ol'o-jist): a specialist in the diagnosis and treatment of heart disease.

carditis (kar-di'tis): inflammation of the heart.

carotene (kar'o-tene): the orange or reddish pigment in foods such as carrots, sweet potatoes, leafy vegetables and egg yolk; provitamin A which can be converted in the body to vitamin A.

carotid (kah-rot'id): relating to the principal artery extending up through the neck to the head.

castration (kas-tra'shun): the removal of the testes or the ovaries.

catalytic (kat-ah-lit'ik): increasing the speed of a chemical or other reaction; said of substances that are not changed themselves but stimulate chemical reactions of other substances. See **enzyme**.

catheter (kath'e-ter): a tube which can be inserted into a body cavity through a canal to remove fluids, such as urine or blood.

celiac (se'le-ak): relating to or located in the abdomen.

cellulitis (sel-u-li'tis): an inflammation of connective tissues, especially those just under the skin.

centigrade (sen'ti-grad): a unit of measurement consisting of 100 steps or degrees of temperature.

centimeter (sen'ti-me-ter): a unit of measurement, being one hundredth part of a meter.

centrifugal (sen-trif'u-gal): moving away from a center. See **centrifuge.**

centrifuge (sen'tri-fuj): a machine by which tubes of a mixture, solution or suspension are rapidly revolved so that floating particles are driven away from the center of rotation. (An example is the separation of the plasma from the formed elements of the blood.)

centrosome (sen'tro-som): a specialized area in the cell protoplasm just outside the nucleus which plays an essential part in cell division. See **mitosis.**

cephalalgia (sef-ah-lal'ji-ah): headache; pain in the head.

cephalopelvic (sef-ah-lo-pel'vik): pertaining to the relationship of the fetal head to the maternal pelvis.

cerebellum (ser-e-bel'um): the part of the hindbrain that lies below the occipital part of the cerebrum on each side concerned with voluntary muscle movement. (The word means "little brain" and it is made of a central vermis and a cerebellar hemisphere on each side.)

cerebrum (ser'e-brum): the largest part of the brain located in the upper portion of the cranium, consisting of 2 cerebral hemispheres which are divided into lobes.

cervical (ser'vi-kal): relating to the neck or any cervix, including the cervix of the uterus.

cervix (ser'viks): any neck or constricted portion of an organ, part, or region of the body.

cheilitis (ki-li'tis): inflammation of the lips.

cheilosis (ki-lo'sis): a disorder often due to riboflavin (B₂) deficiency, marked by fissuring and scaling of the lips.

cheiralgia (ki-ral'ji-ah): pain or aching in the hand; neuritis in the hand.

cheiromegaly (ki-ro-meg'ah-le): abnormally large hands.

chemotaxis (ke-mo-tak'sis): the movement of an organism in response to variations in the concentration of a substance or chemical compound.

chemotherapy (ke-mo-ther'ah-pe): the treatment of disorders by chemicals, especially those that harm the disease organisms without harming the patient.

chirologist (ki-rol'o-jist): one who communicates by using his hands and fingers. See **dactylology.**

chiropodist (ki-rop'o-dist): one who specializes in disorders of the feet. See **podiatry.**

chiropractic (ki-ro-prak'tik): a system of treating all disorders by using one's hands to manipulate body parts, mostly the spinal column.

cholagogue (ko'lah-gog): a substance that stimulates the flow of bile.

cholecyst (ko'le-sist): the gallbladder.

cholecystitis (ko-le-sis-ti'tis): inflammation of the gallbladder (the cholecyst).

cholelithiasis (ko-le-li-thi'ah-sis): the disorder in which stones are present in the gallbladder.

cholesterol (ko-les'ter-ol): an organic fatlike compound, found in animal fat, bile, blood, brain tissue, the nerve fiber sheath (myelin), liver, and other parts of the body. (It is also found in abnormal amounts in gallstones and in some fatlike cysts.)

cholochrome (kol'o-krom): any bile pigment.

chondric (kon'drik): relating to cartilage.

chondrocyte (kon'dro-site): a cartilage cell.

chondroma (kon-dro'mah): an overgrowth of cartilage tissue.

chorion (ko're-on): the outermost layer that serves as a protective and nutritive envelope around the very early embryo.

choroid (ko'roid): pertaining to the thin, dark brown, vascular middle coat of the eyeball; also relating to the capillary fringelike parts of the pia mater that extend into the brain ventricles and produce cerebrospinal fluid

chromosomes (kro'mo-somes): small rod-shaped bodies that stain deeply and appear in the nucleus at the time of cell division (mitosis). (They contain hereditary factors, the genes.)

chronograph (kron'o-graf): a device used for measuring time intervals.

chronology (kro-nol'o-je): the arrangement

of events in the order of their occurrence; a list of dates in proper sequence.

chronophobia (kron-o-fo'be-ah): a psychoneurosis in which there is a fear of time, often seen in prison inmates.

chyle (kile): the milky looking fluid in the lacteals of the small intestine after digestion; a combination of lymph and emulsified fat.

chyme (kime): the semifluid creamy or gruellike material in the stomach; the material formed by the mixing and partial digestion of food in the stomach.

cicatrix (sik-a'triks, or sik'ah-triks): a scar; the new tissue formed during wound healing.

cilia (sil'e-ah): hairs or hairlike processes (may refer to eyelashes or to microscopic extensions of the cell protoplasm). The singular is **cilium** (sil'e-um).

circumcision (ser-kum-sizh'un): removal of the foreskin, the fold over the glans penis of the male.

circumoral (ser-kum-o'ral): situated around or near the mouth.

circumorbital (ser-kum-or'bi-tal): situated near or found around an orbit, such as the eye orbit.

circumrenal (ser-kum-re'nal): situated near or around the kidney.

circumscribed (ser'kum-skribd): confined to a small or limited area.

cirrhosis (sir-ro'sis): a disorder of the liver in which the cells are destroyed (may refer to chronic inflammation of any organ's interstitial tissue).

claudication (klaw-di-ka'shun): lameness, as in intermittent claudication where the symptoms appear upon walking and tend to disappear with rest.

clostridium (klos-trid'e-um): a group of spore-forming, rod-shaped bacteria that grow without oxygen and produce poisons (toxins). **Clostridium botulinum** causes a serious toxemia called botulism (bot'u-lizm).

clysis (kli'sis): the washing out of a cavity.

cocci (kok'si): spherical bacterial cells that resemble dots. The singular is **coccus** (kok'us).

colloids (kol'oids): small particles that are larger than ordinary molecules but small enough to remain suspended in a liquid; may also refer to a substance found in the thyroid gland or to abnormal material (hyalin) in certain tissues.

colostomy (ko-los'to-me): the surgical creation of a new opening from the colon to the body surface.

colpectasia (kol-pek-ta'se-ah): dilation of the vagina.

colposcope (kol'po-skope): an instrument used to examine the vagina; a vaginal speculum.

colpotomy (kol-pot'o-me): cutting of the vaginal wall; incision of the upper vagina to form an opening into the lower abdominal cavity. See **culdocentesis.**

comminuted (kom'i-nut-ed): broken or crushed into small pieces.

compound (kom'pownd): a substance made of 2 or more elements.

conchae (kong'ke): structures that are shell-shaped. The singular is **concha** (kong'kah).

congenital (kon-jen'i-tal): present at and usually before birth.

conjunctiva (kon-junk-ti'vah): the thin delicate membrane that lines the eyelids and is reflected over the front of the eyeball.

conjunctivitis (kon-junk-te-vi'tis): inflammation of the membrane that lines the eyelids and covers the front of the eyeball.

contraindication (kon-trah-in-di-ka'shun): a condition that makes a particular kind of treatment undesirable.

contrastimulus (kon-trah-stim'u-lus): an agent which opposes stimulation.

contrecoup (kon-tr-koo'): a French word that means "counterblow," especially referring to a skull fracture caused by a blow to the opposite side.

convoluted (kon'vo-loot-ed): coiled or rolled together; irregularly tortuous, as are the tubules in the kidney and coils of the small intestine.

convolution (kon-vo-lu'shun): an elevation caused by an infolding of the structure upon itself. See **gyrus.**

corium (ko're-um): the deeper part of the skin found below the epidermis; the dermis or true skin, containing blood vessels, nerves, and connective tissue.

cornea (kor'ne-ah): the transparent front part of the eyeball; the forward continuation of the outer coat (sclera).

coronary (kor'o-na-re): applying to structures that encircle a part or organ in a crownlike manner, as for example, the coronary arteries encircling the base of the heart.

corpus (kor'pus): the main part of a structure or organ. (It may designate the whole organism.)

corpuscle (kor'pus'l): a very small mass or body; a microscopic structure such as a blood cell or nerve ending.

costiform (kos'ti-form): rib-shaped.

costosternal (kos-to-ster'nal): pertaining to a rib and the sternum (breastbone).

counterirritation (kown-ter-ir-i-ta'shun): a superficial stimulant or irritant that serves to relieve a pain, an ache, or other irritation.

countertraction (kown'ter-trak-shun): pulling in the near (or proximal) direction while traction (a pull) is applied in the opposite direction. (It is used to reduce fractures.)

craniectomy (kra-ne-ek'to-me): removal or excision of a part of the skull, as performed for the relief of microcephalus.

craniotomy (kra-ne-ot'o-me): any operation on the skull; the cutting into pieces of the fetal head to make delivery possible.

crepitations (krep-i-ta'shuns): fine crackling sounds, such as may be heard in the lungs (see rales); the gritty sounds one may hear by rubbing together the ends of a fractured bone.

cryalgesia (kri-al-je'ze-ah): pain resulting from a cold application.

crymotherapy (kri-mo-ther'ah-pe): the therapeutic use of cold.

cryogenic (kri-o-jen'ik): relating to or producing low temperatures.

cryptic (krip'tik): hidden, concealed, or in a larval stage.

cryptogenic (krip-to-jen'ik): of doubtful or obscure origin; origin not ascertainable.

cryptorchidism (krip-tor'ki-dizm): a failure of the testis to descend normally; a defect in the normal development and descent of the testis into the scrotum.

crystalloids (kris'tal-loids): molecules or particles that are so small that they pass through animal (or vegetable) membranes easily. (The particles are smaller than those in colloids.)

cul-de-sac (kul'de-sahk): a blind pouch or a cavity which is closed at one end; the rectouterine excavation of the lower abdominal cavity.

culdocentesis (kul-do-sen-te'sis): the removal of fluid from the lower peritoneal cavity (rectouterine excavation) by puncture of the upper posterior vaginal wall. See **culpotomy.**

culdoscopy (kul-dos'ko-pe): the visual examination of the female pelvic organs by means of an instrument (endoscope) introduced through the upper posterior vaginal wall.

cutization (ku-ti-za'shun): the change of exposed mucous membrane into skin.

cycloplegic (si-klo-ple'jik): an agent that causes paralysis of the muscles of accommodation in the eye.

cyesis (si-e'sis): the condition of being pregnant.

cystitis (sis-ti'tis): inflammation of the urinary bladder.

cystocele (sis'to-sele): a bulging of the urinary bladder through the wall of the vagina (a kind of herniation).

cystoscope (sis'to-skope): an instrument used to examine the inside of the urinary bladder.

cytemia (si-te'me-ah): the presence of extra cells in the blood.

cytology (si-tol'o-je): the study of cells, their origin, structure, and functions.

cytolytic (si-to-lit'ik): causing or pertaining to the destruction or dissolution (dissolving) of cells.

cytophagocytosis (si-to-fag-o-si-to'sis): the ingestion (swallowing) of cells by phagocytes.

cytophagy (si-tof'ah-je): the absorption of cells by other cells.

cytoplasm (si'to-plazm): the cell protoplasm outside the nucleus.

dacryagogue (dak're-ah-gog): any substance that induces a flow of tears.

dacryocyst (dak're-o-sist): the tear (lacrimal) sac.

dactylitis (dak-ti-li'tis) inflammation of a finger or toe.

dactylology (dak-til-ol'o-je): the use of hands and fingers for purposes of communication. See **chirologist.**

deciduous (de-sid'u-us): relating to anything that is cast off at maturity, as for example, the first set of teeth.

decubitus (de-ku'bi-tus): the lying-down position (a decubitus ulcer is caused by pressure when a patient is confined to bed for a long period of time).

defecation (def-e-ka'shun): the discharge of excreta (fecal material) from the rectum.

dehydration (de-hi-dra'shun): a condition due to excessive water loss from the body or its parts.

dementia (de-men'she-ah): a disordered or deteriorated mind. See **psychosis.**

dentition (den-tish'un): the position of the teeth in their sockets (alveoli); also used to indicate the process of teething.

dermatitis (der-mah-ti'tis): inflammation of the skin.

dermatology (der-mah-tol'o-je): the medical specialty dealing with skin disorders.

dermatosis (der-mah-to'sis): a general term for any skin disorder.

dermic (der'mik): pertaining to the skin.

deoxyribonucleic (de-ok-se-ri-bo-nu-kle'ik) **acid.** See **DNA.**

desquamation (des-kwah-ma'shun): the shedding of skin or other epithelial layers in sheets or scales.

dialysis (di-al'i-sis): the process of separating crystalloids (smaller particles) from colloids (larger particles) by the difference in their rates of diffusion through a semipermeable membrane.

diapedesis (di-ah-pe-de'sis): the passage of blood cells, especially white cells (leukocytes), through the intact blood vessel walls.

diaphoresis (di-ah-fo-re'sis): perspiring, especially *profuse* sweating.

diaphragm (di'ah-fram): any partition that separates one area from another, especially the somewhat dome-shaped musculomembranous partition between the thoracic and abdominal cavities.

diaphysis (di-af'i-sis): the shaft or part of a long bone between the two ends (epiphyses).

diarrhea (di-ah-re'ah): abnormal frequency of liquid discharges from the bowels.

diastole (di-as'to-le): the relaxing dilatation period of the heart muscle, especially of the ventricles. The adjective is **diastolic** (di-ah-stol'ik).

diathermy (di'ah-ther-me): the generation of heat within the body tissues using high frequency electric currents.

diathesis (di-ath'e-sis): a condition of the body which causes unusual predisposition to disease.

diffusion (di-fu'shun): the process of becoming spread out, as any gaseous substance that spreads throughout a room; the movement of molecules from any area of high concentration to one of lower concentration.

digitalis (dij-i-tal'is): the dried leaf of foxglove **(Digitalis purpurea)** which is used in the treatment of some types of heart disease.

diglossia (di-glos'e-ah): double tongue, or division into two branches (bifid).

dimorphism (di-mor'fizm): the property of existing in two forms, as in sexual dimorphism where properties of both sexes exist.

diopter (di-op'ter): a unit for measuring the bending or refractive power of a lens.

diploe (dip'lo-e): the spongy (cancellous) bone lying between the two layers of compact bone in the cranium.

diplopia (di-plo'pe-ah): double vision where two images of one object are seen.

disarticulation (dis-ar-tik-u-la'shun): the amputation or separation at a joint.

disinter (dis-in-ter'): to take out of the grave or tomb; to dig up a buried body; to exhume.

disinterment (dis-in-ter'ment): the process of taking the body out of a grave after burial. See **exhumation.**

disparate (dis'pah-rat): not alike; not exactly paired.

distal (dis'tal): away from the point of origin. The opposite is **proximal.**

diuresis (di-u-re'sis): increased secretion of urine.

diverticulitis (di-ver-tik-u-li'tis): an inflammation of the abnormal sacs formed as a result of weakness in the muscle wall of a tubular organ, such as the colon.

DNA (deoxyribonucleic acid): a complex compound found in the nuclei of cells which is believed to be the chief (or possibly only) component of genes, the hereditary factors in each cell.

dolichocephalic (dol-i-ko-se-fal'ik): having a long head.

dolicomorphic (dol-i-ko-mor'fik): the tall slender type of build.

dorsiflexion (dor-si-flek'shun): backward bending, as of the hand.

dorsonuchal (dor-so-nu'kal): pertaining to the back of the neck.

duodenal (du-o-de'nal): located in or related to the duodenum.

duodenum (du-o-de'num): the first or proximal part of the small bowel (about 12 inches in length).

dura mater (du'rah ma'ter): the outermost of the 3 coverings that surround the brain and spinal cord; a tough connective tissue membrane that serves as one of the meninges of the central nervous system.

dysentery (dis'en-ter-e): a painful disorder due to intestinal inflammation and accompanied by frequent loose, bloody stools. (Amebic dysentery is caused by **Entamoeba histolytica,** while various bacteria cause bacillary dysentery.)

dysphagia (dis-fa'je-ah): difficulty in swallowing which is often accompanied by pain.

dysphasia (dis-fa'ze-ah): speech impairment; difficulty in speaking, due to a lesion in the brain.

dyspnea (disp'ne-ah); difficult or labored breathing.

ectoderm (ek'to-derm): the outer layer of cells of the embryo from which develop the nervous system, the skin, the teeth, and other structures.

ectogenous (ek-toj'e-nus): originating from outside the organism.

ectopic (ek-top'ik): away from the normal location; congenital malposition. (An ectopic heart beat originates at a point away from its normal origin, the sinoatrial node.)

eczema (ek'ze-mah): an inflammatory skin disorder in which there may be blisters, scales, crusts, redness, and other lesions.

edema (e-de'mah): an abnormal accumulation of fluid in the body tissues, formerly referred to as dropsy.

efferent (ef'er-ent): carrying away from a center.

effusion (e-fu'shun): the escape of fluid into a space or part; the fluid that has escaped.

ego (e'go): that part of the mind which possesses consciousness and deals with reality.

electrocardiogram (e-lek-tro-kar'de-o-gram): the tracing of the electric current produced by heart muscle activity (contraction); the record produced by an electrocardiograph.

electrocardiograph (e-lek-tro-kar'de-o-graf): an instrument used for making records of the heart's electric currents. See **electrocardiogram.**

electroencephalogram (e-lek-tro-en-sef'ah-lo-gram): the tracing of the electric currents developed in the brain; the record produced by the electroencephalograph.

electroencephalograph (e-lek-tro-en-sef'ah-lo-graf): and instrument for making records of the brain's electric currents. See **electroencephalogram.**

electrolyte (e-lek'tro-lite): a solution that conducts electricity by means of ions that are positively or negatively charged.

electron (e-lek'tron): the unit of negative electricity. (When flowing in a conductor, electrons constitute an electric current.)

element (el'e-ment): in chemistry, a simple substance that cannot be decomposed into simpler substances by chemical means; any one of the primary parts of a thing.

elephantiasis (el-e-fan-ti'ah-sis): a disorder in which the lymph channels are obstructed resulting in marked swelling and thickening of the skin. See **filariasis.**

embolus (em'bo-lus): a foreign or abnormal object carried by the bloodstream into a smaller vessel causing its obstruction. (Blood clots, air bubbles, fat globules, a mass of tissue cells, etc., may act as an embolus.) The plural is **emboli.**

emesis (em'e-sis): the act of vomiting.

emetic (e-met'ik): an agent, such as a drug, that causes vomiting.

emphysema (em-fi-se'mah): a swelling or inflation of air passages with resulting stagnation of air in parts of the lungs.

empyema (em-pi-e'mah): an accumulation of pus in a cavity, especially in the chest (the pleural cavity).

emulsion (e-mul'shun): a substance in which there is distribution of small globules of one liquid, such as fat, throughout a second liquid. (To "emulsify" (e-mul'si-fi) means "to make into an emulsion.")

encephalitis (en-sef-ah-li'tis): inflammation of the brain, the encephalon (en-sef'ah-lon).

encephalogram (en-sef'ah-lo-gram): a roentgenogram (x-ray) of the head.

endarterial (end-ar-te're-al): within an artery.

endocarditis (en-do-kar-di'tis): inflammation of the endocardium. (Valvular endocarditis is more common than mural (wall) endocarditis.)

endocardium (en-do-kar'de-um): the membrane which lines the heart chambers and assists in forming the heart valves.

endocervicitis (en-do-ser-vi-si'tis): inflammation of the mucous membrane inside the cervical canal of the uterus (in the cervix uteri).

endochondral (en-do-kon'dral): formed or located within cartilage.

endocrine (en'do-krin): secreting to the inside, into either tissue fluid or blood. The opposite is **exocrine.**

endocrinopathy (en-do-kri-nop'ah-the): any disorder of the glands of internal secretion.

endogenic (en-do-jen'ik). See **endogenous.**

endogenous (en-doj'e-nus): growing from or beginning within the organism.

endolymph (en'do-limf): a fluid found within the membranous portion of the inner ear.

endoscope (en'do-skope): an instrument used to look inside hollow organs, such as the stomach (gastroscope) or urinary bladder (cystoscope).

endosteum (en-dos'te-um): the membrane that lines the medullary cavity of bones.

endothelium (en-do-the'le-um): the layer of cells (serosa) that lines blood and lymph vessels, the heart, and the serous body cavities.

enteritis (en-ter-i'tis): inflammation of the small bowel.

enteroanastomosis (en-ter-o-ah-nas-to-mo'sis): the connection of 2 portions of the intestine by surgery.

enterobius (en-ter-o'be-us): intestinal worms, the most common of which is the seat or pinworm, **Enterobius vermicularis** (ver-mik'u-lar-is).

enterocolitis (en-ter-o-ko-li'tis): inflammation of the small and the large bowel.

enteroptosis (en-ter-op-to'sis): the downward displacement of the intestine.

enterorrhaphy (en-ter-or'ah-fe): the sewing or suturing of a wound or other defect in the intestine.

enzyme (en'zim): a substance that causes chemical changes; a kind of organic catalyst; usually a protein. See **catalytic.**

eosinophil (e-o-sin'o-fil): a cell that stains readily with a rose-colored dye called eosin. (It refers mostly to a white blood cell.)

eosinophilia (e-o-sin-o-fil'e-ah): an increase in the number of eosinophils in the blood; the condition of being easily stained with eosin.

epicardium (ep-i-kar'de-um): the membrane that forms the outer layer of the heart wall and is continuous with the lining of the sac that encloses the heart; the visceral pericardium.

epidermis (ep-i-der'mis): the outer epithelial layer of the skin, which contains no blood vessels and which rests on the dermis (corium).

epidermophytosis (ep-e-der-mo-fi-to'sis): a fungous infection of the skin, especially of the toes and soles of the feet which is called tinea pedis (athlete's foot).

epigastrium (ep-i-gas'tre-um): the upper middle section of the abdominal cavity, just below the breastbone (sternum).

epiglottis (ep-i-glot'is): a lidlike kind of structure made largely of cartilage, which covers the entrance to the larynx (voice box).

epinephrine (ep-i-nef'rin): a hormone produced by the adrenal medulla which may also be produced synthetically.

epiphysis (e-pif'i-sis): the end of a long bone, usually larger in diameter than the shaft (diaphysis).

epistaxis (ep-i-stak'sis): nosebleed; nasal hemorrhage.

epithelium (ep-i-the'le-um): the tissue that forms the outer part (epidermis) of the skin; lines blood vessels, hollow organs and passages that lead to the outside of the body; and makes up the active part of many glands, such as the lacrimal (tear) glands.

ergograph (er'go-graf): an instrument for recording work done by muscle activity.

ergosterol (er-gos'te-rol): a compound found in plant and animal tissues that can be irradiated by ultraviolet rays to make vitamin D_2 (important in combating rickets).

eructation (e-ruk-ta'shun): the forceful expulsion of gas from the stomach; belching.

erythema (er-e-the'mah): skin redness usually due to congestion of the blood in the capillaries.

erythroblast (e-rith'-ro-blast): an immature cell which contains a nucleus and is believed to be an early stage in the development of mature, normal, nonnucleated red blood cells.

erythroblastosis (e-rith-ro-blas-to'sis): the presence of immature red cells (erythroblasts) in the circulating blood. (Erythroblastosis fetalis is a congenital disorder in which an Rh negative mother transmits antibodies against the Rh protein to an Rh positive baby.)

erythrocyte (e-rith'ro-site): a red blood cell; a nonnucleated, circular, disk-shaped cell that contains hemoglobin.

erythrocytopenia (e-rith-ro-si-to-pe'ne-ah): a deficiency in the number of red blood cells (erythrocytes). It is also called **erythropenia.**

erythropoiesis (e-rith-ro-poi-e'sis): the production of red blood cells.

esophageal (e-sof-ah-je'al or e-so-fa'je-al): relating to the gullet. See **esophagus.**

esophagus (e-sof'ah-gus): the gullet; the tubular passage extending from the pharynx to the stomach.

etiology (e-te-ol'o-je): the study of causes of disease, including theories of origin and particularly what organisms, if any, are involved.

euphoria (u-fo're-ah): a feeling of bodily comfort; in psychiatry, an exaggerated sense of well-being.

eupnea (up-ne'ah): normal, easy respiration.

exacerbation (eks-as-er-ba'shun): an increase in severity of symptoms or of disease.

exanthem (ek-san'them): any skin eruption or rash; visible skin lesions often accompanied by fever.

excoriation (eks-ko-re-a'shun): the removal of any superficial pieces of skin, such as that caused by scratching or scraping.

excrement (eks'kre-ment): matter cast out from the body as waste, especially that expelled from the bowels; fecal material.

excrescence (eks-kres'ens): any abnormal projection or outgrowth.

excretion (eks-kre'shun): process of discharging or throwing off waste matter.

exhumation (eks-hu-ma'shun): the process of taking the body out of the earth after burial. See **disinterment.**

exocrine (ek'so-krin or ek-so'krin): secreting toward the outside, or away from the secreting tissue by tubes or ducts. The opposite is **endocrine.**

exogenous (eks-oj'e-nus): developing or originating outside the organism.

exophthalmos (ek-sof-thal′mos), **exoph-thalmus** (ek-sof-thal′mus): an abnormal bulging of the eyeball.

extension (eks-ten′shun): a movement by which two parts are pulled apart toward a straightened position.

extracellular (eks-trah-sel′u-lar): outside of a cell or cells. The opposite is **intracellular.**

extrasystole (eks-trah-sis′to-le): a premature contraction of heart muscle, independent of the normal rhythm.

extravasation (eks-trav-ah-sa′shun): blood, lymph, or serum that escapes from a vessel into the tissues.

exudate (eks′u-dat): escaping fluid or semifluid material that oozes out of a blood vessel (usually as a result of inflammation) which may contain serum, pus, and cellular debris.

facies (fa′she-ez): the appearance or expression of the face; also a specific surface of any part or organ.

facultative (fak′ul-ta-tiv): ability to adjust to various circumstances; not compulsory. The opposite is **obligate.**

falciform (fal′si-form): somewhat crescent-shaped; like a curved blade; sickle-shaped.

fascia (fash′e-ah): a layer or band of connective tissue, especially that which holds the skin to the surface muscles, or any of the sheets enclosing muscles or other organs.

fascial (fash′e-al): relating to the bands or sheets of fibrous connective tissue known as fasciae (fash′e-e). See **fascia.**

feces (fe′sez): the material discharged from the bowel (also called the stool), which is made up of bacteria, secretions, and a little food residue.

fenestra (fe-nes′trah): a windowlike opening.

fenestration (fen-es-tra′shun): forming a window or opening, as in the surgical opening produced in the inner ear for some conditions of deafness.

festination (fes-ti-na′shun): an involuntary tendency to lean forward while walking and to increase speed, as seen in certain nervous disorders (paralysis agitans).

fetal (fe′tal) pertaining to the developing unborn baby after the first 8 weeks. See **fetus.**

fetus (fe′tus): the unborn offspring of the human after 8 weeks. (Before 8 weeks it is called an embryo.)

fibrillation (fi-bri-la′shun): irregular twitching movements of individual muscle cells (fibers) or small groups of muscle fibers, preventing effective action by a muscle or organ.

fibrinogen (fi-brin′o-jen): a protein found in the liquid (plasma) of the blood (so-called coagulation factor I), which is converted into insoluble fibrin during clotting.

fibroblast (fi′bro-blast): a flat elongated connective tissue cell. (Fibroblasts form the fibrous tissues of the body.)

fibroid (fi′broid): a tumor having a structure of threadlike (fibrous) elements; a fibroma; a myoma of the uterus.

fibrositis (fi-bro-si′tis): a disorder in which there is inflammation of certain fibrous connective tissue layers around or near muscles, resulting in pain and stiffness.

filariasis (fil-ah-ri′ah-sis): a disorder caused by tiny threadlike worms called filariae (fi-la′re-e), which may cause inflammation and obstruction of lymph vessels. See **elephantiasis.**

filtrate (fil′trate): a liquid that has passed through a membrane or filter. (The liquid that passes from the blood in the kidney glomerulus constitutes the beginning of urine formation, and is called the glomerular filtrate.)

filtration (fil-tra′shun): the passage of a liquid through a filter or a membrane that acts as a filter. (A pressure that is higher on the liquid to be filtered or a negative pressure on the side of the membrane receiving the filtrate makes filtration possible.)

fimbriated (fim′bre-ated): fringed, as the lateral ends of the uterine tubes (oviducts). "Fimbriae" (fim′bre-e) means "fringe," while one part of the fringe is a fimbria (fim′bre-ah).

fissure (fish′ur): a groove, fold, or slit, which may be normal or abnormal. (The inward folds of the cerebral cortex are normal fissures, while inflammation may cause painful abnormal fissures around the mouth, anus and elsewhere.)

fistula (fis'tu-lah): an abnormal passage between two organs, or between an organ cavity and the outside, which may be formed by tissue injury and disintegration.

flagella (flah-jel'ah): microscopic whiplike processes or threadlike appendages that enable tiny organisms to swim about rapidly. A single process is a **flagellum** (flah-jel'um).

flatus (fla'tus): gas, usually air, in the stomach or bowel. (It means a "blowing" and so can refer to expelling air from the lungs.)

fluoroscope (floo-o'ro-skope): an instrument used to examine deep structures, including movement (of heart, bowels, etc.), by means of roentgen rays (x-rays).

fontanel, fontanelle (fon-tah-nel'): a soft spot in a baby's skull; a membrane-covered space where ossification (bone formation) has not yet occurred.

fossa (fos'sah): a hollow or depressed area; a valleylike region on a bone or other structure.

fovea (fo've-ah): a small pit or cup-shaped depression in the surface of a part or organ, as in the head of the femur and near the center of the retina of the eye; the point of clearest vision.

frenulum (fren'u-lum): a small fold, usually mucous membrane, that limits motion of a part. It is also called **frenum.**

fulguration (ful-gu-ra'shun): the destruction of animal tissue by electric sparks.

fulminate (ful'mi-nate): occurring suddenly and with severity. (A fulminating anoxia is a sudden reduction in the oxygen content of the blood, causing collapse.)

fundus (fun'dus): the part of a hollow organ farthest from the entrance. (The fundus of the stomach is the rounded portion to the left and above the body.)

furuncle (fu'rungk'l): a boil; a painful nodule due to infection and inflammation of a hair follicle or an oil gland.

galactagogue (gah-lak'tah-gog), **galactogogue** (gah-lak'to-gog): a substance that stimulates the flow of milk.

galactemia (gal-ak-te'me-ah): a diseased state of the blood in which milk is present.

galactocele (gah-lak'to-sele): a cyst or tumor in the mammary gland which is filled with milk; a hydrocele containing milklike fluid (chylous); a galactoma.

galactose (gah-lak'tose): a substance obtained from milk sugar (lactose) by enzyme action, or by other procedures.

gamete (gam'ete): a reproductive cell; an ovum or a spermatozoon; the sexual form of the malarial parasite found in the stomach of the mosquito.

gamma globulins (gam'mah glob'u-lins): protein substances often found in immune serums that act as antibodies. (They are used to prevent such diseases as measles and epidemic hepatitis.)

ganglion (gang'gle-on): a small knotlike mass; in the nervous system, a collection of nerve cells; a kind of tumor formed in a tendon of the wrist. The plural is **ganglia** (gang'gle-ah).

gangrene (gang'grene): death of a mass of tissue, accompanied by bacterial invasion and putrefaction, that is usually due to blood vessel obstruction.

gastritis (gas-tri'tis): inflammation of the stomach, usually of the lining mucosa.

gastroenterostomy (gas-tro-en-ter-os'to-me): the surgical production of a passage between the stomach and intestine. See **anastomosis.**

gastroplasty (gas'tro-plas-te): a molding or plastic operation on the stomach.

gavage (gah-vahzh'): feeding through a tube passed into the stomach through the esophagus.

gene (jene): one of the biologic units of heredity. (Genes are made partially or entirely of DNA and each is located in a definite position on a certain chromosome.)

genetics (je-net'iks): the study of heredity.

genitoplasty (jen'i-to-plas-te): plastic surgery on organs of the reproductive system.

genitourinary (jen-i-to-u'ri-nar-e): relating

to the organs of both the urinary and the reproductive systems.

genodermatology (jen-o-der-mah-tol'o-je): the study that deals with inherited skin disorders.

genotype (jen'o-tipe): the basic constitution of an organism in terms of its hereditary traits, or its assortment of genes; the type species of a genus.

genyantrum (jen-e-an'trum): the maxillary sinus; the antrum of Highmore.

genyplasty (jen'e-plas-te): plastic surgery to reconstruct the jaw.

geriatric (jer-e-at'rik): relating to the care and the treatment of the aged.

germicide (jer'mi-side): any substance that destroys disease—producing organisms (pathogens). The adjective is **germicidal.**

giantism (ji'ant-izm), **gigantism** (ji'gan-tizm): excessive growth with resulting large size.

gingiva (jin'ji-vah): the mucous membrane and connective tissue that encircles the neck of the tooth, and overlies the crown of those not as yet erupted.

glans (glanz): a small rounded mass, as the cap-shaped expansion at the end of the penis in the male, or the smaller body at the end of the clitoris (klit'o-ris) in the female.

glaucoma (glaw-ko'mah): a disorder of the eye in which there is increased pressure due to an excess of fluid within the eye.

glioma (gli-o'mah): a tumor of the brain or spinal cord that is made of supporting tissue elements. See **neuroglia.**

glomerulus (glo-mer'u-lus): a ball-like cluster of nerves or blood vessels, especially the microscopic tuft of capillaries that is surrounded by the expanded part of each kidney tubule. See **nephron.**

glossitis (glos-si'tis): inflammation of the tongue.

glossopharyngeal (glos-o-fah-rin'je-al): pertaining to the tongue and pharynx.

glucoprotein (gloo-ko-pro'te-in), **glycoprotein** (gli-ko-pro'te-in): a compound consisting of a protein with a carbohydrate, including mucins, mucoids, and other substances of the human body.

glycemia (gli-se'me-ah): presence of sugar (in the form of glucose) in the blood.

glycogen (gli'ko-jen): the so-called animal starch, the chief storage carbohydrate in animals. (It is stored largely in the liver and is liberated in the form of glucose as it is needed by the body cells.)

glycosuria (gli-ko-su're-ah): an abnormal amount of the simple sugar glucose in the urine.

gonad (gon'ad): an ovary or a testis; a sex gland; the producer of seed (egg cells called ova and sperm cells).

gonadotropic (gon-ah-do-trop'ik): affecting the gonads. (It applies especially to the pituitary hormones that influence the testes in the male or the ovaries in the female.)

gonarthritis (gon-ar-thri'tis): inflammation of a knee or of a knee joint.

gonorrhea (gon-o-re'ah): a contagious venereal disease characterized by discharge of pus from mucous membranes, chiefly of the urethra and other parts of the genitourinary system.

graphology (graf-ol'o-je): the study of handwriting.

gynatresia (jin-ah-tre'ze-ah): a closure of some part of the female reproductive system, as for example, occlusion of the vagina.

gynecology (jin-e-kol'o-je): the branch of medicine related to the study and treatment of disorders of the female reproductive system.

gynecomastia (jin-e-ko-mas'te-ah): excessive development of the male mammary glands (breasts).

gynoplasty (ji'no-plas-te): a surgical operation on the reproductive organs of the female.

gyrus (ji'rus): one of the tortuous elevations (convolutions) of the cerebral cortex. The plural is **gyri.**

helminth (hel'minth): a worm or wormlike parasite.

helminthology (hel-min-thol'o-je): the study of worms including those that are parasitic.

hemacytometer (hem-ah-si-tom'e-ter),

hemocytometer (hem-o-si-tom′e-ter): an instrument used in counting blood cells.

hematemesis (hem-at-em′e-sis): the vomiting of blood.

hematoma (hem-ah-to′mah): a tumor or swelling filled with blood.

hematopoiesis (hem-ah-to-poi-e′sis): the formation and development of blood cells in the body, largely in the red bone marrow.

hematuria (hem-ah-tu′re-ah): the presence of blood in the urine.

hemianopia (hem-e-ah-no′pe-ah): blindness or defective vision affecting half of the visual field.

heminephrectomy (hem-e-ne-frek′to-me): removal of part of the kidney.

hemiplegia (hem-e-ple′je-ah): paralysis of one side of the body.

hemoglobin (he-mo-glo′bin): the oxygen-carrying colored compound in the red blood cells.

hemoglobinometer (he-mo-glo-bi-nom′e-ter): an instrument used for measuring the amount of hemoglobin in the blood. It is also called a **hemometer** (he-mom′e-ter).

hemolysis (he-mol′i-sis): the disintegration of red blood cells which results in the appearance of hemoglobin in the surrounding fluid.

hemolytic (he-mo-lit′ik): having the ability to disintegrate or hemolyze (he′mo-lize) red blood cells. See **hemolysis.**

hemometer (he-mom′e-ter). See **hemoglobinometer.**

hemophilia (he-mo-fil′e-ah): a hereditary blood disorder in which there is deficient production of certain factors involved in blood clotting, resulting in bleeding into joints, deep tissues and elsewhere.

hemophilic (he-mo-fil′ik): pertaining to a fondness of blood; in bacteriology, pertaining to bacteria that grow well in the presence of hemoglobin.

hemoptysis (he-mop′ti-sis): the spitting up of blood or blood-stained sputum.

hemorrhage (hem′or-ij): bleeding; profuse escape of blood from the vessels.

hemostasis (he-mos′tah-sis): the stoppage of the escape of blood; the arrest of blood flow through any part or vessel.

hemostat (he′mo-stat): an instrument or agent used to prevent the flow or escape of blood.

heparin (hep′ah-rin): a complex acid compound, found most abundantly in the liver, which prevents blood clotting; in pharmacy, a mixture obtained from animal livers or lungs which is used in the prevention and treatment of disorders involving blood coagulation.

hepatitis (hep-ah-ti′tis): inflammation of the liver.

hepatogenous (hep-ah-toj′e-nus): coming from or originating in the liver.

herpes (her′peze): a skin disease in which small blisters appear, often in clusters. (Herpes simplex may be referred to as cold sores or fever blisters, and is caused by a virus infection involving mostly the lip borders and the nose. Herpes zoster, shingles, is also a virus infection but involves nerve trunk areas.)

heteradenoma (het-er-ad-e-no′mah): a tumor found on abnormal glandular tissue, or on glandular tissue occurring in an abnormal place.

heterocrine (het′er-o-krin): referring to glands or other tissues that secrete more than one type of substance, such as the pancreas which produces both endocrine and exocrine secretions.

heterogeneous (het-er-o-je′ne-us): made up of differing ingredients; not of uniform quality throughout.

heterosexual (het-er-o-seks′u-al): relating to or directed toward the opposite sex.

hilum (hi′lum), **hilus** (hi′lus): an area, depression or pit where blood vessels and nerves enter or leave the organ.

histiocyte (his′te-o-site): a large cell found in certain connective tissues of the reticuloendothelial system.

histology (his-tol′o-je): the study of minute structure, composition, and function of tissues; microscopical anatomy.

homeomorphous (ho-me-o-mor′fus): of like form or structure.

homeopathy (ho-me-op′ah-the): a system of treatment using minute amounts of drugs that theoretically in larger amounts could produce in healthy persons the symptoms of the disease to be treated.

homeostasis (ho-me-o-sta'sis): a consistency and uniformity of the internal body environment which maintains normal body function; stability of body fluids and their constituents.

homogeneous (ho-mo-je'ne-us): having similar or the same consistency and composition throughout.

homosexual (ho-mo-seks'u-al): pertaining to the same sex; one who is sexually attracted to another individual of the same sex.

homotransplant (ho-mo-trans'plant): a graft or transplant from an individual of the same species.

hordeolum (hor-de'o-lum): a sty; an inflammation of the oil glands of the eyelid.

hydrocele (hi'dro-sele): a fluid-containing sac or tumor; specifically, a collection of fluid formed in the space along the spermatic cord and in the scrotum.

hydrocephalus (hi-dro-sef'ah-lus): a disorder characterized by gross enlargement of the cranium and atrophy of the brain due to an accumulation of excessive amounts of fluid in and around the brain.

hydrophobia (hi-dro-fo'be-ah): an abnormal fear of water; the term for rabies, characterized by severe muscle spasms when attempting to drink water, or even when seeing water.

hyperacidity (hi-per-ah-sid'i-te): an excessive degree of acidity, especially excessive hydrochloric acid in the stomach. See **hyperchlorhydria.**

hyperchlorhydria (hi-per-klor-hid're-ah): an excessive secretion of hydrochloric acid by the gland cells in the stomach.

hyperemia (hi-per-e'me-ah): an excess of blood in an area or part of the body.

hyperesthesia (hi-per-es-the'ze-ah): an abnormal sensitivity of the skin or of the organs of special sense (eye, ear, etc.).

hyperglycemia (hi-per-gli-se'me-ah): an abnormal increase in the amount of sugar (glucose) in the blood.

hypertrophy (hi-per'tro-fe): an excessive enlargement or overgrowth of an organ or part. The adjective is **hypertrophic** (hi-per-trof'ik).

hypochondrium (hi-po-kon'dre-um): the region below the costal cartilages at each side of the upper abdominal cavity.

hypodermic (hi-po-der'mik): administered or applied beneath the skin.

hypodermoclysis (hi-po-der-mok'li-sis): the injection of fluid into the subcutaneous tissues, especially the slow injection of large amounts of physiologic salt solution.

hypogastrium (hi-po-gas'tre-um): the lower central region of the abdominal cavity below the umbilical region.

hypoglycemic (hi-po-gli-se'mik): an agent that acts to lower the amount of glucose in the blood.

hypospadias (hi-po-spa'de-as): a defect in a male, present at birth, in which the urethra opens on the perineum or on the underside of the penis. It occurs less often in the female, where the urethra may open into the vagina.

hypothalamus (hi-po-thal'ah-mus): a part of the forebrain near the 3rd ventricle, containing groups of nerve cells that control temperature, sleep, water balance, and various other chemical and visceral activities.

hysterectomy (his-ter-ek'to-me): the surgical removal of the uterus.

hysteria (his-ter'e-ah): a mental disorder in which there is lack of control over emotions and behavior acts, with simulation of some physical disease; a psychoneurosis.

hysterodynia (his-ter-o-din'e-ah): pain in the uterus.

idiohypnotism (id-e-o-hip'no-tizm): self-induced hypnotism; a spontaneous type of hypnotism.

idiopathic (id-e-o-path'ik): relating to any disorder that is of unknown origin, or apparently of spontaneous origin; self-originating.

idiosyncrasy (id-e-o-sin'krah-se): a habit or quality peculiar to any person; an individual's susceptibility to some drug or other agent.

ileum (il'e-um): the last or distal part of the small intestine, ending at the cecum of the large intestine.

ileus (il'e-us): a disorder in which there is obstruction of the small bowel, which may be due to paralysis or to a mechanical blockage.

iliac (il'e-ak): pertaining to the bone called the ilium (upper os coxae); the 2 regions at each side of the lower abdomen.

iliocolotomy (il-e-o-ko-lot'o-me): a surgical incision into the colon in the flank or iliac region.

iliotibial (il-e-o-tib'e-al): relating to or extending from the ileum (upper os coxae) to the tibia (shin bone), as for example, the connective tissue band in the lateral part of the thigh.

ilium (il'e-um): the upper somewhat wing-shaped portion of the os coxae (hip bone).

impetigo (im-pe-ti'go): a contagious skin disease usually caused by staphylococci, and characterized by pustular eruptions that later become covered with crusts.

implantation (im-plan-ta'shun): the insertion of a tissue or a part into a new body location; the attachment of the preembryonic ball of cells (blastula) into the lining of the uterus.

inanimate (in-an'i-mat): lacking in life; lacking in liveliness.

infarct (in'farkt): an area of tissue death due to the obstruction of the circulation to that area. (The process of developing an infarct is known as infarction.)

infiltration (in-fil-tra'shun): the diffusion or accumulation of liquids or other substances not normal to the tissue.

inguinal (ing'gwi-nal): relating to the groin region (the inguen).

integument (in-teg'u-ment): a covering, especially the skin.

integumentary (in-teg-u-men'tar-e): composed of or relating to the skin; serving as a covering.

intercostal (in-ter-kos'tal): situated between the ribs (costae).

interstitial (in-ter-stish'al): pertaining to spaces or structures between the functioning active tissues of any part or organ.

intracellular (in-trah-sel'u-lar): within the cell itself. The opposite is **extracellular.**

intracranial (in-trah-kra'ne-al): within the cranial cavity.

intraocular (in-trah-ok'u-lar): within the eyeball.

ischemia (is-ke'me-ah): a lack of sufficient blood to a part, usually due to the obstruction of an artery.

isotonic (i-so-ton'ik): having equal tension or tone; the existence of equality of osmotic pressure between 2 different solutions or between 2 elements in a solution.

isotope (i'so-tope): a chemical element that has the same atomic number as another but a different atomic weight. (A radioactive isotope is one that changes into another element with the emission of certain radiations.)

jejunum (je-joo'num): the second portion of the small intestine; the part of the small intestine between the duodenum and the ileum.

keratin (ker'ah-tin): a special protein that is found in the hair, nails, and other horny tissues of the epidermis; a rather insoluble protein also found in the enamel of the teeth.

keratitis (ker-ah-ti'tis): inflammation of the cornea of the eye.

keratoplasty (ker'ah-to-plas-te): plastic surgery of the cornea; a corneal transplant.

kineplasty (kin'e-plas-te): the surgical creation of a skin-lined tunnel through a muscle next to the stump of an amputated limb to aid in the use of an appliance (prosthesis) for movement, etc.

kinesiology (ki-ne-se-ol'o-je): the study of motion and the part muscles play in producing movement.

kyphosis (ki-fo'sis): an increased curvature of the thoracic (chest) spine, giving a hunchback appearance.

lactation (lak-ta'shun): the secretion of milk.

lacteal (lak'te-al): related to milk; one of the intestinal lymph vessels which take up fat from digested food. See **chyle**.

lactogenic (lak-to-jen'ik): stimulating the production of milk, as certain hormones do.

leukemia (lu-ke'me-ah): a cancerlike disorder of the blood-forming organs, characterized by a marked increase in the number of white blood cells plus the presence of many immature cells in the circulating blood.

leukocyte, leucocyte (lu'ko-site): a white blood cell; any colorless ameboid cell mass.

leukocytosis, leucocytosis (lu-ko-si-to'sis): an increase in the number of white blood cells. (There may be a moderate and normal leukocytosis in pregnancy and during digestion. An abnormally increased white cell count is characteristic of many infections and other disorders.)

leukopenia (lu-ko-pe'ne-ah): a decrease in the number of white blood cells, below 5,000 per cubic millimeter. It is also called **leukocytopenia** (lu-ko-si-to-pe'ne-ah).

leukoplakia (lu-ko-pla'ke-ah): a disease in which there are white patches in the mucous membrane of the tongue, gums, and cheeks.

lipoma (lip-o'mah): a painless, fatty tissue tumor.

lithiasis (lith-i'ah-sis): the condition in which there is stone formation; the formation of hard inorganic masses in organs, spaces, or tissues.

litholapaxy (lith-ol'ah-pak-se): the crushing of a bladder stone followed by the immediate flushing out of fragments.

lithopedion (lith-o-pe'de-on): a dead fetus that has become stony (or petrified).

lumen (lu'men): the channel or space inside a tube or a tubular organ.

lymph (limf): a yellowish relatively clear watery fluid found in the lymphatic vessels; a liquid containing cells, mostly lymphocytes, and after a meal, fat globules; any clear watery fluid resembling true lymph.

lymphatic (lim-fat'ik): relating to the system of vessels that contain lymph.

lymphocyte (lim'fo-site): one kind of white blood cell (leukocyte) which is formed in lymph nodes instead of in bone marrow (as other blood cells are).

lymphoid (lim'foid): resembling lymph or relating to the lymphatic system; the name of the tissue of lymph nodes.

lysobacteria (li-so-bak-te're-ah): bacteria that can dissolve other bacteria (both living and dead ones).

macroblast (mak'ro-blast): a very large nucleated red blood cell. It is also called a **megaloblast**.

macrocolon (mak-ro-ko'lon) an excessively large colon. It is also called **megacolon**.

macula (mak'u-lah), **macule** (mak'ule): a discolored spot on the skin that is not raised above the surrounding area, as seen in freckles or measles.

malacoma (mal-ah-ko'mah): a diseased soft part.

malacosarcosis (mal-ah-ko-sar-ko'sis): a softening of muscle tissue.

malignant (mah-lig'nant): referring to disorders that tend to become worse and cause death, as in the case of an invading and spreading cancer.

malnutrition (mal-nu-trish'un): any abnormal assimilation of food; disordered nutrition.

malocclusion (mal-o-kloo'zhun): a displacement or distortion of the teeth so that they do not meet in a normal way during chewing.

malunion (mal-un'yon): an abnormal healing of a fracture due to faulty position, angulation, or other abnormality of alignment of the bone fragments.

mastectomy (mas-tek'to-me): the removal of the breast; mammectomy.

mastitis (mas-ti'tis): inflammation of the breast or mammary gland.

mastocarcinoma (mas-to-kar-si-no'mah): cancer of the breast.

medulla (me-dul'lah): the innermost part of an organ, as seen in the kidneys and adrenal glands; the part of the brain that connects with the spinal cord.

megacolon (meg-ah-ko'lon): a dilated and hypertrophied large intestine; congenital enlargement of the colon (Hirsch-sprung's disease).

megakaryocyte, megacaryocyte (meg-ah-kar'e-o-site): a giant cell found in the bone marrow; a cell with a large irregularly shaped (or lobulated) nucleus, believed to give rise to the blood platelets.

megalencephalon (meg-al-en-sef'ah-lon): an abnormally large brain.

megaloblast (meg'ah-lo-blast): a large primitive red blood cell which is usually found only in the bone marrow in pernicious anemia, but may also enter the circulation.

megalogastria (meg-ah-lo-gas'tre-ah): a dilated, abnormally enlarged stomach.

meiosis (mi-o'sis): a special method of cell division occurring during the development of sex cells (ova and sperm) in which the number of chromosomes is reduced, so that there are only half as many in the mature gamete as there are in other body cells of the species.

melanin (mel'ah-nin): the dark pigment found in some parts of the body, such as the skin, the middle coat of the eye (choroid), and certain tissues in the brain. (Under abnormal conditions it is present in certain tumors called melanomas or melanosarcomas.)

melanoma (mel-ah-no'mah): a tumor containing melanin.

melanosarcoma (mel-ah-no-sar-ko'mah): a malignant tumor usually developing from a mole (nevus); a malignant melanoma; dark masses of cells that have a marked tendency to spread (metastasize).

meninges (me-nin'jez): the 3 membranes that cover the brain and spinal cord.

meningitis (men-in-ji'tis): inflammation of 1 or more of the 3 membranes that cover the brain and spinal cord.

meningocele (me-ning'go-sele): a protrusion of the membranes around the brain or spinal cord through a defect in the skull or vertebral column.

menopause (men'o-pawz): the cessation of the normal monthly uterine bleeding.

menorrhagia (men-o-ra'je-ah): an abnormally profuse menstrual flow; excessive bleeding from the uterus.

menses (men'sez): the monthly flow of blood from the genital tract of women.

menticide (men'ti-side): the destruction of the mind of an individual by psychiatric procedures, drugs, surgery, or by the injection of thoughts by a powerful tyrant.

mentolabial (men-to-la'be-al): relating to the chin and the lip.

mentum (men'tum): the chin.

mesaortitis (mes-a-or-ti'tis): inflammation of the middle coat of the wall of the aorta.

mesencephalon (mes-en-sef'ah-lon): the midbrain; the middle part of the 3 primary divisions of the embryo's neural tube, between the forebrain and hindbrain.

mesoderm (mes'o-derm): the middle layer of the 3 primary germ layers of the embryo; the source of connective tissue, muscles, blood, blood vessels and serous membranes (peritoneum, pleura, etc.).

mesothelium (mes-o-the'le-um): the layer of flat mesodermal cells forming the surface of the true serous membranes (the peritoneum, pericardium, and pleura).

metabolism (me-tab'o-lizm): the physical and chemical changes or processes by which living substance is maintained and by which energy is produced.

metacarpus (met-ah-kar'pus): the part of the hand near the wrist, between the wrist and fingers; the 5 elongated bones in the hand.

metaplasia (met-ah-pla'ze-ah): a change in tissue cells to an abnormal form, or to a form not characteristic of that tissue.

metastasis (me-tas'tah-sis): the transfer of disease from one organ or part of the body to another part that is not connected with it.

microabscess (mic-kro-ab'ses): a very small localized collection of pus, visible only under a microscope.

microbiology (mi-kro-bi-ol'o-je): the science dealing with microscopic plants and animals, including bacteria, fungi, rickettsiae, viruses and protozoa. See **bacteriology.**

microcephalus (mi-kro-sef'ah-lus): an individual or a fetus with an abnormally small head.

microcyte (mi'kro-site): an abnormally small red blood cell, less than 5 microns in diameter (the normal erythrocyte is about 7 microns in diameter).

microorganism (mi-kro-or'gan-izm): a tiny living organism (sometimes called a microbe or a germ) that cannot be seen with the naked eye.

micturition (mik-tu-rish'un): the act of expelling urine from the bladder; urination.

mitochondria (mit-o-kon'dre-ah): very small rod-shaped structures or granules in the cytoplasm of cells which are responsible for oxidative reactions to release energy from the food materials. (They are examples of organelles.)

mitosis (mi-to'sis): a kind of indirect cell division in which a rather complex series of processes result in the equal distribution of cell components to two daughter cells; the characteristic cell division found in all cells of the body except the gametes.

molecule (mol'e-kule): a minute mass of matter; a combination of atoms that form a given chemical substance or compound; the smallest particle in a chemical compound that can exist in a free state.

mucosa (mu-ko'sah): a lining membrane that produces mucus and is found in spaces that are connected with the outside, such as the alimentary and respiratory tract; mucous membrane.

myalgia (mi-al'je-ah): muscle pain or aching.

mycete (mi'seet): a fungus.

mycid (mi'sid): a secondary infection developing in some kinds of skin diseases caused by a fungus.

mycology (mi-kol'o-je) the scientific study of fungi.

mycosis (mi-ko'sis): any disorder caused by a fungus, such as dermatomycosis (der-mah-to-mi-ko'sis), a fungous infection of the skin.

myelin (mi'e-lin): the fatlike substance that forms a covering for many nerve fibers. (These are called myelinated nerve fibers.)

myeloblast (mi'e-lo-blast): a large bone marrow cell believed to be the earliest stage in the process of blood cell development, particularly of white blood cells, but possibly also of red cells.

myelogenous (mi-e-loj'e-nus): relating to or produced in the bone marrow.

myeloid (mi'e-loid): resembling bone marrow.

myenteron (mi-en'ter-on): the muscular coat of the intestine.

myocardium (mi-o-kar'de-um): the middle thick layer of the heart wall. (It is composed of cardiac muscle.)

myodynia (mi-o-din'e-ah): muscular pain or tenderness; myalgia.

myoma (mi-o'mah): a tumor made of muscle tissue, usually involuntary visceral muscle.

myometrium (mi-o-me'tre-um): the middle muscular wall forming the bulk of the uterus. It is also called the **tunica muscularis uteri.**

myopathy (mi-op'ah-the): any disease of a muscle.

myositis (mi-o-si'tis): inflammation of a voluntary muscle.

necrectomy (nek-rek'to-me): the cutting away of dead material.

necropsy (nek'rop-se): the examination of a corpse. See **autopsy.**

necrosis (ne-kro'sis): tissue death, usually in a localized area.

neopathy (ne-op'ah-the): a new complication or condition of a disease, or an entirely new disorder.

neoplasm (ne'o-plazm): any new growth; a tumor.

nephrectomy (ne-frek'to-me): the removal of a kidney.

nephritis (ne-fri'tis): inflammation of the kidney, or any disorder resulting in degeneration of the kidney tissue.

nephrocolopexy (nef-ro-ko'lo-pek-se): the surgical suspension and fixation of the kidney and the colon, using the nephrocolic ligament.

nephroma (ne-fro'mah): a tumor of the kidney.

nephron (nef'ron): the microscopic functional unit of kidney tissue; a combination of a glomerulus with its capsule, convoluted tubules, and Henle's loop, plus the collecting tubule.

nephropathy (ne-frop'ah-the): kidney disease.

nephropexy (nef'ro-pek-se): an operation to suspend and fix a so-called floating kidney.

nephroptosis (nef-rop-to'sis): a so-called floating kidney; downward displacement of the kidney.

nephrosis (ne-fro'sis): any disorder of the kidney, especially one that is not due to infection and inflammation (as is the case in nephritis); a degenerative lesion of the kidney with loss of function of the secreting epithelium of the cortex.

neuralgia (nu-ral'je-ah): an aching or spasmodic pain along the course of a nerve or nerves.

neurilemma (nu-re-lem'mah), **neurolemma** (nu-ro-lem'mah): a very thin membrane wrapping the nerve fibers of the peripheral nervous system (those not in the spinal cord or brain).

neuritis (nu-ri'tis): inflammation of a nerve, usually accompanied by pain, tenderness, and other symptoms, such as loss of sensation.

neurodermatitis (nu-ro-der-mah-ti'tis): a chronic skin disorder, accompanied by itching, believed to be due to a nervous disorder.

neurodynia (nu-ro-din'e-ah): pain in a nerve or in nerves.

neuroglia (nu-rog'le-ah): the special connective tissue of the central nervous system; weblike supporting tissue that contains branching glia or neuroglia cells peculiar to the brain and spinal cord. See **glioma.**

neuroma (nu-ro'mah): a tumor made up mostly of nerve fibers and nerve cells.

neuron (nu'ron): the nerve cell body plus its processes; the structural unit of nerve tissue.

neurosis (nu-ro'sis): a mental or psychic disorder characterized by fears and anxieties. (It is less incapacitating than a psychosis and is sometimes called a psychoneurosis.)

nevus (ne'vus): a small skin tumor, usually congenital in origin, which may be vascular or nonvascular. (It is sometimes called a mole.) The plural is **nevi** (ne'vi).

noctambulation (nok-tam-bu-la'shun): walking while asleep. See **somnambulism.**

noctiphobia (nok-te-fo'be-ah): an abnormal fear of darkness and silence.

nocturia (nok-tu're-ah): excessive urination at night.

nodule (nod'ul): a small solid mass; a little knot; a small node or mass of tissue.

nosema (no-se'mah): any disease or illness.

nosophilia (nos-o-fil'e-ah): an undue wish to be ill; a morbid desire to be sick.

nosophobe (nos'o-fob): a person who has an abnormal fear of a disease.

nucleolus (nu-kle'o-lus): a tiny globule located within the nucleus of a cell.

nucleus (nu'kle-us): a small spherical body within a cell; a general term used to indicate a group of nerve cells, usually connected with the fibers of a particular nerve; in chemistry, the central part of an atom.

nyctophobia (nik-to-fo'be-ah): an abnormal fear of the dark.

nycturia (nik-tu're-ah): frequency of urination at night, particularly the passage of more urine at night than during the day.

obligate (ob'li-gate): compulsory or necessary. The opposite is **facultative.**

obstetrics (ob-stet'riks): the medical specialty dealing with pregnancy, labor, and the confinement of the mother immediately following the birth of the child.

occipital (ok-sip'i-tal): relating to the back part of the head (the occiput).

occlusion (o-kloo'zhun): the process of closing or the state of being closed; also applied to the manner of bringing the upper and lower teeth together.

oculist (ok'u-list): an older term for a physician who specializes in eye disorders. (He is now called an ophthalmologist.)

oculomotor (ok-u-lo-mo′tor): relating to eye movements, as the oculomotor nerve supplying many of the eye muscles.

oculomycosis (ok-u-lo-mi-ko′sis): any disease of the eye that is caused by a fungus.

odontalgia (o-don-tal′je-ah): a toothache; pain in a tooth.

odontiasis (o-don-ti′ah-sis): the eruption of the teeth, or a disorder caused by this eruption.

odontology (o-don-tol′o-je): dentistry; the science dealing with the anatomy and diseases of the teeth.

oligemia (ol-i-ge′me-ah): a deficiency of blood volume.

oligophrenia (ol-i-go-fre′ne-ah): defective mental development.

oligospermia (ol-i-go-sper′me-ah): deficient numbers of spermatozoa in the semen.

oliguria (ol-i-gu′re-ah): a diminished amount of urine secretion in relation to the fluid intake.

ontogeny (on-toj′e-ne): the biological development of an individual; the life cycle of an organism.

onychia (o-nik′e-ah), **onychitis** (on-i-ki′tis): inflammation of the nail matrix (the tissue on which the nail rests).

onychoma (on-i-ko′mah): a tumor of the nail or the nail bed.

oocyte (o′o-site): an immature ovum or egg cell; a cell undergoing the maturation process to become an ovum. It is also called an **ovocyte.**

oophorectomy (o-of-o-rek′to-me): the removal or destruction of an ovary (or ovaries).

oophoritis (o-of-o-ri′tis): inflammation of an ovary.

oophorocystectomy (o-of-o-ro-sis-tek′to-me): surgical removal of an ovarian cyst.

ophthalmia (of-thal′me-ah): a severe inflammation of the eye, or of the conjunctiva.

ophthalmic (of-thal′mik): relating to the eye, as the ophthalmic arteries, veins, and nerves.

ophthalmologist (of-thal-mol′o-jist): a physician who specializes in eye disorders. (He was formerly called an oculist.)

ophthalmoscope (of-thal′mo-skope): an instrument that includes a perforated mirror used for inspecting the inside portions of the eyeball (especially the retina and related structures).

opisthotonos (o-pis-thot′o-nos): a form of severe muscle spasm in which the head and heels are bent backward and the body is arched forward.

organelle (or-gah-nel′): a tiny specific particle of living material present in most cells and serving a specific function in the cell. See **mitochondria.**

organism (or′gan-ism): an individual animal or plant; any organized living thing.

orthesis (or-the′sis): a brace or other device used in treating physical impairment or disability.

orthodontist (or-tho-don′tist): a dentist who specializes in the prevention and correction of tooth irregularities, malocclusion, etc.; one who straightens teeth.

osmosis (os-mo′sis): the passage of a pure solvent, such as water, from a solution of lesser concentration to the one of greater concentration through a semipermeable membrane.

ossature (os′a-tur): the arrangement of the bones of the body.

osseous (os′e-us): bony; resembling or having the quality of bone.

ossicle (os′sik′l): a small bone, such as those within the middle ear.

ossification (os-i-fi-ka′shun): the process of forming bone, or the conversion of fibrous tissue, or cartilage, into bone.

osteitis (os-te-i′tis): inflammation of bone tissue. See **osteomyelitis.**

osteoma (os-te-o′mah): a firm tumor of bone or bonelike tissue; a kind of connective tissue.

osteomalacia (os-te-o-mah-la′she-ah): a disorder in which bones become softened, accompanied by pain, tenderness, and loss of weight. (The cause is believed to be a deficiency of vitamin D or of certain minerals—calcium and phosphorus.)

osteomyelitis (os-te-o-mi-e-li′tis): inflammation of bone by a pus-producing organism. (It may be a localized inflammation or it may spread through the marrow and bone tissue to the periosteum.)

otalgia (o-tal′je-ah): earache; pain in the ear.

otitis (o-ti′tis): inflammation of the ear, most often the middle ear (otitis media).

otomycosis (o-to-mi-ko′sis): a fungous infection of the external auditory canal.

otorhinolaryngology (o-to-ri-no-lar-in-gol′o-je): the branch of medicine dealing with disorders of the ear, nose, and throat (E.N.T.).

ovariectomy (o-va-re-ek′to-me): the removal or destruction of the ovary (or ovaries); oophorectomy.

ovariopathy (o-va-re-op′ah-the): ovarian disease.

ovariorrhexis (o-va-re-o-rek′sis): the rupture of an ovary.

oviduct (o′vi-dukt): the tube through which the egg cells (ova) pass; the uterine tube; the fallopian tube.

ovoplasm (o′vo-plazm): the living material (protoplasm) of an unfertilized ovum.

ovulation (ov-u-la′shun): the discharge of a mature egg cell (ovum) from the follicle of the ovary.

palsy (pawl′se): a paralysis; a loss or impairment of nerve or muscle function; motor paralysis with muscle weakness and loss of function. See **paresis.**

papilla (pah-pil′lah): any small projection or elevation. The plural is **papillae** (pah-pil′e).

papilloma (pap-i-lo′mah): a projecting or branching type of benign tumor made of epithelial cells, such as warts.

papule (pap′ul): a small solid elevation on the skin; a pimple.

paracentesis (par-ah-sen-te′sis): a puncture through the wall of a cavity usually to remove fluid or to promote drainage from that space (abdomen, middle ear, etc.).

paramedical (par-ah-med′i-kal): related to or adjunctive to the science of medicine.

parametrium (par-ah-me′tre-um): the tissues near the margins of the lower part of the uterus, located between the layers of the broad ligament and around the uterosacral ligaments.

paraplegia (par-ah-ple′je-ah): a paralysis of half of the body; loss of sensation and motion in the lower half of the body or of the legs.

parasite (par′ah-site): any organism that lives within or upon another (the host) at the host's expense.

parasitology (par-ah-si-tol′o-je): the study of those organisms that live in or on another at the latter's expense.

parathyroid (par-ah-thi′roid): located near the thyroid gland in the neck; any of the 4 small glands embedded in the capsule covering the thyroid gland.

paresis (pah-re′sis or par′e-sis): a slight or incomplete paralysis; a disorder due to syphilis. It is also called **dementia paralytica.**

paresthesia (par-es-the′ze-ah): abnormal sensations such as burning, prickling, numbness, etc.

parietal (pah-ri′e-tal): relating to the walls of a space or cavity.

paronychia (par-o-nik′e-ah): an inflammation involving the tissues surrounding the fingernail.

parturition (par-tu-rish′un): the process of giving birth to a child.

pathema (pah-the′mah): any disease condition.

pathogen (path′o-jen): any disease-producing organism.

pathognomonic (path-og-no-mon′ik): distinctive or characteristic of a disease.

pathology (pah-thol′o-je): the study or branch of medicine that deals with disease and the changes in the body tissues and organs caused by the disease.

pedialgia (ped-e-al′je-ah): neuralgic pain in the foot.

pediatrician (pe-di-ah-trish′un): a physician who specializes in the care and treatment of children and their illnesses.

pediatrics (pe-di-at′riks): the medical specialty dealing with the care and treatment of children and their illnesses.

pedometer (pe-dom′e-ter): an instrument used to measure infants; an instrument which measures approximate distances by recording the number of steps taken when walking.

pedophobia (pe-do-fo′be-ah): fear of children.

pellagra (pel-lag′rah or pel-la′grah): a vitamin-deficiency disease caused by a lack of niacin (one of the B vitamins), and characterized by symptoms that involve the skin, digestive system, and nervous system.

pelvimetry (pel-vim′e-tre): the measurement of the dimensions and capacity of the pelvis (lower part of the abdominal cavity).

pelvis (pel′vis): any basinlike structure; an oblong trough; the lower portion of the trunk of the body bounded by the sacrum and coccyx at the back, the 2 hip bones at the sides and front, and the tissues of the pelvic floor at the outlet (see perineum). (The renal pelvis is the basinlike expansion of the upper ureter, usually lodged within the renal sinus at the kidney hilum.)

peracidity (per-ah-sid′it-te): excessive acidity.

percutaneous (per-ku-ta′ne-us): performed through the skin.

perfusion (per-fu′zhun): pouring liquid over or through something; passage of a fluid through the vessels of an organ.

pericardium (per-i-kar′de-um): the serous membrane that lines the sac enclosing the heart, plus the reflection that attaches itself to the heart itself. See **epicardium.**

perichondrium (per-i-kon′dre-um): a membrane that covers the surface of cartilage.

perineorrhaphy (per-i-ne-or′ah-fe): the sewing up of a tear or other defect in the pelvic floor (perineum).

perineum (per-i-ne′um): the pelvic floor; the space between the anus and the scrotum (of the male); the parts and structures occupying the pelvic outlet in the female.

periosteum (per-e-os′te-um): the special fibrous connective tissue membrane covering the bones of the body; the surface tissue which plays an important part in the repair of bone fractures and other injuries.

periostitis (per-e-os-ti′tis): inflammation of the membrane that covers all bones.

peripheral (pe-rif′er-al): related to or located at the surface.

peritoneoscopy (per-i-to-ne-os′ko-pe): the examination of the peritoneal (abdominal) cavity by using an endoscope. See **abdominoscopy.**

peritoneum (per-i-to-ne′um): the large serous membrane that lines the abdominal cavity and is reflected over the organs within.

perivascular (per-i-vas′ku-lar): located around blood vessels.

petechia (pe-te′ke-ah): a tiny reddish pinpoint spot due to a small hemorrhage just under the skin or mucous membrane which later turns blue or yellow. See **thrombocytopenia.**

phage (faj): a virus that eats and destroys bacteria; a bacteriophage.

phagocyte (fag′o-site): any cell that engulfs other cells, including bacteria, or any small foreign particles. (Among phagocytes there are white blood cells plus certain cells in the spleen, liver, and lymph nodes.) See **reticuloendothelial.**

pharynx (far′inks): the saclike tube extending from the nose and mouth above to the larynx and esophagus below; the "throat."

phlebitis (fle-bi′tis): an inflammation of a vein, often resulting in pain and sometimes in thrombus formation, a condition known as thrombophlebitis.

phleboclysis (fle-bok′li-sis): injection of a solution into a vein. (It is often a slow drop-by-drop instillation.)

phlebotomy (fle-bot′o-me): the cutting of a vein to allow the escape of blood.

phobic (fo′bik): pertaining to a morbid fear.

photophobia (fo-to-fo′be-ah): undue intolerance of or unusual sensitivity to light.

physiology (fiz-e-ol′o-je): the science which deals with the activities or dynamics (functions) of the body and its parts.

pileous (pi′le-us): hairy.

piliation (pi-le-a'shun): the formation and production of hair.

pilonidal (pi-lo-ni'dal): containing hairs, often resembling a tuft or nest inside a cyst or sinus.

pineal (pin'e-al): pertaining to the flattened cone-shaped body or glandlike organ near the midbrain, the endocrine function of which has been disputed.

pleurisy (ploor'i-se): inflammation of the serous membrane covering the lungs and lining the chest cavity (the pleura). It is also known as **pleuritis.**

pleuritis (ploor-i'tis): See **pleurisy.**

pleurothotonos (ploor-o-thot'o-nos), **pleurothotonus** (ploor-o-thot'o-nus): a spasmodic bending of the body to one side.

pleurotomy (ploor-o'to-me): an incision into the pleura.

pneumatics (nu-mat'iks): the science which deals with a study of the physical properties of gases.

pneumatocardia (nu-mah-to-kar'de-ah): the presence of air in the heart.

pneumectomy (nu-mek'to-me): the cutting away of lung tissue.

pneumograph (nu'mo-graf): an instrument that registers respiratory movements.

pneumonia (nu-mo'ne-ah): inflammation of the lungs. (It usually refers to lobar pneumonia, an acute infection caused by a diplococcus.)

pneumonitis (nu-mo-ni'tis): an acute localized inflammation of the lung without the serious generalized symptoms seen in lobar pneumonia.

podiatry (po-di'ah-tre): the diagnosis and treatment of foot disorders. See **chiropodist.**

pododynia (pod-o-din'e-ah): pain in the heel and sole of the foot, often burning, though there is no redness.

polioclastic (po-le-o-klas'tik): referring to the viruses of rabies, epidemic encephalitis and poliomyelitis which destroy the gray matter in the brain.

polioencephalitis (po-le-o-en-sep-ah-li'tis): inflammation of the gray matter in the brain; a cerebral poliomyelitis.

poliomyelitis (po-le-o-mi-e-li'tis): an acute virus disease involving the gray matter of the central nervous system, especially the motor cells of the spinal cord. (The symptoms include fever, headache, vomiting, and stiffness of the neck and back.)

polyarthritis (pol-e-ar-thri'tis): an inflammation of several joints at the same time.

polycystic (pol-e-sis'tik): referring to many saclike structures or tumors in a part.

polydactylia (pol-e-dak-til'e-ah): the presence of extra digits on the hands or feet (extra fingers or toes).

polydipsia (pol-e-dip'se-ah): an excessive persistent thirst.

polyp (pol'ip): a protruding, often grapelike growth from a mucous membrane, such as the lining of the nose or the uterus.

polyphagia (pol-e-fa'je-ah): excessive eating; a craving for all kinds of food.

postnatal (post-na'tal): occurring after birth.

postocular (post-ok'u-lar): situated behind the eye.

postpartum (post-par'tum): occurring after the delivery of the baby.

posttussis (post-tus'is): after coughing.

precancerous (pre-kan'ser-us): the early stage or beginning of a cancerous growth.

preclinical (pre-klin'i-cal): occurring before the disease is actually recognized by observation.

precursor (pre-kur'sor): a forerunner; something that goes before.

prenatal (pre-na'tal): present or occurring before the baby is born.

prepatellar (pre-pah-tel'ar): located in front of or over the kneecap.

presbyophrenia (pres-be-o-fre'ne-ah): a defective memory and loss of sense of location, often seen in old age.

presbyopia (pres-be-o'pe-ah): a visual change due to advancing age; loss of elasticity of the lens in the eye.

procidentia (pro-si-den'she-ah): a falling down, especially of the uterus so that the cervix protrudes from the vaginal outlet; a prolapse.

proctitis (prok-ti'tis): inflammation of the rectum.

proctocele (prok'to-sele). See **rectocele.**

proctologist (prok-tol'o-jist): a physician who specializes in the diagnosis, care, and treatment of rectal disorders.

proctopexy (prok'to-pek-se): the operative fixation of the rectum to some other part by suturing.

prodromal (pro-dro'mal), **prodromic** (pro-dro'mik): relating to something that indicates the approach of a disease; premonitory.

progeny (proj'e-ne): refers to children or descendants.

prognosis (prog-no'sis): a forecast of the probable results of a disorder; the outlook for recovery.

prolapse (pro-laps'): the sinking or falling down of a part of an organ. See **procidentia.**

pronation (pro-na'shun): the act of lying in a face-down or prone position. (In the case of the hand, it is the act of turning the hand so that the palm faces backward.)

prophylaxis (pro-fi-lak'sis): the prevention of disease; preventive care and treatment.

proprietary (pro-pri'e-ta-re): referring to a drug (or other preparation used in the treatment of diseases) that is protected against free competition by a patent, trademark, copyright, or other means.

proprioceptive (pro-pre-o-sep'tiv): receiving stimulations within the body tissues, especially in muscles, tendons, and in the inner ear.

prosencephalon (pros-en-sef'ah-lon): the forebrain, which includes the cerebral hemispheres, the thalamus, hypothalamus, and related parts.

prosthesis (pros'the-sis): an artificial substitute for a missing part of the body, such as a leg, denture, eye, any appliance that will aid natural function (hearing aid, dental bridge, etc.).

protean (pro'te-an): changeable in form; of varying shapes, assuming different characteristics.

protein (pro'te-in): any of a group of complex organic compounds consisting of carbon, hydrogen, oxygen, and nitrogen (some contain sulfur and phosphorus); the principal constituent of cell protoplasm.

prothrombin (pro-throm'bin): a substance in the blood plasma that is converted into thrombin during the second stage of blood clotting (coagulation).

protoplasm (pro'to-plazm): the living building material of all organisms, plants and animals; the only matter in which life is manifested.

prototype (pro'to-tipe): the original form or type, after which various forms are developed.

protozoa (pro-to-zo'ah): one-celled animals which form the lowest division of the animal kingdom. The singular is **protozoan** or **protozoon.**

protozoology (pro-to-zo-ol'o-je): the study of one-celled animals.

protractor (pro-trak'tor): an instrument used to remove bits of foreign material, such as bone chips, from a wound.

provitamin (pro-vi'tah-min): a substance from which a vitamin can be produced by the human (or other animal) organism. (Carotene is provitamin A.)

proximal (prok'si-mal): near the point of origin; referring to the nearest part. The opposite is **distal.**

pseudarthrosis (su-dar-thro'sis): a so-called false joint; a disorder in which a weight-bearing long bone softens, leading to fractures that do not heal.

pseudomania (su-do-ma'ne-ah): a pretended mental disorder; pathologic lying.

pseudopodia (su-do-po'de-ah): temporary protrusions of the outer protoplasm of an ameba or other cell which allow it to move and obtain food. See **ameboid.** The singular is **pseudopodium** (su-do-po'de-um).

psoriasis (so-ri'ah-sis): a chronic recurring skin disorder characterized by the appearance of scaly red or silvery patches, sometimes elevated and other times like plaques.

psychasthenia (si-kas-the'ne-ah): a functional nervous disorder (neurosis) in which there are stages of anxiety, fear, fixed ideas, obsessions and other mental disturbances.

psychogenic (si-ko-jen'ik): of an origin related to the mind; of an emotional or psychologic origin (as contrasted with one of organic origin).

psychoneurosis (si-ko-nu-ro'sis): a mental disorder of the functional type in which there isn't such deep nor far-reaching abnormalities as in the true psychoses. (Examples of psychoneuroses are hysteria, neuresthenia, and psychasthenia.)

psychosis (si-ko'sis): any mental disorder, but especially one involving far-reaching and prolonged behavior disorders. See **dementia.**

psychosomatic (si-ko-so-mat'ik): pertaining to both mind and body; the effect of the mind on the body or of body disorders on the mind.

psychotherapy (si-ko-ther'ah-pe): a treatment designed to produce response by mental rather than physical means.

ptosis (to'sis): a drooping or falling down of a part or organ, such as the eyelid, the kidney, the stomach, and the intestine. See **nephroptosis** and **splanchnoptosis.**

puerperium (pu-er-pe're-um): the period of confinement after the delivery of the baby.

pulmonic (pul-mon'ik): referring to or relating to the lungs, the pulmonary artery or the pulmonary valve.

pulmonitis (pul-mo-ni'tis): inflammation of the lung tissues; pneumonia.

pulmonology (pul-mo-nol'o-je): the science concerned with the anatomy, physiology and pathology of the lungs.

pulmotor (pul'mo-tor): an apparatus that forces oxygen (or air) into the lungs and then sucks it out, producing artificial respiration.

purpura (pur'pu-rah): a disorder in which hemorrhages occur in the skin and mucous membranes, often accompanied by a low platelet count. See **thrombocytopenia.**

pustule (pus'tule): a small pus-containing elevation on the skin; a pimple that is filled with pus.

pyelitis (pi-e-li'tis): inflammation of the kidney pelvis.

pyelogram (pi'e-lo-gram): a roentgenogram (x-ray) of the kidney and ureter, including especially the kidney pelvis.

pyelonephritis (pi-el-o-ne-fri'tis): an inflammation involving the kidney pelvis and the tissues of the kidney itself, usually due to an infection with microorganisms.

pyelonephrosis (pi-el-o-ne-fro'sis): any disease of the kidney and its pelvis, not necessarily an infection.

pyogenic (pi-o-jen'ik): pus producing, as in the case of certain bacteria.

pyorrhea (pi-o-re'ah): a discharge or flow of pus, often related to the tooth sockets and the tissues of the gums.

pyosalpinx (pi-o-sal'pinks): pus in an oviduct (fallopian or uterine tube).

pyuria (pi-u're-ah): the presence of pus cells in the urine.

rachicentesis (ra-ke-sen-te'sis), **rachiocentesis** (ra-ke-o-sen-te'sis): a puncture into the spinal canal.

rachischisis (ra-kis'ki-sis): a fissure in the spine present at birth; a congenital anomaly of the vertebral column.

rales (rahls): abnormal breath sounds heard (usually with a stethoscope) in certain disorders of the lungs; rattling, bubbling, whistling, or crackling sounds heard in the chest.

rectocele (rek'to-sele): a protrusion of a part of the rectum into the vaginal canal. It is also called **proctocele.**

reflected (re-flekt'ed): to be bent back; to be folded back; said of membranes, of light rays, and of nervous transmissions that are returned from a center toward the periphery.

renal (re'nal): pertaining to the kidney.

renopathy (re-nop'ah-the): disease of the kidney; nephropathy.

reticuloendothelial (re-tik-u-lo-en-do-the'le-al): pertaining to a combination of certain cells of the spleen, lymph nodes, bone marrow, and liver, that play roles in defense against infection, in metabolism, and in blood cell formation; pertaining to cells of both endothelium and reticulum.

reticulum (re-tik'u-lum): a network of connective tissue cells and fibers; a web-like mesh of protoplasmic cell extensions.

retina (ret'i-nah): the innermost coat of the eyeball; the nerve coat of the eye, made of nerve cells and fibers.

retrocecal (ret-ro-se'kal): located behind the cecum.

retroperitoneal (re-tro-per-i-to-ne'al): located behind the peritoneum as are the kidneys, pancreas, and abdominal aorta. (Retro may also be pronounced ret'ro.)

rheology (re-ol'o-je): the study of the flow of matter, such as the flow of blood through the heart and vessels.

rheoscope (re'o-skope): an instrument used to detect an electric current.

rhinitis (ri-ni'tis): inflammation of the lining of the nasal cavities.

rhinology (ri-nol'o-je): the study of the nose and its disorders. See **otorhinolaryngology.**

rhinophyma (ri-no-fi'mah): a chronic form of rosacea involving the skin of the nose in which there are large, nodular swellings and redness of the nose.

rickettsiae (rik-et'se-e): microscopic oval to rod-shaped organisms that resemble bacteria, but are smaller and cannot grow in nonliving matter.

roentgen (rent'gen): the international unit of radiation; a standard quantity of x or gamma radiation.

roentgenogram (rent-gen'o-gram): a film produced by means of x-rays, also called roentgen rays; named after the discoverer of the x-rays (gamma rays).

rosacea (ro-za'se-ah): a skin disorder in which the capillaries of the nose, forehead and cheeks are dilated, causing flushing and redness, and accompanied by a breaking out of pustules and papules.

salpingitis (sal-pin-ji'tis): inflammation of the uterine (fallopian) tube or of the auditory (eustachian) tube.

salpingoscopy (sal-ping-gos'ko-pe): inspection of the auditory (eustachian) tube by means of an instrument called the salpingoscope (sal-ping'go-skop).

sarcoma (sar-ko'mah): a tumor made of a kind of connective tissue, often highly malignant.

sclera (skle'rah): the tough opaque white coat that forms the outer protective layer of the eyeball. (It is continuous with the transparent colorless cornea at the front.)

scleredema (skle-re-de'mah): hardening of the skin with excessive fluid retention in the tissues.

scleroderma (skle-ro-der'mah): a connective tissue disorder involving the skin and other organs, and resulting in hardening, thickening and rigidity.

sclerosis (skle-ro'sis): a hardening with loss of elasticity of the tissues.

scoliosis (sko-le-o'sis): an abnormal curvature sideways (laterally) from the normal vertical line of the spine.

scoliosometer (sko-le-o-som'e-ter): an instrument for measuring deformities of the spinal column.

sebaceous (se-ba'shus): secreting or pertaining to oil or an oily substance called sebum (se'bum).

seborrhea (seb-o-re'ah): the excessive secretion of oil (sebum) with a resulting formation of greasy scales on the skin.

secretion (se-kre'shun): the process of producing a new substance from materials in the blood; the new substance produced by glandular activity using materials in the blood.

semen (se'men): the thick whitish secretion from the male reproductive organs; a combination of male germ cells (spermatozoa) and secretions from the several glands of the reproductive system.

semicanalis (sem-e-kah-na'lis): a channel open on one side or at one end only.

semicoma (sem-e-ko'mah): a mild state of unconsciousness (coma) from which the patient usually arouses easily.

semipermeable (sem-e-per'me-ah-b'l): permitting the passage of some particles (molecules) and not others; referring to membranes that allow the passage of a pure solvent such as water but not of the substances dissolved in it.

sepsis (sep'sis): poisoning due to products from decay, putrefaction, infection or contamination.

septicemia (sep-ti-se′me-ah): blood poisoning; the presence of bacterial toxins in the blood.

serosa (se-ro′sah): a serous membrane; one that is found lining the so-called body cavities, such as the pleural and peritoneal cavities.

somatalgia (so-mah-tal′je-ah): bodily pain.

somatotype (so-mat′o-tipe): a category of body build based on certain physical characteristics.

somnambulism (som-nam′bu-lizm): the habit of walking while asleep; a hypnotic state with full possession of one's senses but with no recollection afterward. See **noctambulation.**

specificity (spes-i-fis′i-te): the quality of having a certain action affecting only a particular substance, tissue, or organism.

speculum (spek′u-lum): an instrument for dilating the opening of a body cavity or passage so that the interior can be examined.

sphygmomanometer (sfig-mo-mah-nom′e-ter): an instrument for measuring arterial blood pressure.

spirilla (spi-ril′ah): corkscrew or spiral-shaped bacteria. The singular is **spirillum.**

splanchnic (splank′nik): relating to internal organs, such as splanchnic nerves.

splanchnoptosis (splank-no-to′sis): the falling down of the internal organs. See **visceroptosis.**

sporozoa (spo-ro-zo′ah): one-called parasitic animals that are unable to move about by themselves; a class of protozoa.

staphylococci (staf-i-lo-kok′si): spherical bacteria that are found in bunches, or clusters, resembling a bunch of grapes.

staphyloma (staf-i-lo′mah): a bulging of the cornea or sclera of the eye due to inflammation.

stasis (sta′sis): a stoppage or standstill in the flow of a fluid in a part, such as the blood, lymph, or the contents of the digestive tract.

static (stat′ik): not in motion; at rest; in equilibrium.

stenosis (ste-no′sis): the narrowing or contraction of a tube or canal; a stricture.

stenostomia (sten-o-sto′me-ah): a narrowing or contraction of the mouth.

stethoscope (steth′o-skope): an instrument used for conveying sounds from the patient's body to the examiner's ears.

sthenometry (sthen-om′e-tre): the measurement of muscular strength.

sthenophotic (sthen-o-fo′tik): pertaining to the ability to see in a strong light.

strabismus (strah-biz′mus): a disorder involving the muscles of the eyeballs so that the eyes cannot work together properly.

stricture (strik′ture): the abnormal narrowing or contraction of a passageway, resulting from deposits of abnormal material or contraction of scar tissue within or around the canal or tube.

subclavian (sub-kla′ve-an): located under the clavicle (collarbone).

subcutaneous (sub-ku-ta′ne-us): occurring or located beneath the skin.

subluxation (sub-luk-sa′shun): a partial or incomplete dislocation.

sudoriferous (su-dor-if′er-us), **sudoriparous** (su-dor-ip′ah-rus): producing or secreting sweat.

suicide (soo′i-sid): the taking of one's own life.

sulcus (sul′kus): a groove or depression between parts, especially a fissure between the convolutions of the brain; any furrow, as in the teeth, the bones, or in the lung surfaces. The plural is **sulci.**

superego (su-per-e′go): a part of the psyche that acts as a monitor or restraint over the ego, functioning largely in the unconscious zone.

supernatant (su-per-na′tant): overlying or situated on top of, as the liquid after precipitation (settling down) of the solids.

supranasal (su-prah-na′sal): located above the nose.

suprarenal (su-prah-re′nal): located above the kidney; relating to the adrenal gland.

suture (su′tur): a type of joint, especially in the skull where bone surfaces are dovetailed and closely united; a stitch used in surgery to bring parts and edges together.

symbiosis (sim-bi-o′sis): the close association of 2 different organisms which may be beneficial to one or both of them; a condition in which a symptom becomes a part of the patient's personality.

symphysis (sim′fi-sis): a line of union; a cartilaginous joint such as that between the bodies of the pubic bones.

synapse (sin′aps): the region where parts of 2 neurons are anatomically related so that impulses are transmitted from one neuron to another. It is also called the **synaptic junction.**

syndrome (sin′drome): a set or group of symptoms that indicate a certain disorder; a complex of symptoms and signs that occur together.

synovial (si-no-ve-al): relating to a thick fluid found in joints, bursae and tendon sheaths.

syringectomy (sir-in-jek′to-me): the removal of the walls of a fistula. See **fistula.**

syringomyelia (si-ring-go-mi-e′le-ah): a disorder of the spinal cord marked by abnormal liquid-containing cavities in the cord substance.

systemic (sis-tem′ik): affecting the whole body; generalized.

systole (sis′to-le): the period of heart muscle contraction, especially that of the ventricles. The adjective is **systolic** (sistol′ik).

tachogram (tak′o-gram): a graphic record to show the movement and velocity of blood flow.

tachycardia (tak-e-kar′de-ah): an excessively rapid heart rate. (It is usually applied to a pulse rate over 100 a minute.)

tachypnea (tak-ip-ne′ah): very rapid breathing. (It may accompany neurotic disorders.)

talipes (tal′i-peze): a deformity of the foot present at birth; clubfoot.

tarsitis (tahr-si′tis): inflammation of a bone in the instep of the foot, or inflammation of the eyelid edge. See **blepharitis.**

tarsoplasty (tahr′so-plas-te): plastic surgery on the eyelids.

tarsoptosis (tahr-sop-to′sis): falling of the bones in the arch of the foot, especially certain tarsus bones; flatfoot.

tensor (ten′sor): any muscle that stretches or pulls on a part to make it tense.

thalamus (thal′ah-mus): the part of the brain at each side of the 3rd ventricle, which acts as the chief relay center for sensory impulses to the cerebral cortex. (It includes 2 large masses of gray matter.)

therapy (ther′ah-pe): the treatment of disease or of any disorder.

thermalgesia (ther-mal-je′ze-ah): a condition in which pain is experienced upon the application of heat.

thermanalgesia (therm-an-al-je′se-ah): a condition in which no pain is felt when heat is applied; thermoanalgesia (thermo-an-al-je′se-ah).

thermhyperesthesia (therm-hi-per-es-the′se-ah): an abnormal sensitivity to heat.

thermocautery (ther-mo-kaw′ter-e): the removal of a growth or a part by use of a heated wire or pointed surface.

thermotaxis (ther-mo-tak′sis): the adjustment of the body temperature to heat production and heat loss; the movement of an organism as a result of a change in temperature.

thoracic (tho-ras′ik): relating to the chest portion of the body.

thorax (tho′raks): the chest; the part of the body between the neck and the abdominal cavity (from which it is separated by the diaphragm).

thrombocyte (throm′bo-site): a tiny particle of protoplasm found in the circulating blood; a blood platelet, believed to play a part in the process of blood clotting.

thrombocytopenia (throm-bo-si-to-pe′ne-ah): a decrease in the number of blood platelets, often resulting in hemorrhaging (petechiae, purpura, etc.).

thrombophlebitis (throm-bo-fle-bi′tis): a disorder in which inflammation of a vein wall is followed by the formation of a blood clot (thrombus).

thymus (thi′mus): an elongated mass of lymphatic tissue, usually consisting of 2 lobes, located in the upper chest cavity beneath the sternum. (It is believed to play a part in the immunity responses of the body.)

thyroidectomize (thi-roid-ek'to-mize): to deprive one of the thyroid gland as by surgical removal; thyroidectomy.

thyrotropic (thi-ro-trop'ik): pertaining to an influence on the thyroid gland, as is the case with certain pituitary hormones.

tonsillectomy (ton-si-lek'to-me): the surgical removal of a tonsil or tonsils.

toxemia (toks-e'me-ah): a general toxic condition in which poisonous bacterial products are absorbed into the bloodstream.

toxicology (tok-si-kol'o-je): the study of poisons, their detection, effects, and the treatment of their effects.

toxicosis (tok-si-ko'sis): any disorder caused by poisons from bacteria or from any other sources.

trachea (tra'ke-ah): a membranous and cartilaginous tube, commonly called the windpipe, extending from the larynx (the voice box) to its 2 branching bronchi.

tracheitis (tra-ke-i'tis): inflammation of the trachea.

tracheobronchial (tra-ke-o-brong'ke-al): relating to the trachea and the bronchi.

tracheostomy (tra-ke-os'to-me): a surgical opening into the trachea, for the introduction of a tube through which the patient may breathe.

tracheotomy (tra-ke-ot'o-me): an incision into the trachea to remove a specimen of tissue for laboratory examination, to remove a growth or foreign body, or to explore the area.

traction (trak'shun): a pulling on certain parts of the body to aid in the treatment of fractures or other disorders.

transanimation (trans-an-i-ma'shun): resuscitation, using mouth-to-mouth breathing.

transatrial (trans-a'tre-al): referring to procedures done through the walls of the heart atrium, especially surgery on a heart valve.

transection (tran-sek'shun): a cross section; a cut across the long axis of a part or an organ.

transorbital (trans-or'bi-tal): referring to a procedure performed through the bony socket of the eye.

transpiration (trans-pi-ra'shun): the discharge of air, vapor or sweat through the skin.

transplantation (trans-plan-ta'shun): the transfer or implantation of body tissue from one part of a person's body to another, or from one individual to another.

trauma (traw'mah): an injury or wound which may be produced by external force or by shock, as in psychic trauma.

triad (tri'ad): a group of 3 parts, objects, symptoms, or other entities.

triceps (tri'seps): having 3 heads or 3 points of origin, especially in referring to the attachments of muscles.

trichiasis (tri-ki'ah-sis): ingrowing hairs about an opening, or ingrowing eyelashes; also hairlike filaments in the urine.

trichinosis (trik-i-no'sis): a disease caused by the tiny roundworm parasite **Trichinella spiralis** that invades muscles. (It is often transmitted by insufficiently cooked pork.)

trichocardia (trik-o-kar'de-ah): a hairy appearance of the heart due to a pericarditis in which there is a fibrinous exudate.

trichosis (tri-ko'sis): abnormal growth of hair.

umbilical (um-bil'i-kal): relating to the umbilicus or navel; also referring to the section of the abdominal cavity around the umbilicus (navel) in the central part of the abdomen.

umbilicus (um-bi-li'kus): a small scar on the abdomen which marks the former attachment of the umbilical cord to the fetus, the navel.

unilateral (u-ne-lat'er-al): pertaining to one side only.

uniovular (u-ne-ov'u-lar): arising from one ovum, as in the case of certain twin pregnancies.

urea (u-re'ah): a nitrogen waste product

excreted in the urine; an end product of protein metabolism.

uremia (u-re′me-ah): an accumulation of urea and other waste products in the blood; a toxic condition seen in nephritis or other disorders of the urinary system in which urinary waste products remain in the blood in excessive amounts.

urticaria (ur-ti-ka′re-ah): a skin reaction to certain foods, drugs, or other substances to which a person may be allergic; an eruption of smooth, slightly elevated patches that differ from the rest of the skin in color; hives.

uvula (u′vu-lah): a soft fleshy mass, especially the V-shaped pendant part hanging down from the soft palate.

varices (var′i-sez): enlarged veins; varicose veins. The singular is **varix** (var′iks).

varicose (var′e-kose): pertaining to an unnatural swelling, as in the case of a varix or varicose vein.

vascular (vas′ku-lar): relating to or containing many vessels.

vasectomy (vas-ek′to-me): the surgical removal of part or all of the tube, the ductus deferens, from the testis.

vasoconstriction (vas-o-kon-strik′shun): a decrease in the caliber (diameter) of blood vessels, especially the constriction of the smallest arteries (arterioles), resulting in a decrease of blood to a part. The opposite is **vasodilation.**

vasodilation (vas-o-di-la′shun): an increase in the caliber (diameter) of blood vessels, especially the dilation of the smallest arteries (arterioles) resulting in an increase in the blood to a part. The opposite is **vasoconstriction.**

vector (vek′tor): a carrier of disease-producing organisms from one person to another (especially insects, such as mosquitoes).

venule (ven′ul): a very small vein that collects blood from capillaries. It is also called, a **venula** (ven′u-lah).

vernix caseosa (ver′niks ka-se-o′sah): an oily substance resembling cream cheese which covers the skin of the fetus.

verruca (ver-rooh′kah): a wart; a small growth on the skin caused by a virus infection; an elevated lesion on a heart valve found in certain cases of endocarditis (a form of heart disease).

vertebra (ver′te-brah): any one of the bones of the spinal column. The plural is **vertebrae** (ver′te-bre), while the adjective is **vertebral** (ver′te-bral).

vesicle (ves′e-kal): a small sac or blister filled with fluid.

viable (vi′ah-b′l): capable of living.

vibrios (vib′re-os): slightly curved, rod-shaped bacteria that are very active (motile); comma-shaped microbes. The singular is **vibrio** (vib′re-o).

viscera (vis′er-ah): the organs in the 3 large body cavities, such as the stomach and the liver in the abdominal cavity. The singular is **viscus** (vis′kus).

visceroptosis (vis-er-op-to′sis): a prolapse or falling down of the abdominal organs. See **splanchnoptosis.**

wen (wen): an oil-containing sac; a sebaceous cyst.

xeroderma (ze-ro-der′mah): a disorder in which there is dryness, roughness, and discoloration of the skin.

xerophthalmia (ze-rof-thal′me-ah): a dry and lusterless appearance of the eye due to a deficiency of vitamin A; a conjunctivitis with atrophy and lack of secretion over the eyeball.

xerosis (ze-ro′sis): an abnormal dryness, as may be found in the skin or the eye.

x-ray. See **roentgenogram.**

APPENDIX

TYPICAL DISEASE CONDITIONS AND CAUSATIVE ORGANISMS

TABLE 1. BACTERIAL DISEASES

ORGANISM	DISEASE AND DESCRIPTION
COCCI *Neisseria gonorrhoeae* (Gonococcus)	Gonorrhea. Acute inflammation of mucous membranes of the genitalia with possible spread to other membranes. Organism also causes ophthalmia neonatorum, an eye inflammation of newborn.
Neisseria meningitidis (Meningococcus)	Epidemic meningitis. Inflammation of the membranes covering brain and spinal cord.
Diplococcus pneumoniae (Pneumococcus)	Pneumonia. Inflammation of the alveoli, bronchioles and lesser bronchi.
Staphylococci	Boils, carbuncles, impetigo, osteomyelitis, staphylococcal pneumonia, cystitis, pyelonephritis, empyema, septicemia, and food poisoning.
Streptococci	Septicemia; septic sore throat; scarlet fever (an acute infectious disease characterized by red skin rash, sore throat, "strawberry" tongue, high fever, enlargement of lymph nodes); puerperal sepsis ("childbed fever"); erysipelas (an acute infection of skin, occurring in lymph channels, usually of face); streptococcal pneumonia; rheumatic fever (an inflammation of the joints, usually progressing to heart disease); subacute bacterial endocarditis (an inflammation of the heart valves).
BACILLI *Mycobacterium tuberculosis* (Tubercle bacillus)	Tuberculosis. An infectious disease in which the organism causes primary lesions called tubercles. These break down into cheeselike masses of tissue, a process known as caseation. Any body organ can be infected, but in adults the usual site is the lungs.

TABLE 1 *(Cont.)*

ORGANISM	DISEASE AND DESCRIPTION
Mycobacterium leprae (Hansen's bacillus)	Leprosy. A chronic illness in which hard swellings occur under the skin, particularly of the face, causing a grotesque appearance. Internal organs may be destroyed, and in one form of leprosy the nerves are affected, resulting in loss of sensation in the extremities.

NOTE: the following 4 organisms are spore-forming rods.

Clostridium tetani	Tetanus. Acute, often fatal poisoning caused by introduction of the organism into deep wounds. Characterized by severe muscular spasms. Also called lockjaw.
Clostridium perfringens	Gas gangrene. Another acute wound infection. The organisms cause death of tissues accompanied by the generation of gas within them.
Clostridium botulinum	Botulism. A very severe poisoning caused by eating food in which this organism has been allowed to grow and excrete its toxin. Can cause paralysis of the muscles, death from asphyxiation.
Bacillus anthracis	Anthrax. A disease acquired from animals. Characterized by a primary lesion called a pustule. Can develop into a fatal septicemia.
Corynebacterium diphtheriae	Diphtheria. Acute inflammation of the throat with the formation of a leathery membranelike growth (pseudomembrane) which can obstruct air passages and cause death by asphyxiation. Toxin produced by this organism can damage heart, nerves, kidneys, etc.
Bordetella pertussis	Pertussis (whooping cough). Severe infection of the trachea and bronchi. The "whoop" is caused by the effort to recover breath after coughing.
Hemophilus influenzae	Organism was thought originally to be cause of influenza, now known as a virus disease. However, can cause nonepidemic meningitis in children, inflammation of larynx, trachea and upper bronchi, and bacterial endocarditis.
Pasteurella pestis	Plague. The "Black Death" of the Middle Ages. A disease of animals, chiefly rats, transmitted to man by fleas. The usual form of this disease is bubonic plague, characterized by swollen lymph nodes called buboes. Usually this disease ends in fatal septicemia. In another form of plague lymph nodes are unaffected, but a rapid septicemia develops.
Pasteurella tularensis	Tularemia. An animal disease, transmitted to man chiefly through contact. Generalized fever with swollen lymph glands. In another form, the infection begins in the eye.

TABLE 1 *(Cont.)*

ORGANISM	DISEASE AND DESCRIPTION
Salmonella typhosa	Typhoid fever. A generalized infection, though manifesting mainly intestinal symptoms. Organisms show up in "rose spots" on skin. Infected areas of intestinal wall form ulcers which perforate, causing peritonitis.
Shigella dysenteriae	Bacillary dysentery. Inflammation of the intestine with diarrhea, possibly accompanied by blood. Epidemics may occur wherever sanitation is poor. Dangerous in infants and young children.
Brucella Types are: *abortus* *melitensis* *suis*	Brucellosis. A disease of cattle and goats, usually milk-borne. It is called *undulant fever* in man. Generalized infection; symptoms disappear and recur, hence "undulant."
Escherichia coli and *Proteus* bacilli	Normal inhabitants of colon, and usually harmless there. However, under certain conditions, they can cause infections particularly of urethra, urinary bladder and gallbladder.
CURVED RODS Spirilla *Vibrio comma* (comma bacillus)	Cholera. Acute infection of the intestine characterized by prolonged vomiting and diarrhea, leading to severe dehydration and in many cases, death.
Spirochetes *Borrelia vincentii* NOTE: always accompanied by a type of cigar-shaped (fusiform) bacillus.	Vincent's angina (trench mouth). Infection of the mouth and throat accompanied by formation of a pseudo-membrane, and with ulceration.
Borrelia (several types)	Relapsing fever. A generalized infection in which attacks of fever alternate with periods of apparent recovery. Organisms spread by lice, ticks, etc.
Leptospira	Infectious jaundice. An infection acquired from rats. Chief symptoms are jaundice, fever, and enlargement of spleen.
Treponema pallidum	Syphilis. An infectious disease transmitted mainly by sexual intercourse. Characterized by 3 stages. Primary: formation of primary lesion (chancre). Secondary: skin eruptions and infectious patches on mucous membranes. Tertiary: development of generalized lesions (gummas), destruction of tissues resulting in aneurysm, heart disease, degenerative changes in brain, spinal cord and ganglia, meninges.
Treponema pertenue	Yaws. A tropical disease characterized by lesions of the skin, deformities of hands, feet and face.

TABLE 2. FUNGOUS DISEASES

DISEASE	DESCRIPTION
Ringworm (tinea capitis) Barber's itch (tinea sycosis) Athlete's foot (epidermophytosis)	Common fungous infections of the skin, all caused by similar organisms from a group of fungi called dermatophytes. These are easily transmitted from person to person and from animals to people.
Actinomycosis	"Lumpy jaw," which occurs in cattle and man. The organisms cause large masses of tissue to form, and these masses are often accompanied by abscesses.
Thrush (moniliasis)	An infection of the mucous membranes of the mouth and the throat, very common in children.
Blastomycosis	A deep and severe fungous infection which may involve the skin and the internal organs. It can be fatal.
Coccidioidomycosis	Also called San Joaquin Valley fever. It is another systemic fungous disease. Because it often attacks the lungs, it may be mistaken for tuberculosis.

TABLE 3. RICKETTSIAL DISEASES

ORGANISM	DISEASE AND DESCRIPTION
Rickettsia prowazekii	Epidemic typhus. A louse-borne disease associated with overcrowded and unsanitary conditions. Main symptoms are headache, delirium, prostration and a skin rash which becomes hemorrhagic. It often ends fatally.
Rickettsia typhi	Endemic typhus. A flea-borne disease of rats, transmissible to man, similar to epidemic typhus but less severe. This disease cannot be spread from person to person.
Rickettsia rickettsii	Rocky Mountain spotted fever. A tick-borne disease common to most areas of the United States, characterized by fever, prostration, hemorrhagic rash covering entire body, and destruction of small blood vessels. It can be fatal.
Rickettsia akari	Rickettsialpox. A comparatively mild mite-borne infection transmitted from mice to men. Initial lesion is a small ulcer where patient has been bitten, followed by fever, headache, chills and a generalized rash.
Coxiella burnetii	Q fever. An infection transmitted from cattle, sheep and goats to man by contaminated dust—the only rickettsial disease not carried by arthropods. Symptoms are fever, headache, chills and pneumonitis. Practically never fatal.

TABLE 4. VIRAL DISEASES

DISEASE	DESCRIPTION
Smallpox (variola)	Fever, followed by a generalized outbreak of skin lesions (pustules). Smallpox was highly widespread until the advent of vaccination. A milder form of this disease is cowpox (vaccinia) found in cattle and men.
Chickenpox (varicella)	A usually mild infection, almost completely confined to children, characterized by blisterlike skin eruptions.
Shingles (herpes zoster)	The cause of this disease is a virus practically identical to that of chickenpox. Herpes is a very painful eruption of blisters of the skin which follow the course of certain peripheral nerves. These blisters eventually dry up and form scabs which resemble shingles.
Cold sores (herpes simplex)	Cold sores or fever blisters appearing about the mouth and nose of patients with colds or other illnesses accompanied by fever. This condition should not be confused with herpes zoster.
Measles (rubeola)	Acute respiratory inflammation followed by fever and a generalized skin rash. Patients are prone to develop dangerous complications such as bronchopneumonia and other secondary infections caused by staphylococci and streptococci.
Yellow fever	An acute infectious tropical disease transmitted by the bite of an infected mosquito. The disease is marked by jaundice, severe gastrointestinal symptoms, stomach hemorrhaging and nephritis which may be fatal.
Viral hepatitis	Two types of hepatitis (liver inflammation) are caused by viruses; infectious hepatitis and serum hepatitis. In the former, the portal of entry and exit is the digestive tract. The virus of the second type must be introduced into the blood; this can occur by way of contaminated needles, surgical instruments, blood specimens, etc. Both infections are accompanied by jaundice with damage to liver cells. Serum hepatitis usually is the more severe type and is often fatal.
German measles (rubella)	A less severe form of measles, but especially dangerous during the first 3 months of pregnancy because the disease organism can cause heart defects, deafness, mental deficiency and other permanent damage in the fetus.
Common cold (coryza)	Viral infection of the upper respiratory tract. Victims are highly susceptible to complications such as pneumonia and influenza.
Influenza	An epidemic viral infection, marked by chills, fever, muscular pains and prostration. The most serious complication is bronchopneumonia caused by *Hemophilus influenzae* (a bacillus) or streptococci.

TABLE 4 *(Cont.)*

DISEASE	DESCRIPTION
Poliomyelitis	An acute viral infection which attacks the anterior horns of the spinal cord, resulting in paralysis of certain voluntary muscles. The degree of permanent paralysis depends upon the extent of damage sustained by the motor nerves. Three types of causative viruses are known (Types 1, 2 and 3).
Rabies	An acute, fatal disease transmitted to man through the saliva of an infected animal. Rabies is characterized by violent muscular spasms induced by the slightest sensations. Because the swallowing of water causes spasms of the throat, the disease is also called hydrophobia ("fear of water"). There is a final stage of paralysis ending in death.
Viral encephalitis	"Encephalitis" usually is understood to be any brain inflammation accompanied by degenerative tissue changes, and it can have many causes besides viruses. There are several forms of viral encephalitis (Western and Eastern epidemic, equine, St. Louis, Japanese B, etc.), some of which are known to be transmitted from birds and other animals to man by insects, principally mosquitoes.
Mumps (epidemic parotitis)	Acute inflammation with swelling of the parotid salivary glands. Mumps can have many complications, such as orchitis (an inflammation of the testes), especially in children.
Psittacosis	A disease of parrots, transmitted by contact with infected birds or their droppings. Primary symptoms are chills, headache and fever, possibly accompanied by a rash. Pneumonia and bronchitis can be complications.
Lymphogranuloma venereum ("L.G.V.")	A venereal disease, characterized by swelling of inguinal lymph nodes, accompanied by signs of general infection. Later scar tissue forms in the genital region, possibly resulting in complete rectal stricture.

TABLE 5. PROTOZOAL DISEASES

ORGANISM	DISEASE AND DESCRIPTION
AMEBAE *Entamoeba histolytica*	Amebic dysentery. Severe ulceration of the wall of the large intestine caused by amebae. Acute diarrhea may be an important symptom. This organism also may cause liver abscesses.
CILIATES *Balantidium coli*	Gastrointestinal disturbances and ulcers of the colon.

TABLE 5 *(Cont.)*

ORGANISM	DISEASE AND DESCRIPTION
FLAGELLATES *Giardia lamblia*	Gastrointestinal disturbances.
Trichomonas vaginalis	Inflammation of the vagina accompanied by a whitish discharge called leukorrhea. This is a fairly common infection.
Trypanosoma	African sleeping sickness. Disease begins with a high fever, followed by invasion of the brain and spinal cord by the organisms. Usually the disease ends with continued drowsiness, coma, and death.
Leishmania (donovani and other types)	Kala-azar. A disease in which there is enlargement of the liver and spleen, as well as skin lesions.
SPOROZOA *Plasmodium;* varieties include *vivax, falcipa-* *rum, malariae*	Malaria. Characterized by recurrent attacks of chills followed by high fever. Severe attacks of malaria can be fatal because of kidney failure, cerebral disorders and other complications.

INDEX

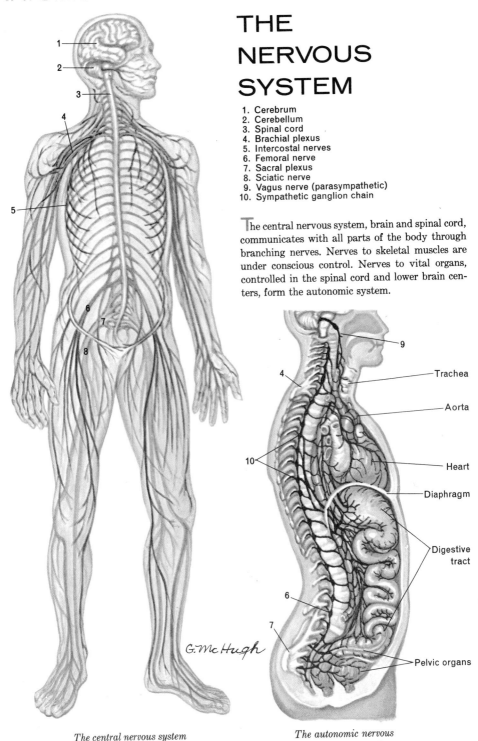

THE NERVOUS SYSTEM

1. Cerebrum
2. Cerebellum
3. Spinal cord
4. Brachial plexus
5. Intercostal nerves
6. Femoral nerve
7. Sacral plexus
8. Sciatic nerve
9. Vagus nerve (parasympathetic)
10. Sympathetic ganglion chain

The central nervous system, brain and spinal cord, communicates with all parts of the body through branching nerves. Nerves to skeletal muscles are under conscious control. Nerves to vital organs, controlled in the spinal cord and lower brain centers, form the autonomic system.

Trachea

Aorta

Heart

Diaphragm

Digestive tract

Pelvic organs

G. McHugh

The central nervous system and branches

The autonomic nervous system (in black)

Plate 1

MUSCLES and SKELETON

front view

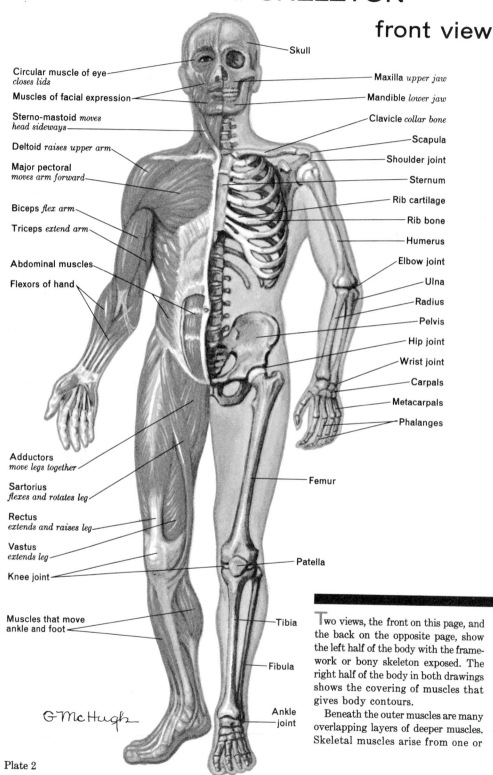

Skull

Circular muscle of eye *closes lids*

Maxilla *upper jaw*

Muscles of facial expression

Mandible *lower jaw*

Sterno-mastoid *moves head sideways*

Clavicle *collar bone*

Deltoid *raises upper arm*

Scapula

Shoulder joint

Major pectoral *moves arm forward*

Sternum

Rib cartilage

Biceps *flex arm*

Rib bone

Triceps *extend arm*

Humerus

Abdominal muscles

Elbow joint

Flexors of hand

Ulna

Radius

Pelvis

Hip joint

Wrist joint

Carpals

Metacarpals

Phalanges

Adductors *move legs together*

Femur

Sartorius *flexes and rotates leg*

Rectus *extends and raises leg*

Vastus *extends leg*

Patella

Knee joint

Muscles that move ankle and foot

Tibia

Fibula

Ankle joint

G. McHugh

Two views, the front on this page, and the back on the opposite page, show the left half of the body with the framework or bony skeleton exposed. The right half of the body in both drawings shows the covering of muscles that gives body contours.

Beneath the outer muscles are many overlapping layers of deeper muscles. Skeletal muscles arise from one or

Plate 2

SKELETON and MUSCLES

back view

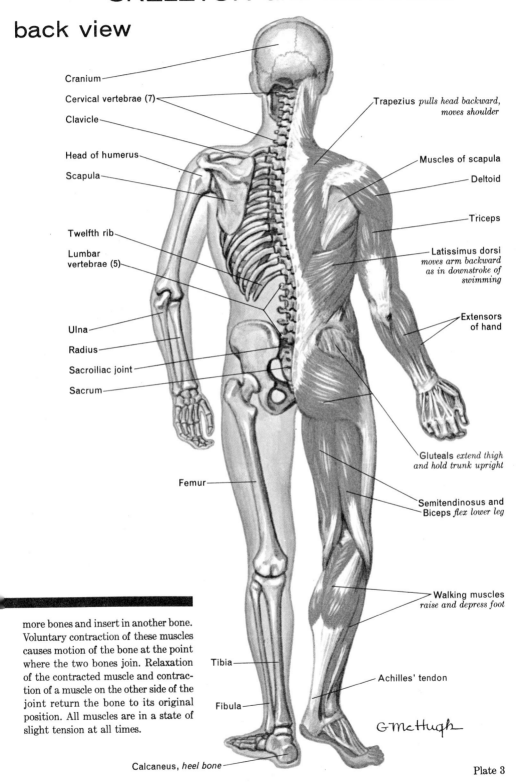

Cranium

Cervical vertebrae (7)

Clavicle

Head of humerus

Scapula

Twelfth rib

Lumbar vertebrae (5)

Ulna

Radius

Sacroiliac joint

Sacrum

Femur

Tibia

Fibula

Calcaneus, *heel bone*

Trapezius *pulls head backward, moves shoulder*

Muscles of scapula

Deltoid

Triceps

Latissimus dorsi *moves arm backward as in downstroke of swimming*

Extensors of hand

Gluteals *extend thigh and hold trunk upright*

Semitendinosus and Biceps *flex lower leg*

Walking muscles *raise and depress foot*

Achilles' tendon

G McHugh

more bones and insert in another bone. Voluntary contraction of these muscles causes motion of the bone at the point where the two bones join. Relaxation of the contracted muscle and contraction of a muscle on the other side of the joint return the bone to its original position. All muscles are in a state of slight tension at all times.

Plate 3

THE CIRCULATORY SYSTEM

1. Jugular vein
2. Carotid artery
3. Brachial artery and vein
4. Superior vena cava
5. Aorta
6. Pulmonary artery
7. Inferior vena cava
8. Portal vein
9. External iliac artery and vein
10. Femoral artery and vein

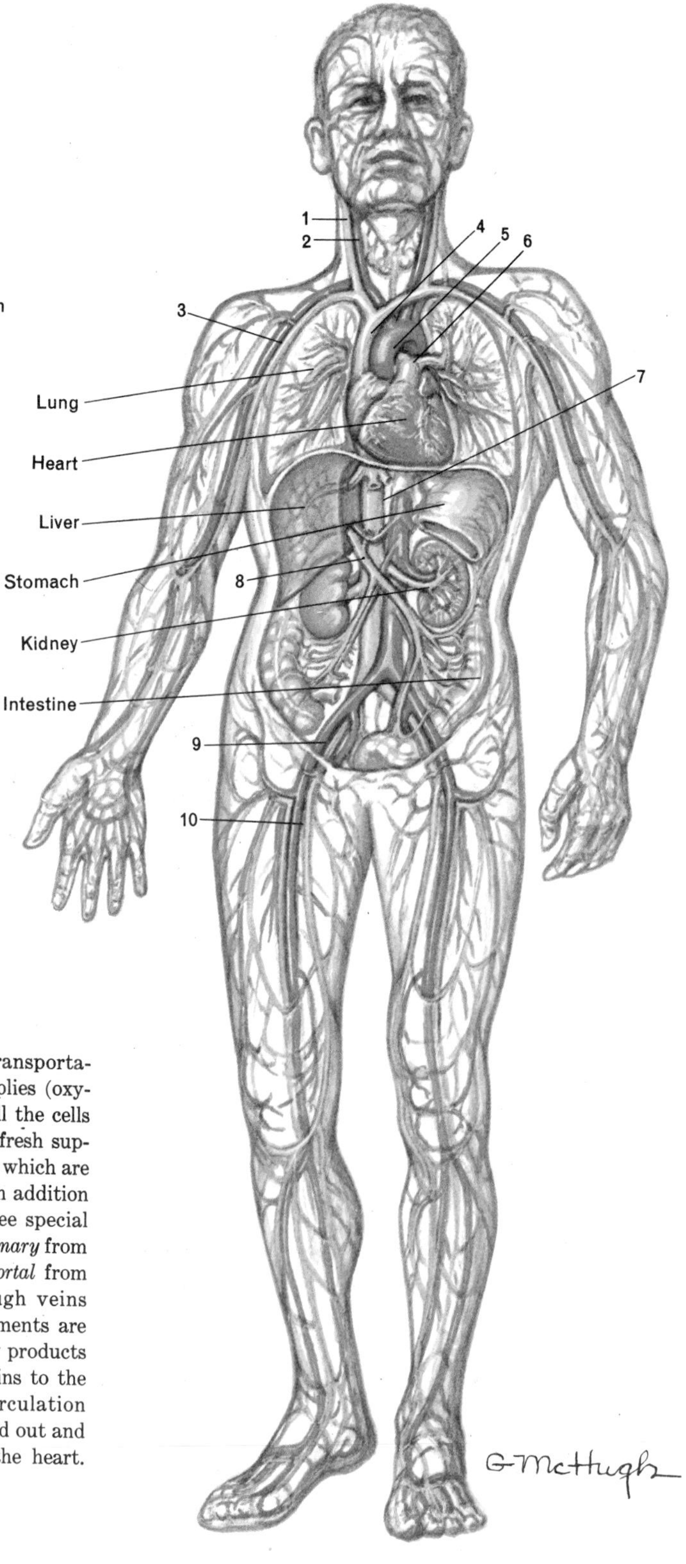

Lung

Heart

Liver

Stomach

Kidney

Intestine

The circulating blood is a transportation system carrying vital supplies (oxygen, nutrients, chemicals) to all the cells of the body. The cells take in fresh supplies and return waste products which are carried away for elimination. In addition to the general circulation, three special systems are depicted: (1) *Pulmonary* from heart to lungs to heart. (2) *Portal* from digestive tract to liver through veins shown in blue-green. Food elements are converted by the liver into new products which pass through hepatic veins to the heart. (3) *Renal* or kidney circulation where waste products are filtered out and purified blood is returned to the heart.

G. McHugh

Plate 4

THE HEART, or PUMPING STATION

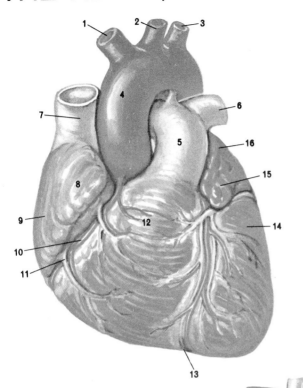

1. Innominate artery
2. Left carotid artery
3. Left subclavian artery
4. Aorta
5. Pulmonary artery
6. Left branch of pulmonary artery
7. Superior vena cava
8. Right auricle
9. Right atrium
10. Right coronary artery
11. Cardiac vein (anterior)
12. Right ventricle
13. Location of septum
14. Left ventricle
15. Left auricle
16. Left atrium
17. Left pulmonary veins
18. Septum between ventricles
19. Tricuspid valve (between left atrium and ventricle, open)
20. Inferior vena cava
21. Pulmonary semilunar valve (closed)

To lung

From lung

The top figure shows the outside of the heart with its powerful muscle walls. The figure at right shows the inside of the right half of the heart, with arrows indicating direction of blood flow. The heart receives blood through veins and pumps it out through arteries. Throughout the body arteries carry fresh oxygenated blood, are depicted in red and the veins in blue, but in the lungs this situation is reversed.

G. McHugh

Plate 5

THE RESPIRATORY SYSTEM

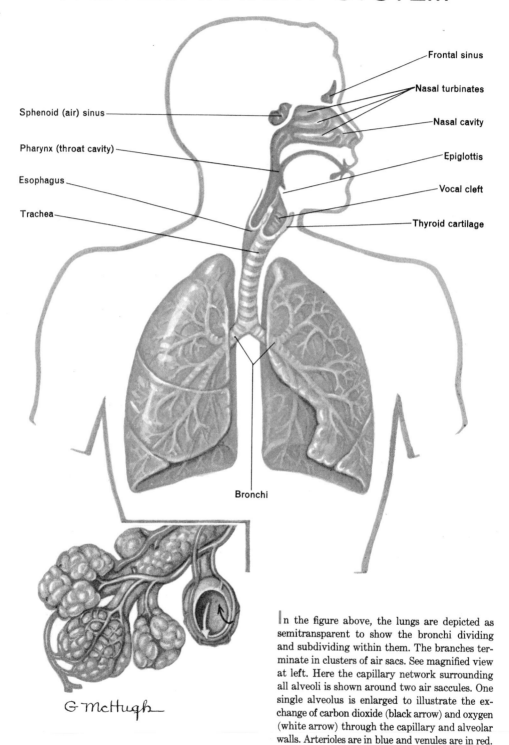

Frontal sinus

Nasal turbinates

Sphenoid (air) sinus

Nasal cavity

Pharynx (throat cavity)

Epiglottis

Esophagus

Vocal cleft

Trachea

Thyroid cartilage

Bronchi

G. McHugh

In the figure above, the lungs are depicted as semitransparent to show the bronchi dividing and subdividing within them. The branches terminate in clusters of air sacs. See magnified view at left. Here the capillary network surrounding all alveoli is shown around two air saccules. One single alveolus is enlarged to illustrate the exchange of carbon dioxide (black arrow) and oxygen (white arrow) through the capillary and alveolar walls. Arterioles are in blue and venules are in red.

Plate 6

THE DIGESTIVE SYSTEM

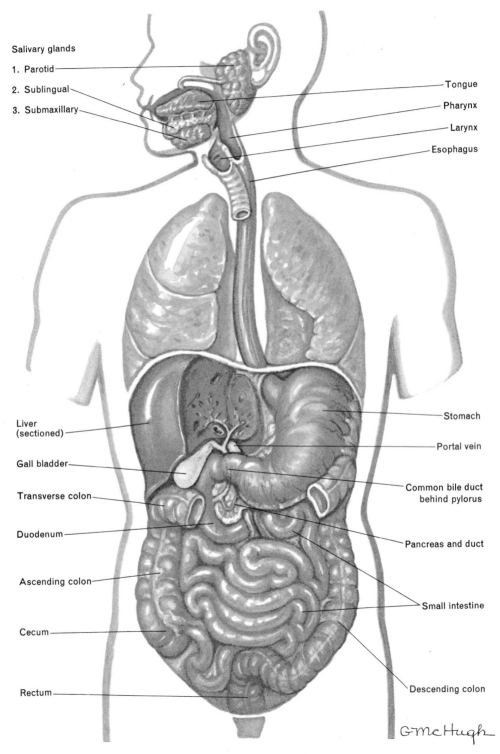

Salivary glands

1. Parotid
2. Sublingual
3. Submaxillary

Tongue
Pharynx
Larynx
Esophagus

Liver (sectioned)
Gall bladder
Transverse colon
Duodenum
Ascending colon
Cecum
Rectum

Stomach
Portal vein
Common bile duct behind pylorus
Pancreas and duct
Small intestine
Descending colon

G. McHugh

Plate 7

THE ENDOCRINE GLAND SYSTEM

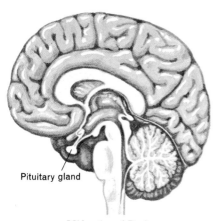

Midsection of Brain

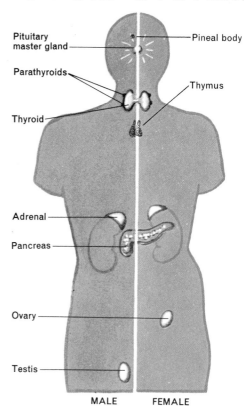

Pituitary master gland

Pineal body

Parathyroids

Thymus

Thyroid

Adrenal

Pancreas

Ovary

Testis

MALE   FEMALE

Pituitary gland

Hormones are chemical products of the endocrine glands distributed by the blood. This chemical system controls and regulates rate of body functions such as growth and metabolism. Hormones bring about development of male and female characteristics, as illustrated below in the changing contours of a growing boy and girl. Each gland produces specific hormones with special functions. The pituitary produces hormones which regulate all the other endocrine glands.

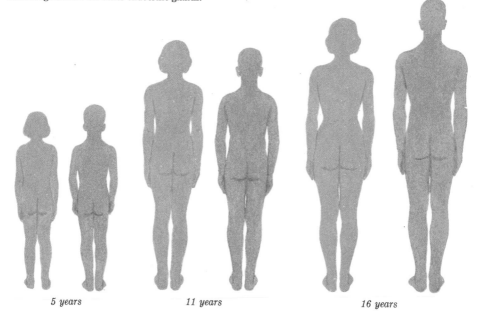

5 years   *11 years*   *16 years*

G McHugh

Plate 8